# ELECTRICAL MEASUREMENTS
# AND INSTRUMENTATION

# ELECTRICAL

ALLYN and BACON, Inc.

Boston

# MEASUREMENTS

## and

# INSTRUMENTATION

## Davis Bartholomew

Consulting Engineer

*formerly* Professor of Electrical Engineering
Brigham Young University and
University of Arizona

This book is part of the

Allyn and Bacon Electrical Engineering Series

under the consulting editorship of Norman Balabanian

*First printing: May 1963*

*Second printing: April 1965*

# ACKNOWLEDGMENT

The author wishes to express his sincere appreciation to Brigham Young University for clerical and drafting assistance in preparing the notes that evolved into this book, and to the many commercial companies who so generously supplied illustrations. He also wishes to express his appreciation to his wife Fern, who assisted with the proofreading and did much of the clerical work.

# PREFACE

The static test of a solid-state missile engine may last only a minute, but the cost of this test may be more than a hundred thousand dollars. This vast sum of money for research, used up in such a short period of time, demands that an enormous amount of information be obtained during the test. This information is gathered with modern high-speed data-acquisition systems that can read data at the rate of several thousand samples per second. There are some commercial systems that read more than a million samples of data per second. Once the data are acquired, the problem of computing the desired information from these data arises. But modern data-computation speeds are even faster than the data-acquisition speeds. Modern data-acquisition and data-reduction systems are being utilized in every field of engineering. They are used in engineering research and development, in quality control, and to obtain optimum operation of industrial plants and utility transmission networks. The accuracy, efficiency, and speed of these systems will reduce to a minimum the process of observing an indicating instrument or adjusting a null-type instrument and writing the data observed on a paper pad attached to a clipboard. The basic theory and the operation of these instruments and modern instrumentation systems are described in this book.

The first chapter is an introduction to the characteristics of instruments and instrumentation systems. It defines accuracy, sensitivity, resolution, discrimination, noise, repeatability, instrument efficiency, linearity, and response. The concept of error, introduced in Chap. 1, is amplified in Chap. 2, where limiting, known, and probable errors are applied to measurement problems. The concepts of the dynamic response, as defined in Chap. 1, are illustrated with the analysis of d-c and ballistic galvanometers in Chap. 3. The principles developed in this chapter are used in Chap. 4 to analyze the operation of d'Arsonval-type strip-chart recorders and in Chap. 7 to analyze the amplitude and phase distortion of galvanometer oscillographs.

Although the block diagram of a modern data-acquisition system does not show the flow of information through indicating instruments, the panels of data-acquisition systems are replete with indicating instruments which are used for monitoring and servicing this equipment. Therefore, it is necessary to understand the theory, operation, and application of these indicating instruments. These instruments are discussed in Chaps. 4 and 5. A short analysis of instrument transformers and their application is given in Chap. 6.

A comprehensive analysis of indicating instruments and galvanometers, given in Chaps. 3, 4, and 5, prepares the reader for the analysis of analog recording instruments in Chap. 7. This includes the theory, operation, and application of the galvanometer oscillographs, the tape recorder, and the cathode-ray oscilloscope.

These subjects are followed by the theory, operation, and application of null-type instruments, including d-c and a-c bridges, and potentiometers, in Chaps. 8, 9, and 10. The bridge circuits are important not only for measuring resistance, inductance, and capacitance, but also for strain gage and thermistor-transducer circuits, which are described in Chap. 12. Similarly, the potentiometer is used not only for precise voltage measurements; when used with a feedback servoloop, it becomes an effective strip-chart recorder. It can also be used with a spatial-type analog-to-digital converter, as described in Chap. 14.

The theory and application of several representative types of transducers, covering the topics from strain gage transducers to scintillation counters, are given in Chap. 11. This is a very extensive subject, and only a limited discussion of it can be included here, but the philosophy of this chapter characterizes the philosophy of the complete book; that is, to obtain an optimum balance between the depth of the topics discussed and the breadth of the material covered.

An introduction to the theory of summing, integrating, and differentiating circuits; limiting circuits; function generators; and multiplying and dividing circuits, as applied to analog computation and simulation, is given in Chap. 12.

The theory and application of digital operations are preceded by Chap. 13, which develops the concept of digital-number systems, the use of binary codes to represent decimal numbers, and the methods of converting from one number system to another. Then, with an understanding of the fundamental concepts of binary numbers and binary-coded decimal numbers, the theory and application of analog-to-digital conversion are developed in Chap. 14.

An introduction to the theory and application of digital computers is given in Chap. 15. It outlines the basic components of a digital computer and shows the flow of information through these components. It further illustrates this operation by describing the flow of information through a typical digital computer. The methods of writing instructions and data are given, and the types of operations performed by the computer are described. A program using these operations and instructions is then written in machine language for the solution of a simple problem. This is followed by a brief introduction to Boolean algebra, and the circuits for addition and subtraction are developed and applied to a binary serial adder and subtractor. Then a binary serial multiplier circuit and a binary serial divider circuit are developed, using repetitive addition and subtraction.

The purpose of this chapter is not to produce either computer programmers or digital-circuit designers, but to remove from the mind of the reader the mystery of the operation of a modern digital computer and to give him a rational concept of basic logic circuits and their operation in arithmetic and control units. It removes the shell of the big-black-box concept of a computer and replaces it with *and*, *or*, and *not* circuits and shift registers that produce the desired digital computations.

The concluding chapter presents the operation of a complete data-acquisition and data-reduction system. It includes the correlation of transducers, signal conditioning circuits, analog computers, galvanometer oscillographs, FM tape recorders, multiplex systems, sample-and-hold circuits, analog-to-digital converters, digital tape recorders, digital tape translators, digital computers, digital tabulators, and digital plotters. A brief discussion as to which of these components would be required to solve a given systems problem is given. Methods for calibrating a data-acquisition system and for determining the accuracy, linearity, drift, noise, cross talk, sensitivity, and frequency response of the system are discussed.

The demands of research, quality control, and industrial systems control for faster and more accurate acquisition of data and the reduction of these data to the desired quantities make it imperative that engineers in every branch of engineering understand the basic theory and operation of modern instrumentation systems in order to apply efficiently these powerful engineering tools to their problems. This book is designed to give a comprehensive understanding of the basic theory and application of these systems and to point the way to further study in this field.

# Contents

Chapter 1

INTRODUCTION TO INSTRUMENT
CHARACTERISTICS                                                    2

Introduction / Accuracy / Sensitivity / Resolution or Discrimination /
Noise and Repeatability / Instrument Efficiency / Instrument Range
and Scales / Linearity / Dynamic Systems / Dynamic Response /
Overshoot / Dead Time / Problems

Chapter 2

ERRORS                                                           14

Limiting Errors / Known Errors / Error in Instruments / Probable
Error / Summary / Problems

Chapter 3

DIRECT-CURRENT AND BALLISTIC
GALVANOMETERS                                              32

Introduction / Torque and Deflection of a Current Galvanometer /
Dynamic Analysis of a Galvanometer / The Underdamped Motion of
a Galvanometer / The Undamped Motion of a Galvanometer / Critical
Damped Motion of a Galvanometer / Relative Damping / Logarithmic
Decrement / Overdamped Motion of a Galvanometer / Nondimensional
Curves of a Galvanometer Motion / Galvanometer Sensitivity /
Measuring the Galvanometer Current / Measuring the Resistance of
the Galvanometer / Measuring the Current Sensitivity of a Galvano-
meter / Measurements of the Voltage Sensitivity of a Galvanometer /
Measurement of the Megohm Sensitivity of a Galvanometer / Measure-
ment of the Ballistic Sensitivity of a Galvanometer / Measuring the
Logarithmic Decrement of a Galvanometer / Computing Relative
Damping / Critical Damping Resistance External / Galvanometer
Protection / The Ayrton Shunt / The Ballistic Galvanometer / Measure-
ments of the Quantity of Electricity / Measurement of the Time
Integral of the EMF / Measuring the EMF-time or Flux-linkage
Sensitivity of a Galvanometer / Problems

xi

Chapter 4

DIRECT-CURRENT INDICATING
INSTRUMENTS                                                  70

Construction of a d'Arsonval Movement / Current Measurements /
Ammeter Shunts and Multirange Ammeters / Voltmeters / Voltmeter–
Ammeter Measurements / Series-type Ohmmeter / Shunt-type Ohm-
meter / Cross-coil Ohmmeters / Megger / Volt–Ohm-milliammeter /
Direct-current Watthour Meter / Direct-current Recording Instru-
ments / Problems


Chapter 5

ALTERNATING-CURRENT INDICATOR
INSTRUMENTS                                                 102

Introduction / Rectifier-type A-C Instruments / Thermocouple In-
struments / Electrodynamic Instruments / Iron-vane Instruments /
Electrostatic Instruments / Power Measurements / Watthour Meters /
Phase-sequence Measurements / Power-factor Measurements and
Phasemeters / Synchroscopes / Frequency Measurements / Alternat-
ing-current Recording Meters / Problems


Chapter 6

INSTRUMENT TRANSFORMERS                                     132

The Ideal Transformer / Losses in a Transformer / Impedance Transformation / Potential Transformers / The Current Transformer /
Problems


Chapter 7

OSCILLOGRAPHS, TAPE RECORDERS, AND
CATHODE-RAY OSCILLOSCOPES                                   148

Introduction / The Galvanometer-type Oscillograph / Magnetic Tape
Recorders / The Cathode-ray Oscilloscope / Problems

Chapter 8

DIRECT-CURRENT BRIDGES 172

Introduction / Wheatstone Bridge / Kelvin Bridge / Application of
Bridge Circuits / Problems

Chapter 9

ALTERNATING-CURRENT BRIDGES 184

Introduction / The Inductance-comparison Bridge / The Capacitance
Bridge with a Wagner Ground / The Bridge-T Network / The Parallel-
T Circuit / The Storage-factor and the Dissipation-factor Measure-
ments / Residuals of A-C Bridge Components / Shielding / Problems

Chapter 10

POTENTIOMETERS 202

The Potentiometer and Its Operation / Duo-range Potentiometer /
Multiple-range Potentiometers / Zero-suppression Potentiometers /
Leeds and Northrup Type K-2 Potentiometer / Leeds and Northrup
Type K-3 Universal Potentiometer / Multirange Portable Potentio-
meters / Volt Box / Current Measurement with a Potentiometer /
Ammeter and Voltmeter Calibration / Potentiometer Sensitivity /
Protection of the Standard Cell and Galvanometer in a Potentiometer
Circuit / Self-balancing Potentiometers / Problems

Chapter 11

NONELECTRICAL QUANTITIES 230

Introduction / Bonded-resistance Strain Gages / Unbonded-resistance
Strain Gages / Differential Transformer / Variable-capacity Displace-
ment Instruments / Reluctance-type Displacement Instruments /
Dynamic Displacement Measurements / Load Cells and Load Rings /
Piezoelectric Devices / Velocity Measurements / Acceleration Mea-
surements / Vibration Measurements / Pressure Measurements /
Thermocouples / Resistance Thermometers / Thermistors and Their
Characteristics / Radiant-energy Measurements / Nuclear Instrumen-
tation / Magnetic Flux and Hysteresis Measurements / $p$H Measurements / Time Measurements / Problems

Chapter 12

ELECTRICAL ANALOG COMPUTERS                                    284

Introduction / Averaging Circuits / Summing Circuit / Integrating Circuits / Differentiating Circuits / Solution of Linear Differential Equations / Representation of Physical Forces / Amplitude and Time Factors / Division with a Servo Circuit / Multiplication with a Servo Circuit / Electrodynamometer-type Multiplier and Divider Circuit / Feedback Dividing and Multiplying Circuits / Nonlinear-potentiometer-function Generator / An Electronic Function Generator / Resolvers and Transformation for the Polar to the Rectangular Form / The Transformation of Rectangular Cartesian Coordinates to the Polar Form / Solution of Simultaneous Equations / Commercial Analog Computers / Problems


Chapter 13

DIGITAL NUMBER SYSTEMS                                        322

Digital Versus Analog Systems / Basic Theory of Digital Numbers / The Decimal-number System / The Binary System / The Conversion from Binary to Decimal and Decimal to Binary Numbers / The Ternary-number System / The Octonary-number System / The Duodecimal-number System / The Binary-coded Decimal System / The Reflected Binary-number System / The Cyclic-decimal-number System / The Biquinary Code / Fractions / Summary / Problems


Chapter 14

ANALOG-TO-DIGITAL CONVERSION                                  346

Introduction / Number-indicator Switching Systems / Diode Matrix / Number Indicators / Time-base Encoders / Feedback or Voltage-comparison Encoder / Spatial Encoders / Commercial Encoders / Positive- and Negative-reading Encoders / Summary / Problems


Chapter 15

THE DIGITAL COMPUTER AND
DIGITAL-COMPUTER PROBLEMS                                     372

Introduction to Digital Computers / Typical Digital-computer Operation and Programming / Boolean Algebra / Arithmetic Processes / Summary / Problems

Chapter 16

DATA-ACQUISITION AND
REDUCTION SYSTEMS                                    420

Introduction / Sensing Elements / Conditioning Equipment / Calibrating Equipment / Integrating Equipment / Analog Computers /
Analog Recorders / Multiplexing Equipment / Analog-to-digital Converters / Telemetering Equipment / Digital Recorders / Digital Plotters / High-speed Cameras and TV Equipment / Progress Monitor /
Central-clock Control / Requirements of a Complete Data-acquisition
and Reduction System / Checking the Performance of a Data-acquisition System / Problems

INDEX                                                450

# ELECTRICAL MEASUREMENTS
# AND INSTRUMENTATION

# Chapter 1

# INSTRUMENT

## 1-1. INTRODUCTION

During the early growth of the electrical industry, reliable instruments were developed for measuring electrical quantities. These basic instruments have received only slight improvements during the past half century. Recent developments, however, have produced instrument systems which will measure thousands of electrical and nonelectrical quantities per second and will transform them into signals which can be interpreted by high-speed computers or high-speed recording systems. As an introduction to the study of these devices, this chapter will define and describe some of the characteristics of these instruments and instrument systems.

## 1-2. ACCURACY [1]*

The most important characteristic of an instrument or instrumentation system is its accuracy. This is defined as the agreement of the instrument

* Superior numbers in the text material refer to the references given at the ends of the chapters.

2

# NTRODUCTION TO

# CHARACTERISTICS

reading with the true value of the quantity measured. The accuracy of an instrument is measured in terms of its error.

*Error* is defined as the difference between the indicated quantity and the true quantity. Then

$$E = I - T \tag{1-1}$$

where

$E$ = error
$I$ = indicated quantity
$T$ = true quantity

*Correction* is defined as the difference between the true quantity and the indicated quantity, or

$$C = T - I \tag{1-2}$$

where $C$ is the correction.

To calibrate an instrument, the quantity to be measured is varied until the instrument reads a given value. This is the indicated quantity. Then the true amount being measured is determined. The error of the reading is obtained by Eq. (1-1). Often, an error chart is drawn with the error plotted as a function of the reading of the instrument, but it is more common to plot the correction as a function of the instrument reading. Thus, if the corrections were +0.05 and the readings were 8.70, the true reading would be the algebraic sum of the correction term and the reading, or 8.75.

## 1-3. SENSITIVITY

Next to accuracy, the most important characteristic in a measuring instrument is its sensitivity. The sensitivity of an instrument or instrumentation system is the ratio of the magnitude of the response to the magnitude of the quantity being measured.[2] Its units are expressed in millimeters per microampere, counts per volt, etc.

Sensitivity is often expressed as the ratio of the magnitude of the measured quantity to the magnitude of the response. Then these units are expressed in microamperes per millimeter, volts per count, etc. This ratio is defined as the *deflection factor or inverse sensitivity*.[2] It is the reciprocal of the sensitivity as defined above. Manufacturers often specify the sensitivity of their instruments as the ratio of the magnitude of the quantity being measured to the magnitude of the response. Thus the inverse sensitivity is often used for the sensitivity.

## 1-4. RESOLUTION OR DISCRIMINATION[3]

The resolution of an instrument is defined as the smallest increment of the quantity being measured which can be detected with certainty by the instrument. For example, if an ordinary indicating voltmeter has a uniform scale with 100 divisions, the full-scale reading is 200 volts and 1/10 of a division can be estimated with a fair degree of certainty, then 1/10 of a division, or 0.2 volt, is the resolution of this instrument. If the indication of the instrument were produced in digital form, then the smallest number of the least significant figure in the digital readout would be the discrimination or resolution of the instrument. For example, a digital instrument has a maximum count or reading of 999. The resolution of this instrument would be 1, or 1 count in 999.

## 1-5. NOISE AND REPEATABILITY[4]

Repeatability is a very important item in instrumentation. Many instruments have a tendency to drift; that is, with a given input the measured values will vary with time. The calibration of an instrument cannot compensate for these variations. In the process of making an electrical measurement, the instrument may respond to environmental disturbances as well as to the signal being measured. Fluctuations in electrical or magnetic fields in the neighborhood of the instrument are common sources of trouble. They may be minimized by adequate shielding or relocation of the components of the instrument. Similarly, mechanical vibrations are another source of trouble that can be eliminated by proper mounting devices. Thermal emfs also produce noise and vary the readings of the instruments. Temperature changes while making a measurement are to be avoided. All disturbances which may produce unwanted inputs are defined as *noise*.

A resistor generates thermal agitation noise owing to random thermal motion of the electrons in its interior. The effect increases with increased temperature of the resistor. The magnitude of this fluctuation is

$$V = 2\sqrt{kTR\,\Delta f} \tag{1-3}$$

where

$k$ = Boltzmann's constant

$T$ = absolute temperature of the resistor

$R$ = resistance

$\Delta f$ = frequency range over which voltage is measured

Many modern instruments use electronic amplifiers. Each vacuum tube in these amplifiers produces a noise. This noise is due to the random emission of electrons from the cathode and other elements in the tube. These noise voltages are present in resistors and vacuum tubes at all times. They are very small in magnitude and are not troublesome except when minute values are measured.

## 1-6. INSTRUMENT EFFICIENCY

Instrument efficiency is defined as the reading of the instrument divided by the power taken from the quantity being measured by the instrument. It is expressed as the unit being measured per watt. Inasmuch as the efficiency is the function of the magnitude of the quantity being measured, the magnitude of the measured quantity must be stated in order to specify the efficiency. This is very troublesome and hard to evaluate. To overcome this difficulty, the definition of efficiency is sometimes broadened to the ratio of the measured quantity at full scale to the power taken by the instrument at full scale. The efficiency should be as high as possible, as the higher the efficiency the less effect the instrument will have upon the circuit being measured.

The efficiency of a voltmeter is expressed in *ohms per volt*. This quantity is the ratio of the resistance of the voltmeter to the full-scale reading of the voltmeter. Thus

$$\text{Ohms per volt} = \frac{R_m}{V_{FS}} \tag{1-4}$$

where

$V_{FS}$ = full-scale reading of the voltmeter
$R_m$ = resistance of the voltmeter

By definition, the instrument efficiency of a voltmeter is

$$\text{Instrument efficiency} = \frac{V_{FS}}{P_{FS}} = \frac{I_{FS}R_m}{I_{FS}V_{FS}} = \frac{R_m}{V_{FS}} \tag{1-5}$$

where

$I_{FS}$ = current in the voltmeter at full-scale reading
$P_{FS}$ = power consumed by the voltmeter at full-scale reading

Thus the instrument efficiency is shown by the ohms per volt.

The full-scale current in a voltmeter can be determined by the ohms per volt of the instrument. Thus

$$I_{FS} = \frac{V_{FS}}{R_m} = \frac{1}{\text{ohms per volt}} \tag{1-6}$$

The efficiency of an instrument is a criterion of the quality of the instrument being used. This term is seldom expressed in the specifications of an instrument, but when the impedance of the instrument is known, and the full-scale current or voltage applied to that instrument is given, the power consumed from the quantity being measured can be computed and the efficiency of the instrument can be obtained. High-efficiency voltmeters are a prerequisite for measurements in electronic circuits where the current and the power are small.

### 1-7. INSTRUMENT RANGE AND SCALES[4]

The choice of proper range instruments is important in instrumentation. The *scale range* of an instrument is defined as the difference between the largest and the smallest reading of the instrument. For example, a standard voltmeter with a linear scale may have a range of 0 to 150 volts, and a thermometer may have a scale of $-20°$ to $300°F$. Thus, in expressing the scale range of an instrument, the minimum as well as the maximum quantity that the instrument will read is given. An instrument may be considered as a mechanism which has an input of the quantity being measured, and an output, which is usually a displacement. For instance, an ordinary d'Arsonval movement measures current which produces a displacement of the pointer. The degree of the displacement of the pointer is indicated by uniformly spaced marks on the arc of the movement of the pointer. These divisions indicate the number of units the pointer has moved. This set of marks forms an *index scale*, and the number of divisions moved is the *index reading*. When numbers are placed on the scale, they convert the scale movement into the current reading. This scale conversion gives the output readings of the instrument in units of the quantity measured. If an ammeter has 100 divisions on its index scale and the instrument is a 0–100-ma instrument with range-multiplier switches of 1, 10, and 100, the range of this instrument would be from 0 to 10 amp, and the index-scale range would be from 0 to 100.

In a digital voltmeter the theory is the same. In a spatial encoder the measured quantity produces a displacement of the mechanism. This displacement is converted into a digital number. Other types of analog-to-digital converters employ electronic circuits to convert a voltage to a digital number.

There is another factor that must be considered in determining the range of an instrument. This is the *frequency range*, which is defined as frequencies over which measurements may be taken with a specified accuracy. For example, a vane-type, a-c voltmeter may have a 0–150-volt range and a 0–135-cycles-per-second frequency range with an accuracy of 1/2 of 1 percent of full-scale reading.

## 1-8. LINEARITY

It is often necessary to have instrument scales and electrical components vary linearly with displacement. For example, the resistance used in a potentiometer should vary linearly with displacement in order for the displacement to be directly proportional to the slider contact voltage. Deviation from linearity of the resistance would cause an error in the readout system. Referring to Fig. 1-1, the resistance is plotted as a function of the displacement. If the resistance to the sliding contact were proportional to the displacement on this potentiometer, the values of the resistance would all fall on the straight line. If the resistance varied as shown by the curved line deviating from the straight-line characteristics, then the percent linearity is

$$\text{Percent linearity} = \left(\frac{\text{maximum resistance deviation}}{\text{full-scale resistance}}\right)100$$

$$= \left(\frac{\text{maximum displacement deviation}}{\text{full-scale displacement}}\right)100$$

It is desirable to keep this small. In many potentiometers this quantity is less than 0.05 percent. For example, if a potentiometer in a self-balancing potentiometer readout system had a linearity of 0.1 percent, its accuracy would be within 1 part in 1,000. With a 1,000-count digital encoder connected to the driving shaft, the variation in the resistance of the potentiometer

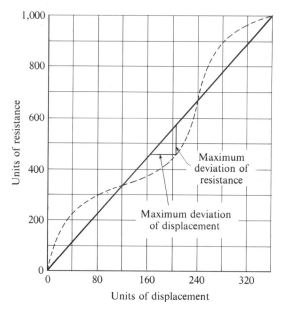

**Fig. 1-1.** *Nonlinearity*

would produce an error equal to 1 count in 1,000 counts. If a potentiometer and encoder were required to read 2,000 counts, then the linearity of the potentiometer would have to be less than 0.05 percent for an accuracy of 1 count in 2,000 counts.

## 1-9. DYNAMIC SYSTEMS

The quantities defined thus far have been based on the static operation of the instrument; that is, the instrument reads a steady, established quantity. It is important to know the characteristics of an instrument during changes in the quantity being measured. The changes used for the dynamic analysis of an instrument are usually of standard forms. A common form is the *step function*, which is a sudden change from one magnitude of the measured quantity to another magnitude. A second form is the *linear change*, in which the measured quantity varies linearly with time. The third, and perhaps the most common form is the *sinusoidal change*, in which the quantity being measured varies sinusoidally with a constant maximum amplitude. For any given type of change, the *dynamic error* of an instrument system is defined as the difference between the indicated quantity and the true quantity being measured. The *fidelity*[4] of a system or a portion of a system is defined as the degree to which a system or a portion of a system actually reproduces the output form of the signal which is impressed upon it. It is the ability of the instrument to produce a wave shape identical to the wave shape of the input with respect to time. If the input were a sine wave, then the output would be a sine wave having 100 percent fidelity. In this definition there is no requirement upon the time lag or the phase angle between the input and the output of the instrument. The total dynamic error of the instrument would be the combination of its fidelity and the time lag or phase angle between the input and the output.

## 1-10. DYNAMIC RESPONSE

The dynamic response of a system depends on its construction and the magnitude and type of the components. This subject can better be analyzed by considering specific instruments, therefore the response of instrument systems will not be discussed in detail in this chapter. Yet there are some terms relative to the response of an instrument that would appropriately be defined here. First, the *response time* is defined as the time after a step function is applied until a specified portion of the required change is made. This specified portion may be 90 percent, 99 percent, etc. In the *American Standard Definition of Electrical Terms*, published by the American Institute of Electrical Engineers, the response time of an instrument is defined as the time required for the pointer of the instrument to come to apparent rest after a specified change in the value of the measured quantity. For portable instruments the pointer is considered as having come to apparent rest when it has reached the actual rest point within $\pm 0.3$ percent of the final scale length. For switchboard instruments the corresponding tolerance is $\pm 1$ percent of the final scale length. In general, it may be considered to be the time required for an instrument to reach its rest position after a specific input has been applied to the instrument.

Other terms are also used to express the response of an instrument. The *speed of response*[5] is defined as the rapidity with which an instrument responds to a change in the measured quantity, and the *measuring lag*[5] is defined as the retardation or delay in the response of an instrument to a change in the measured quantity. This lag of the indicated quantity behind the actual quantity is usually small compared with the overall time taken to make a measurement, but in some controlled devices and where high-speed measurements are required, this becomes a very important factor and should be reduced to a minimum.

## 1-11. OVERSHOOT

The pointer and movement of an indicating instrument have a mass. If the measured quantity is suddenly applied to the instrument, the force applied to the movement will accelerate the movement, giving it a definite momentum. This momentum may carry the pointer beyond the desired quantity tó be measured. Thus there is an overshoot of the rest point. The overshoot is defined as the maximum amount, usually in percent of the step magnitude, by which the response exceeds the required change. As will be illustrated later, a slight amount of overshoot may be desirable to bring the instrument to rest in the minimum time, but any excess value of overshoot is undesirable.

## 1-12. DEAD TIME

Dead time[5] is defined as the time required for an instrument to begin to respond to a change in the measured value. Referring to Fig. 1-2, the measured quantity and the instrument readings are plotted as a function of time. The dead time is indicated as the time before the instrument begins to move after the measured variable has been changed. This quantity is closely associated with the dead zone. The *dead zone* is defined as the largest change

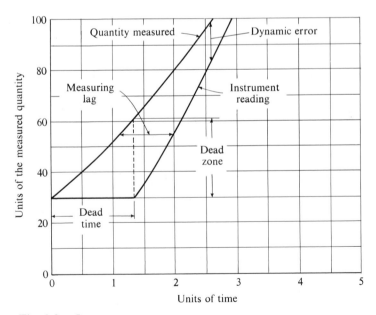

**Fig. 1-2.** *Instrument response*

of the measured quantity to which the instrument does not respond. This dead zone is produced by friction, backlash, or hysteresis in the instrument. *Hysteresis* is the retardation of the effect when a force acting upon a system is changed. It is produced by external friction or internal friction such as that produced in magnetic circuits or highly stressed materials. Although the hysteresis loops seldom are important in instrumentation, the dead zone is often an important factor and should be reduced to the minimum. The dead time, dead zone, and dynamic error are graphically shown in Fig. 1-2.

## PROBLEMS

**1-1.** A meter reads 125.5 volts, and the true voltage is 125.11 volts. Determine: (*a*) the error; (*b*) the correction of this instrument.

**1-2.** A meter reads 108.5 volts. The error taken from an error curve is +0.37 volt. Determine the true voltage.

**1-3.** An ammeter reads 5.15 amp. The correction given on a correction curve is −0.07. Determine the true current.

**1-4.** A 0–150-volt voltmeter has 75 scale divisions which can be read to 1/10 division. Determine the resolution of the meter in volts.

**1-5.** A digital voltmeter has a range from 0 to 9.999 counts. Determine the resolution of the instrument in volts when the full-scale reading is 9.999 volts.

**1-6.** A Wheatstone bridge requires a change of 7 ohms in the unknown arm of the bridge to produce a change in the deflection of the galvanometer of 3 mm. Determine the bridge sensitivity.

**1-7.** A 0–3-amp meter has a resistance of 0.012 ohm. Determine the efficiency of the ammeter.

**1-8.** A 250,000-ohm and a 750,000-ohm resistor are connected in series across a 75-volt source. (*a*) Determine the error in measuring the voltage across each of these resistances when the voltage is read with 0–150-volt, 1,000-ohms-per-volt meter. (*b*) Determine the error in measuring the voltage across each of these resistances when read with a 0–75-volt, 20,000-ohms-per-volt meter. (*c*) Determine the error in measuring the voltage across each of the resistors when a vacuum-tube voltmeter is used with an input impedance of 25 megohms.

**1-9.** A 0–150-volt voltmeter has 75 divisions. It reads 128 volts. Determine the index scale and the index reading.

**1-10.** An ammeter has a 0–1-, a 0–2.5-, and a 0–5-amp range and 50 scale divisions. Determine the range and the index scale of the meter.

**1-11.** A 10,000-ohm variable resistance has a linearity of 0.1 percent and the total movement of the contact arm is 320 deg. (*a*) Determine the maximum position deviation in degrees and the resistance deviation in ohms. (*b*) If this resistor is to be used as a potentiometer with a linear scale from 0 to 1.6 volts, determine the maximum voltage error.

**1-12.** Determine the linearity of a potentiometer to obtain an error not to exceed 1 part in 10,000.

**1-13.** List three types of changing input signals used in the dynamic analysis of instruments and instrumentation systems.

**1-14.** Define the dynamic error of an instrument or an instrumentation system.

**1-15.** What is the difference between dynamic error and fidelity?

**1-16.** What is the difference between time lag, or phase angle error, and fidelity?

**1-17.** Give the definition of response time.

**1-18.** A step input of 5 amp is applied to an ammeter. The needle swings to a maximum reading of 5.17 amp and finally comes to rest at 5.02 amp. (*a*) Determine the overshoot of the reading in amperes and in percent of final reading. (*b*) Determine the error in the instrument reading in percent.

**1-19.** A recording ammeter requires a current of 0.05 amp to overcome the initial friction of the instrument and produce motion of the movement. Define this effect, and list the factors that produce it.

**1-20.** Define (*a*) speed of response, (*b*) measuring lag, (*c*) hysteresis, and (*d*) backlash.

## REFERENCES

1. *American Standard Definitions of Electrical Terms*, American Institute of Electrical Engineers, New York, 1942.

2. *American Standard Definitions of Electrical Terms Group 30, Instruments, Meters, and Meter Testing*, American Institute of Electrical Engineers, New York, 1957.

3. D. P. Eckman, *Industrial Instrumentation*, John Wiley & Sons, Inc., New York, 1950.

4. I. F. Kinnard, *Applied Electrical Measurements*, John Wiley & Sons, Inc., New York, 1956.

5. J. D. Trimmer, *Response of Physical Systems*, John Wiley & Sons, Inc., New York, 1950.

## 2-1. LIMITING ERRORS[1]

The accuracy and precision of an instrument depend on the workmanship of those who make the instrument, the material used, and the design. These factors are blended into the type of instrument desired. If the design is such that only fair accuracy is obtainable, it is not economical to put expensive materials and skill into the production of the instrument. Likewise, it is wasteful for an instrument, designed to be an accurate product, to be poorly built. The economical production of any instrument requires the proper choice of material, design, and skill. In order to assure the purchaser of the quality of the instrument, the manufacturer guarantees a certain accuracy. In most indicating instruments the accuracy is guaranteed to be within a certain percent of full-scale reading. Circuit components, such as inductance, capacitance, and resistance are guaranteed to be within a certain percent of rated value. Many of these accuracies are maintained through careful inspection of the finished product. The limits of these deviations from the specified value are defined as limiting errors.

The magnitude of a quantity $q$ having a specified magnitude $q_1$ and a maximum error or limiting error $\pm q_e$ must have a magnitude between the limits $q_1 - q_e$ and $q_1 + q_e$ or

$$q = q_1 \pm q_e \qquad (2\text{-}1)$$

For example, the specified magnitude of a resistor is 200 ohms with a limiting error of $\pm 20$ ohms. The magnitude of the resistor will lie between the limits

$$R = 200 \pm 20 \text{ ohms}$$

or

$$R \geq 200 - 20 = 180 \text{ ohms}$$

and

$$R \leq 200 + 20 = 220 \text{ ohms}$$

The limiting error $q_e$ expressed in percent of the specified magnitude $q_1$ is

$$\%q_e = \left(\frac{q_e}{q_1}\right)100 \tag{2-2}$$

or

$$q_e = q_1\left(\frac{\%q_e}{100}\right)$$

Then

$$q = q_1 \pm q_1\left(\frac{\%q_e}{100}\right)$$

$$= q_1\left(1 \pm \frac{\%q_e}{100}\right) \tag{2-3}$$

Referring to the above example, the percent limiting error is 10 percent. Then

$$R = 200 \left(1 \pm \frac{10}{100}\right)$$

$$= 200 \, (1 \pm 0.1)$$

$$= 200 \pm 20 \text{ ohms}$$

The *fractional error* $e$ is defined as the ratio of the error to the specified magnitude of the quantity. Then

$$e = \frac{q_e}{q_1} \tag{2-4}$$

or

$$q_e = e q_1$$

Then, by Eq. (2-1),

$$q = q_1 \pm e q_1$$

$$= q_1(1 \pm e) \tag{2-5}$$

In the above example the fractional error is

$$e = \frac{20}{200} = 0.1$$

Then

$$R = 200 \, (1 \pm 0.1)$$

$$= 200 \pm 20$$

Consider another example: a 0–150-volt voltmeter reads 83 volts. The meter has a guaranteed accuracy of 1 percent of full scale. The magnitude of the limiting error of the instrument is $0.01 \times 150$ or 1.5 volts. The magnitude of the voltage measured is 83 volts. The fractional limiting error at this voltage is

$$e = \frac{1.5}{83} = 0.0181$$

and the voltage measured is between the limits of

$$E = 83(1 \pm 0.018) = 83 \pm 1.5$$

The limiting error in percent is

$$\%q_e = \frac{1.5}{83} (100) = 1.81\%$$

It is important to note that this meter is guaranteed to have an error of less than 1 percent of full scale, or the limiting error is 1.0 percent at a full-scale reading of 150 volts. But when the meter reads 83 volts, the limiting error is

1.81 percent. The percent limiting error will be greater if a smaller voltage is measured. If the meter reads 75 volts, the percent limiting error is

$$\%q_e = \frac{1.5}{75}(100) = 2\%$$

If the meter reads 37.5 volts, the limiting error is

$$\%q_e = \frac{1.5}{37.5}(100) = 4\%$$

This increase in the percent limiting error as smaller voltages are measured occurs because the magnitude of the limiting error $q_e$ is based on the full-scale reading of the meter and is a fixed quantity, while the voltage readings $q$ can be any magnitudes from zero to 150 volts. In this example $q$ has been assigned a series of decreasing magnitudes to illustrate that the percent error by Eq. (2-2) increases as the voltage being measured decreases. For this reason, meters which read well up on their scales should be chosen wherever possible.

In limiting errors the specified quantity $q_1$ is taken as the true quantity, and the quantity which has the maximum deviation from $q_1$ is taken as the erroneous quantity. Solving for the limiting error in Eq. (2-1) gives

$$q_e = q - q_1 \qquad (2\text{-}6)$$

Substituting this value of $q_e$ into Eq. (2-4) gives

$$e = \frac{q - q_1}{q_1}$$

$$= \frac{\text{erroneous quantity} - \text{true quantity}}{\text{true quantity}} \qquad (2\text{-}7)$$

**Combinations of Quantities with Limiting Errors[1]**

When two or more quantities, each having a limiting error, are combined, it is advantageous to be able to compute the limiting error of the combination; that is, when the quantities with limiting errors are combined in networks, such as resistances in series or in parallel, or in a Wheatstone bridge circuit, etc., it is desirable to be able to compute the fractional error of the resistance in series or in parallel or in other circuit combinations. Methods of determining the limiting error of (1) the sum of two quantities, (2) the difference of two quantities, (3) the product of two quantities, and (4) the quotient of two quantities will now be derived. These terms can be applied to the solution of basic network problems.

LIMITING ERROR OF THE SUM OF TWO QUANTITIES, EACH HAVING A LIMITING ERROR. The fractional limiting error of the sum of the quantities

$$q_a = q_{1a}(1 \pm e_a)$$

and

$$q_b = q_{1b}(1 \pm e_b)$$

can be determined by Eq. (2-7) where the erroneous value of $(q_a + q_b)$ is

$$(q_a + q_b) \text{ erroneous} = q_{1a}(1 \pm e_a) + q_{1b}(1 \pm e_b)$$

and the true value of $(q_a + q_b)$ is

$$(q_a + q_b) \text{ true} = q_{1a} + q_{1b}$$

Then substituting in Eq. (2-7) gives

$$e_{a+b} = \frac{[q_{1a}(1 \pm e_a) + q_{1b}(1 \pm e_b)] - (q_{1a} + q_{1b})}{q_{1a} + q_{1b}}$$

$$= \frac{(\pm e_a q_{1a}) + (\pm e_b q_{1b})}{q_{1a} + q_{1b}}$$

The signs in the numerator must be both $(+)$ or both $(-)$ to give the maximum or limiting error. Then

$$e_{a+b} = \pm \frac{e_a q_{1a} + e_b q_{1b}}{q_{1a} + q_{1b}} = \pm \frac{q_{ea} + q_{eb}}{q_{1a} + q_{1b}} \tag{2-8}$$

where $q_{ea}$ and $q_{eb}$ are the limiting errors of $q_a$ and $q_b$. To illustrate, let $q_a = 250 \pm 2.1$ and $q_b = 100 \pm 1.5$. Then, by Eq. (2-8),

$$e_{a+b} = \pm \frac{2.1 + 1.5}{250 + 100}$$

$$= \pm \frac{3.6}{350} = \pm 0.0103$$

Then

$$q_{(a+b)} = (q_{1a} + q_{1b})(1 \pm e_{a+b})$$
$$= (250 + 100)(1 \pm 0.0103)$$
$$= 350 \pm (350)(0.0103)$$
$$= 350 \pm 3.6$$

Referring to Eq. (2-8),

$$e_{a+b} \cong e_a$$

when

$$q_{1a} \gg q_{1b}$$

and

$$e_{a+b} \cong e_b$$

when

$$q_{1b} \gg q_{1a}$$

LIMITING FRACTIONAL ERROR OF THE DIFFERENCE OF TWO QUANTITIES, EACH HAVING A LIMITING ERROR. The fractional limiting error of the difference of the quantities

$$q_a = q_{1a}(1 \pm e_a)$$

and

$$q_b = q_{1b}(1 \pm e_b)$$

by Eq. (2-7) is

$$e_{a-b} = \frac{[q_{1a}(1 \pm e_a) - q_{1b}(1 \pm e_b)] - (q_{1a} - q_{1b})}{q_{1a} - q_{1b}}$$

$$= \frac{(\pm e_a q_{1a}) - (\pm e_b q_{1b})}{q_{1a} - q_{1b}}$$

The signs of $e_a$ and $e_b$ in this equation must be different to obtain the maximum or limiting error. Then

$$e_{a-b} = \pm \frac{e_a q_{1a} + e_b q_{1b}}{q_{1a} - q_{1b}}$$

$$= \pm \frac{q_{ea} + q_{eb}}{q_{1a} - q_{1b}} \tag{2-9}$$

where $q_{ea}$ and $q_{eb}$ are the limiting errors of $q_a$ and $q_b$. The value of $e_{a-b}$ can become very large when $q_{1a}$ and $q_{1b}$ are nearly equal. For example, the fractional limiting error of the difference of the quantities $q_a$ and $q_b$ given above will be

$$e_{a-b} = \pm \frac{2.1 + 1.5}{250 - 100} = \pm \frac{3.6}{150}$$

$$= \pm 0.024$$

and $q_{a-b}$ becomes

$$q_{a-b} = (q_{1a} - q_{1b})(1 \pm e_{a-b})$$
$$= (250 - 100)(1 \pm 0.024)$$
$$= 150 \pm 3.6$$

FRACTIONAL LIMITING ERROR OF THE PRODUCT OF TWO QUANTITIES. The fractional limiting error of the product of two quantities

$$q_a = q_{1a}(1 \pm e_a)$$

and

$$q_b = q_{1b}(1 \pm e_b)$$

is obtained by using Eq. (2-7). Then

$$e_{ab} = \frac{[q_{1a}(1 \pm e_a)][q_{1b}(1 \pm e_b)] - q_{1a}q_{1b}}{q_{1a}q_{1b}}$$
$$= 1 + e_a + e_b + e_a e_b - 1$$
$$= e_a + e_b + e_a e_b \tag{2-10}$$

The $(+)$ signs of $e_a$ and $e_b$ are chosen to obtain the maximum or limiting fractional error. If second-order errors are neglected, the fractional limiting error of the product of $q_a$ and $q_b$ is

$$e_{ab} \cong e_a + e_b \qquad (2\text{-}11)$$

If the values of $q_a$ and $q_b$ given above are used, the fractional error of $q_a$ is

$$e_a = \frac{2.1}{250} = 0.0084$$

and

$$e_b = \frac{1.5}{100} = 0.015$$

By Eq. (2-10), the fractional limiting error of the product of $q_a$ and $q_b$ is

$$e_{ab} = 0.0084 + 0.015 + (0.0084)(0.015)$$
$$= 0.023526$$

By Eq. (2-11),

$$e_{ab} \cong 0.0084 + 0.015$$
$$= 0.0234$$

By neglecting the second-order errors, the answer is correct to two significant figures, which is sufficient for error computations, as the error itself is an approximation.

FRACTIONAL LIMITING ERROR OF THE QUOTIENT OF TWO QUANTITIES. The fractional limiting error of the quotient of two numbers

$$q_a = q_{1a}(1 \pm e_a)$$

and

$$q_b = q_{1b}(1 \pm e_b)$$

is obtained by using Eq. (2-7). Then

$$e_{a/b} = \frac{\dfrac{q_{1a}(1 \pm e_a)}{q_{1b}(1 \pm e_b)} - \dfrac{q_{1a}}{q_{1b}}}{\dfrac{q_{1a}}{q_{1b}}}$$

$$= \frac{1 \pm e_a}{1 \pm e_b} - 1$$

$$= \frac{(1 \pm e_a) - (1 \pm e_b)}{1 \pm e_b}$$

$$= \frac{(\pm e_a) - (\pm e_b)}{1 \pm e_b}$$

The sign of $e_a$ must be $(+)$ and the sign of $e_b$ must be $(-)$ to obtain the maximum or limiting fractional error of the quotient of $q_a$ and $q_b$. Then

$$e_{a/b} = \pm \frac{e_a + e_b}{1 - e_b} \qquad (2\text{-}12)$$

when $1 \gg e_b$

$$e_{a/b} = \pm(e_a + e_b) \qquad (2\text{-}13)$$

Again using the above values of $q_a$ and $q_b$, the quotient of the fractional limiting error of the quotient of $q_a$ divided by $q_b$, using Eq. (2-12), is

$$e_{a/b} = \frac{0.0084 + 0.015}{1 - 0.015}$$

$$= \frac{0.0234}{0.985} = 0.023756$$

Using Eq. (2-13),

$$e_{a/b} = 0.0084 + 0.015$$

$$= 0.0234$$

This approximation is correct to two significant figures, which is sufficient for computing errors.

## 2-2. KNOWN ERRORS[1]

When the error of an instrument or a component of a circuit is known, the effect of this error, when combined with other known errors, can be computed in a manner similar to the combinations of the limiting error, except that the signs of the fractional errors $e_a$ and $e_b$ are given and must be preserved in the computations. The value of $q$ is no longer

$$q = q_1(1 \pm e)$$

but

$$q = q_1(1 + e)$$

The expressions for $e_{a+b}$, $e_{a-b}$, $e_{ab}$, and $e_{a/b}$ are given, using positive values for $e_a$ and $e_b$. These fractional errors can be either positive or negative and will carry their own signs when they are substituted into the following equations.

1. The fractional known error of the sum of $q_a$ and $q_b$ is

$$e_{a+b} = \frac{e_a q_{1a} + e_b q_{1b}}{q_{1a} + q_{1b}} \qquad (2\text{-}14)$$

2. The fractional known error of the difference of $q_a$ and $q_b$ is

$$e_{a-b} = \frac{e_a q_{1a} - e_b q_{1b}}{q_{1a} - q_{1b}} \tag{2-15}$$

3. The fractional known error of the product of $q_a$ and $q_b$ is

$$e_{ab} = e_a + e_b \tag{2-16}$$

4. The fractional known error of the quotient of $q_a$ divided by $q_b$ is

$$e_{a/b} = e_a - e_b \tag{2-17}$$

## 2-3. ERROR IN INSTRUMENTS[1,2]

Error in instruments can be divided into two classes: first, systematic errors; second, accidental or random errors. Systematic errors, in turn, can be divided into three groups: instrumental errors, environmental errors, and observer errors.

### Systematic Errors

Instrumental errors are errors within the instrument, owing to its construction, its calibration, or its operation. Calibration errors may result in the instrument reading either high or low. Improper setting of the zero point would have a similar effect. Poor construction, variation in the air gap, irregular spring tension, etc., in d'Arsonval movements may cause instrumental errors. Instrumental errors can be corrected by the proper calibration of the instrument itself.

Environmental errors are due to external conditions. These may be the effects of temperature, barometric pressure, magnetic fields, electrostatic fields, humidity, dust, vibrations, and other conditions. The corrective methods used to reduce these effects include air conditioning, shielding, hermetically sealing, etc.

Observer errors are recording errors made when the data are read by an observer; they may include parallax, wrong scale, etc.

Much of our modern data is taken by readout systems. Errors involved in these systems would constitute *machine errors*. These errors are due to improper zero adjustment, wrong scale calibration, etc. Errors incurred in the data reduction equipment are instrumental errors if these errors are due to the construction and calibration of the instrument; they are environmental errors if these errors are conditions reacting upon the readout system.

## Random Errors

Random errors are errors due to unknown causes, and they occur even when all known means of correction have failed. To illustrate these errors better, suppose that a current of 15 amp is supplied to an instrument and the instrument is read at hourly intervals. It is found that the readings vary from time to time, although the source of current is accurately measured and known to be correct, and the instrument is operated under the best-known environmental conditions. This variation cannot be corrected by calibration. These errors cannot be explained. Variations in these readings can be analyzed by statistical methods to obtain the best approximation of the true magnitude of the quantity being measured.

ARITHMETIC MEAN.[1,3,4]  The best approximation that can be made of a number of readings of the same quantity is the arithmetic mean of the numbers read, and the most probable quantity would be obtained from an infinite number of readings. The arithmetic mean $\bar{X}$ is

$$\bar{X} = \frac{x_1 + x_2 + x_3 + \ldots + x_n}{n} = \frac{\sum x}{n} \tag{2-18}$$

where

$$\bar{X} = \text{arithmetic mean}$$
$$x_1, x_2, x_3, \text{ to } x_n = \text{readings or samples}$$
$$n = \text{number of readings taken or degrees of freedom}$$

DEVIATION.  Deviation is the departure of the observed reading from the arithmetic mean of the group of readings. Let the deviation of reading $x_1$ be $d_1$ and the deviation of reading $x_2$ be $d_2$, etc. Then

$$d_1 = x_1 - \bar{X}$$

and

$$d_2 = x_2 - \bar{X} \tag{2-19}$$

It will be noted that the algebraic sum of the deviation is zero.

*Average Deviation.*[1,3,4]  The average deviation is defined as the sum of the deviations without respect to sign; that is, the sum of the absolute values of the deviation divided by the number of readings. Thus the average deviation is

$$\bar{D} = \frac{|d_1| + |d_2| + \ldots + |d_n|}{n}$$
$$= \frac{\sum |d|}{n} \tag{2-20}$$

This quantity is an indication of the precision of the instrument.

*Standard Deviation.*[1,3,4] Another valuable term in the analysis of random errors is the standard deviation or root-mean-square (rms) deviation. The standard deviation is defined as the square root of the sum of the individual deviations squared, divided by the number of readings. Thus

$$\sigma = \sqrt{\frac{d_1{}^2 + d_2{}^2 + \ldots + d_n{}^2}{n}}$$

$$= \sqrt{\frac{\sum d^2}{n}} \tag{2-21}$$

It will be noted that, regardless of the sign of the deviation, the deviation squared is positive. This term is used extensively in statistical work.

THE NORMAL DISTRIBUTION CURVE.[1,3,4] The law of probability states that the normal occurrence of deviations from the average value of an infinite number of measurements can be expressed by

$$y = \frac{h}{\sqrt{\pi}} \epsilon^{-h^2 x^2} \tag{2-22}$$

where

$y =$ number of readings at any particular deviation $x$

$h =$ a factor, the significance of which will be shown later

$\epsilon =$ base of the natural logarithms.

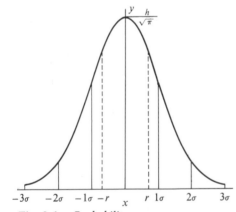

Fig. 2-1. *Probability curve*

The curve showing $y$ plotted as a function of $x$ is given in Fig. 2-1 and is defined as the normal probability curve. This curve is symmetrical about the arithmetic mean value, and the area under the curve is equal to unity. Under the conditions here specified the total number of readings taken is represented by 1. The fraction of the total number of readings occurring between the values $x_1$ and $x_2$ will be equal to the area under the curve between these two values of $x$, or

$$n_{1-2} = \frac{h}{\sqrt{\pi}} \int_{x_1}^{x_2} \epsilon^{-h^2 x^2} \, dx \tag{2-23}$$

If the area between $x_1$ and $x_2$ were 0.25, then 0.25 of the total deviations, or 25 percent, would fall between $x_1$ and $x_2$. If, in plotting the value of $y$ with respect to $x$ for any given set of readings, the readings do not follow the general law of probability, then the curve is not a normal distribution curve.

This would indicate that some factor that was not a pure random value was entering into the measurements. In the following analysis it will be assumed that the values follow the normal law of probability and thus have a normal distribution curve as represented by Fig. 2-1.

If the lower value $x_1$ were zero in Eq. (2-23) and $x_2$ were $x$, then the fraction of the total number of deviations falling between zero and $x$ could be determined by

$$n_{0-x} = \frac{h}{\sqrt{\pi}} \int_0^x \epsilon^{-h^2 x^2} \, dx \qquad (2\text{-}24)$$

This value as a function of $x$ is given in tables of the probability integrals.

## 2-4. PROBABLE ERROR[1,3,4]

The $h$ term in the above equations determines the sharpness of the normal probability curve. When $x = 0$,

$$y = \frac{h}{\sqrt{\pi}} \qquad (2\text{-}25)$$

and thus the maximum value of $y$ depends on $h$. The larger the value of $h$, the sharper is the curve, and the deviations are more closely grouped around $x = 0$. Also, the larger the value of $h$, the more precise is the instrument. Precision can also be measured by the probable error. The *probable error* is defined as the value of $x$ at which half the total number of deviations lie between $\pm x$. This value of $x$ will be symbolized by $r$. Then 25 percent of the deviations will lie between 0 and $x$, when $x = r$. By Eq. (2-23),

$$0.25 = \frac{h}{\sqrt{\pi}} \int_0^r \epsilon^{-h^2 x^2} \, dx$$

which has been evaluated for $r$, giving

$$r = \frac{0.4769}{h} \qquad (2\text{-}26)$$

### Average Deviation as a Function of $h$ and Probable Error

The number of deviations at a given $x$ through a distance of $dx$ is equal to $y \, dx$ or the area of the element $dx$ at $x$. This area multiplied by $x$ will give the sum of the deviations through the element $dx$, as $x$ is the magnitude of the deviations and $y \, dx$ is the number of these deviations. Thus

$$|x| y \, dx = \sum d \Big|_x^{x+dx}$$

Now the summation of $|x|y\,dx$ for the area under the normal probability curve, without regard as to the sign of the deviation, will be the sum of all the deviations forming the normal probability curve. Thus

$$\bar{D} = \int_{-\infty}^{+\infty} |x|y\,dx = \frac{2h}{\sqrt{\pi}} \int_0^\infty \epsilon^{-h^2 x^2} x\,dx$$

$$= \frac{1}{\sqrt{\pi}h} \int_0^\infty \epsilon^{-h^2 x^2}(-2h^2 x)\,dx$$

$$= \frac{1}{\sqrt{\pi}h} \tag{2-27}$$

Solving Eq. (2-26) for $h$ gives

$$h = \frac{0.4764}{r}$$

Substituting this in Eq. (2-27) gives

$$\bar{D} = \frac{r}{0.8453} \tag{2-28}$$

This represents the sum of the absolute values of the deviation in terms of the dimension of the normal probability curve. The sum of the absolute value of the deviations divided by the number of deviations is, by definition, the average deviation. The dimension of the normal probability curve is such that the area under the curve is 1, or the total number of deviations, if taken as a whole, is equal to unity. Then Eq. (2-27) divided by 1 is the average deviation. Thus the summation listed in Eq. (2-27) is the desired average deviation, and the average deviation can be determined by the factor $h$ in Eq. (2-27) or the factor $r$ in Eq. (2-28).

**Relationship of Standard Deviation, Probable Error, and Average Deviation**

From Eq. (2-21) the standard deviation is given by the expression

$$\sigma^2 = \frac{\sum d^2}{n}$$

Referring to the normal distribution curve, this becomes

$$\sigma^2 = \frac{2h}{\sqrt{\pi}} \int_0^\infty \epsilon^{-h^2 x^2} x^2\,dx$$

Integrating this gives

$$\sigma^2 = \frac{1}{2h^2}$$

or

$$\sigma = \frac{1}{\sqrt{2}h} = \frac{r}{0.6745} \tag{2-29}$$

Thus, in Eqs. (2-26), (2-27), and (2-29), the probable error, the average deviation, and the standard deviation are given in terms of $h$.

If $y$ were plotted as a function of $\sigma$ instead of $x$, there would be a fixed relationship between $h$, the magnitudes of $y$, and the standard deviation. These relationships are briefly given in Table 2-1. An extended list of these values can be obtained in normal error tables.

### Table 2-1

| 'Standard Deviation $\sigma$ | Area Between Zero and $\sigma$ | $y$ |
|---|---|---|
| 0.00 | 0.0000 | 0.3989 |
| 0.32 | 0.1255 | 0.3790 |
| 0.68 | 0.2518 | 0.3166 |
| 1.00 | 0.3413 | 0.2450 |
| 2.00 | 0.4773 | 0.0540 |
| 3.00 | 0.4987 | 0.0044 |
| 4.00 | 0.5000 | 0.0001 |

**Probable Error of a Finite Number of Readings**

In the above analysis using the probability curve, it was assumed that an infinite number of readings were taken to obtain this curve and the derived expressions. With a finite number of readings, there is a slight difference between the computed values given above and the values obtained for a set of finite readings. For example, substituting Eq. (2-21) into Eq. (2-29) gives the probable error as

$$r = 0.6745 \sqrt{\frac{d_1{}^2 + d_2{}^2 + \ldots + d_n{}^2}{n}}$$

for an infinite number of deviations forming the normal probability curve where $n$ is infinite. But for a finite number of deviations, the probable error for one reading is

$$r_1 = 0.6745 \sqrt{\frac{d_1{}^2 + d_2{}^2 + \ldots + d_n{}^2}{n - 1}} \qquad (2\text{-}30)$$

This states that, for a computed $r_1$ obtained from $n$ readings, one more reading would have an even chance of being above or below $r_1$.

In an infinite number of readings with random dispersion, the true value is the average value. With a finite number of readings, the average reading has a probable error of

$$r_{\text{avg}} = \frac{1}{\sqrt{n}} r_1$$

$$= 0.6745 \sqrt{\frac{d_1{}^2 + d_2{}^2 + \ldots + d_n{}^2}{n(n - 1)}} \qquad (2\text{-}31)$$

This states that for $n$ finite readings the probable error is $r_{avg}$, and that if a second set of $n$ readings were taken, the average of the second set would have an even chance of being either greater or less than $r_{avg}$.

It will be noted that when

$$n \gg 1$$

then

$$n - 1 \cong n$$

and

$$r_1 \cong 0.6745\sigma \tag{2-32}$$

and

$$r_{avg} = 0.6745 \frac{\sigma}{\sqrt{n}} \tag{2-33}$$

From Eq. (2-31) it is observed that the accuracy of the average value varies inversely as the square root of the number of readings. Thus the probability of the average of 81 readings is improved by only a factor of 3 over the probable of the average of 9 readings. With these criteria it will be observed that the accuracy does not increase proportionally with the number of readings; therefore, few readings may have nearly as valid an approximation as a great number. Often, in scientific work, the probable error is given to specify the variation of the quantity which has been measured; therefore, it is advantageous to understand this term and to be able to work with quantities where the probable error is given.

## Probable Error of Combinations of Components
### Where the Probable Error is Given

The probable error of a function of components whose probable error is known is not computed in the same manner as the combined error where the limiting or known error is given, as the probable error functions are not linear. Consider the variables $V_1$, $V_2$, to $V_n$ where $R$ is

$$R = f(V_1, V_2, \ldots V_n) \tag{2-34}$$

and $\Delta V_1$, $\Delta V_2$, etc., are the probable errors of $V_1$, $V_2$, etc. Then the probable error $\Delta R_1$ of $R$ due to the error in $V_1$ is

$$\Delta R_1 = \Delta V_1 \frac{\delta R}{\delta V_1}$$

and the probable error $\Delta R_2$ of $R$ due to the error in $V_2$ is

$$\Delta R_2 = \Delta V_2 \frac{\delta R}{\delta V_2} \quad \text{etc.} \tag{2-35}$$

Then the probable error $\Delta R$ due to the error of all the components is

$$\Delta R = \sqrt{(\Delta R_1)^2 + (\Delta R_2)^2 + \ldots (\Delta R_n)^2} \tag{2-36}$$

For example, suppose that a current of 10 amp with a probable error of $\pm 0.1$ amp is passing through a resistance of 100 ohms with a probable error of $\pm 2$ ohms. To determine the power dissipated in heat and the probable error of the computed power, let

$$V_1 = \text{the current} = 10, \text{ and } \Delta V_1 = \pm 0.1$$
$$V_2 = \text{the resistance} = 100, \text{ and } \Delta V_2 = \pm 2$$
$$R = \text{the power} = V_1{}^2 V_2 = (10)^2(100) = 10{,}000 \text{ watts}$$
$$\Delta R_1 = \Delta V_1 \frac{\delta R}{\delta V_1} = \Delta V_1 \frac{\delta}{\delta V_1}(V_1{}^2 V_2) = (\Delta V_1)(2V_1 V_2)$$
$$= (0.1)(2)(10)(100) = 200$$

and

$$\Delta R_2 = \Delta V_2 \frac{\delta R}{\delta V_2} = \Delta V_2 \frac{\delta}{\delta V_2}(V_1{}^2 V_2) = (\Delta V_2)(V_1{}^2)$$
$$= (2)(100) = 200$$

Then

$$\Delta R = \sqrt{\Delta R_1{}^2 + \Delta R_2{}^2} = \sqrt{200^2 + 200^2}$$
$$= 283 \text{ watts probable error}$$
$$R = 10{,}000 \pm 280 \text{ watts}$$

The error term in this answer is carried to only two significant figures, as it is an approximation and there is no necessity of carrying a probable error to more than two significant figures.

## 2-5. SUMMARY

In this chapter, limiting and known errors were first discussed. These are fixed quantities. The magnitude of the limiting errors and the magnitude and the sign of the known errors are known. With these fixed quantities the procedure follows linear computations, and the result of their combination is given in the forepart of this chapter. Distinct from these limiting and known errors are the probable errors. It must be kept in mind that the probable error is not the maximum error or limiting error; rather, it is a quantity obtained by the application of the law of probability, which is the most probable guess that can be made. The probable error states that, in the law of averages, the error will be larger than the probable error 50 percent of the trials, and less than the probable error 50 percent of the trials. The computations of the probable errors are based on the normal probability curve and follow the rules given in the latter part of this chapter. The definition of these errors must be clearly understood. When an error is defined, it should be defined as a probable error, a known error, or a limiting error. Sometimes the type of error is not specified. In most instrumentation problems the error specified is a probable error, but, in specifying components, the limiting error is usually given.

## PROBLEMS

**2-1.** The solution for the unknown resistance in a Wheatstone bridge is

$$R_X = \frac{R_2 R_3}{R_1}$$

where

$$R_1 = 100 \pm 0.5 \text{ percent}$$
$$R_2 = 1{,}000 \pm 0.5 \text{ percent}$$
$$R_3 = 728 \pm 0.5 \text{ percent}$$

Determine the magnitude of the unknown resistance and the fractional limiting error in ohms and in percent of the unknown resistance $R_X$.

**2-2.** A resistance is rated at 3,200 ohms, and the measured current through this resistor is 64 ma. (*a*) Compute the watts dissipated in the resistor. (It was later found that the resistance of the resistor was 0.2 percent greater than the specified resistance and the ammeter read 0.75 percent more than the true current.) (*b*) Determine the known error in the computed power in part (*a*) in watts and in percent of the computed power.

**2-3.** Three resistors have the following ratings:

$$R_1 = 37 \pm 5 \text{ percent}$$
$$R_2 = 75 \pm 5 \text{ percent}$$
$$R_3 = 50 \pm 5 \text{ percent}$$

(*a*) Determine the magnitude and the limiting error in ohms and in percent of the resistance of these resistances connected in series. (*b*) Determine the magnitude and the limiting error in ohms and in percent of the resistance of these resistances connected in parallel.

**2-4.** The following magnitudes were obtained from the measurements of a given quantity: 147.2, 147.4, 148.1, 147.9, 147.1, 147.5, 147.6, 147.4, 147.6, and 147.7. Determine: (*a*) the arithmetic mean; (*b*) the average deviation; (*c*) the standard deviation; (*d*) the probable error of the average of 10 readings.

**2-5.** The voltage across a resistance is 220 volts with a probable error of ± 1.5 percent, and the resistance is 52 ohms with a probable error of ± 2.0 percent. Determine the probable error and magnitude of the power.

**2-6.** Two resistors have the following magnitudes and probable errors:

$$R_1 = 121 \pm 2 \text{ percent}$$
$$R_2 = \phantom{0}87 \pm 2 \text{ percent}$$

Determine the magnitude and the probable error in ohms and in percent of the magnitude of the resistance of: (*a*) these resistances in parallel; (*b*) these resistances in series.

**2-7.** The side of a cube is 12.7 in. long with a probable error of $\pm 0.31$ in. Determine the volume of the cube and the probable error of the volume.

**2-8.** A 250-ohm, a 500-ohm, and a 375-ohm resistor are connected in parallel. The 250-ohm resistor has a $+0.025$ fractional error, the 500-ohm resistor has a $-0.036$ fractional error, and the 375-ohm resistor has a $+0.014$ fractional error. Determine (*a*) the total resistance of these resistors in parallel neglecting the errors, (*b*) the total resistance of these resistors considering the error of each resistor, and (*c*) the fractional error of the parallel resistance based on the rated values.

**2-9.** Successive calibration readings of a pressure transducer for full-scale reading are as follows: 25,250, 25,150, 25,175, 25,095, 25,075, 25,140, 25,190, 25,210, 25,110, and 25,105 psi. Determine (*a*) the standard deviation and (*b*) the probable error.

**2-10.** In Prob. 9 determine the probable error of one more reading.

**2-11.** In Prob. 9 determine the probable error of the average of ten more readings.

**2-12.** The sides of a rectangular parallelepiped are: width, 10.24 in.; length, 22.56 in.; height, 5.12 in. as measured with a vernier caliper. The probable error of these measurements are: width, $\pm 0.014$ in.; length, $\pm 0.026$ in.; height, $\pm 0.007$ in. Determine the probable error of the volume computed from these measurements.

**2-13.** Determine (*a*) the value of $x$ in terms of $\sigma$ when the area under the probability curve between 0 and $x$ is 0.1255, (*b*) the value of $y$ at this value of $x$.

**2-14.** Resistors $a$ and $b$ are connected in parallel, and this combination is connected in series with resistor $c$. The magnitude and limiting error in percent of these resistors are $a = 12.2 \pm 5$ percent, $b = 20.5 \pm 10$ percent, and $c = 30.4 \pm 10$ percent. Determine (*a*) the magnitude and (*b*) the percent limiting error of the combined resistors.

**2-15.** Define (*a*) instrumental errors, (*b*) recording errors, (*c*) machine errors, (*d*) limiting errors, (*e*) known errors, (*f*) calibration errors, (*g*) environmental errors, (*h*) recording errors, (i) random errors, and (*j*) probable errors.

**2-16.** What is known or assumed when the probable error and standard deviation are computed?

## REFERENCES

1. M. B. Stout, *Basic Electrical Measurements*, First Edition, Prentice-Hall, Inc., Englewood Cliffs, N.J., 1951.

2. I. F. Kinnard, *Applied Electrical Measurements*, John Wiley & Sons, Inc., New York, 1956.

3. A. E. Waugh, *Elements of Statistical Method*, McGraw-Hill Book Company, Inc., New York, 1943.

4. O. L. Davis, *Statistical Methods in Research and Production*, Oliver & Boyd, Ltd., Edinburgh and London, 1949.

5. B. Ostle, *Statistics in Research*, Iowa State College Press, Ames, Iowa, 1956.

# Chapter 3

# AND BALLISTIC

A galvanometer is an instrument which employs the reaction between a field produced by a permanent magnet and the electrical current in a coil to produce a deflection of the indicating device. The construction of a galvanometer can take many forms. One type has a thin needle-shaped bar magnet suspended in the center of a narrow circular coil, in which the horizontal components of the earth's magnetic field provide the restoring force and the force deflecting the needle is the field produced by the current flowing through the coil. A second type has a small bar magnet suspended in a coil, with the instrument thoroughly shielded and the restoring force being supplied by the elasticity of the suspending mechanism. A third type, which is the most commonly used at the present time, is a coil suspended in the air gap of a permanent magnet. The current is supplied to the coil through the conducting material used in the suspension, and the stiffness of the suspension supplies the restoring force. The current through the coil produces the driving torque. In these instruments the deflection of the movement is usually measured by the reflection of a light beam from a mirror mounted on the moving coil of the instrument. Other types of galvanometers use bearing mountings and spiral springs to supply the restoring force.

# DIRECT-CURRENT

# GALVANOMETERS

Referring to the galvanometer shown in Fig. 3-1, the coil is suspended in a flux density $B$. The length of the coil in this flux is $L$, and the width of the coil is $b$. Then the force produced on each side of the coil is

$$F = iBNL \qquad (3-1)$$

In mks units

$F =$ force, in newtons (a newton is equal to a force of $10^5$ dynes, or the weight of 0.102 kg, 0.224 lb, or 3.6 oz)

$B =$ webers/square meter

$i =$ amperes

$N =$ turns

$L =$ meters (length)

$b =$ meters (width)

(Unless otherwise stated, the mks units will be used in this text.) Then the displacing torque produced by the current in the coil is

$$\tau_d = (2F)\left(\frac{b}{2}\right) = Fb$$

$$= iBNLb \tag{3-2}$$

where $\tau_d$ is the torque in newton-meters.

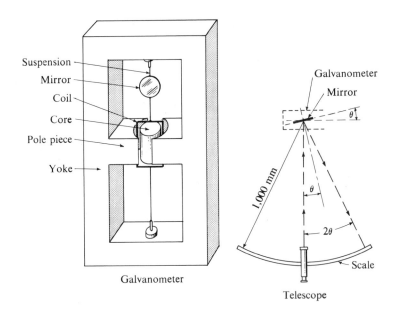

**Fig. 3-1.** *Current galvanometer*

For a given instrument, $B$, $N$, $L$, and $b$ are constant. Then let

$$G = BNLb \tag{3-3}$$

Substituting Eq. (3-3) in Eq. (3-2) gives

$$\tau_d = Gi \tag{3-4}$$

The restoring torque due to the elasticity of the suspension is

$$\tau_r = S\theta$$

where

$S$ = suspension restoring torque per radian deflection

$\theta$ = deflection of the coil from the zero position, in radians

At equilibrium,

$$Gi = S\theta \tag{3-5}$$

Then the deflection of the coil is

$$\theta = \frac{\tau_r}{S} = \frac{Gi}{S} \tag{3-6}$$

In Eq. (3-6), the *stiffness coefficient* or *torque constant* $S$ is constant, so let

$$K_s = \frac{2G}{S} \tag{3-7}$$

Then

$$2\theta = K_s i \tag{3-8}$$

The deflection registered on the mirror-type galvanometer scale in Fig. 3-1 is

$$d = 2L_g\theta \tag{3-9}$$

where

$d$ = scale deflection, in millimeters
$L_g$ = distance from the line about which the coil rotates to the scale, in millimeters

Substituting Eq. (3-7) in Eq. (3-9) gives

$$d = K_s L_g i$$

Then

$$\frac{d}{i} = K_s L_g = S_i \tag{3-10}$$

when, and only when, $L_g$ is constant. This constant $S_i$ is the current sensitivity of the galvanometer expressed in millimeters per microampere.

### 3-3. DYNAMIC ANALYSIS OF A GALVANOMETER[1]

In order to analyze the dynamic characteristics of a galvanometer, consider the circuit in Fig. 3-2 where

$E$ = the step function of emf applied to the circuit at time $t = 0$
$R$ = resistance of the galvanometer circuit
$\phi$ = the flux through the coil (webers)
$\theta$ = angular deflection of the coil from the zero current position
$Lb$ = area of coil (length $L$ and width $b$)
$J$ = moment of inertia of the coil
$S$ = stiffness coefficient or torque factor of the coil suspension
$D_m$ = mechanical damping coefficient
$D$ = total damping coefficient

The emf generated in the coil is

$$e = -N\frac{d\phi}{dt}$$

$$= -NBLb\frac{d\theta}{dt} \tag{3-11}$$

where

$B$ = flux density in the coil

$Lb$ = area of the coil

By Eq. (3-3)

$$G = NBLb$$

Then

$$e = -G\frac{d\theta}{dt} \tag{3-12}$$

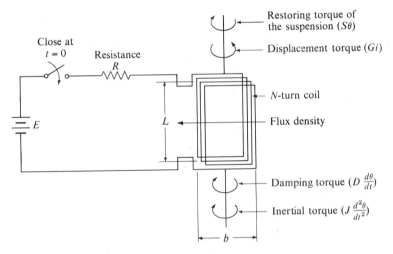

**Fig. 3-2.** *Current-galvanometer circuit*

The total emf in the galvanometer circuit after $t = 0$ is $E + e$, and the current in the circuit is

$$i = \frac{E + e}{R} = \frac{E}{R} + \frac{e}{R}$$

$$= \frac{E}{R} - \frac{G}{R}\frac{d\theta}{dt} \tag{3-13}$$

The displacing torque due to the current is

$$\tau_d = Gi = \frac{EG}{R} - \frac{G^2}{R}\frac{d\theta}{dt} \tag{3-14}$$

This is the driving torque and is equal to the sum of the mechanical forces acting on the movement. The equation of these forces is

$$J\frac{d^2\theta}{dt^2} + D_m\frac{d\theta}{dt} + S\theta = \frac{EG}{R} - \frac{G^2}{R}\frac{d\theta}{dt}$$

or

$$J\frac{d^2\theta}{dt^2} + \left(D_m + \frac{G^2}{R}\right)\frac{d\theta}{dt} + S\theta = \frac{EG}{R}$$

where $G^2/R$ is the electromagnetic damping factor, and the total damping factor is the sum of the electromagnetic damping and the mechanical damping. Then

$$D = D_m + \frac{G^2}{R} \tag{3-15}$$

and

$$J\frac{d^2\theta}{dt^2} + D\frac{d\theta}{dt} + S\theta = \frac{EG}{R}$$

Dividing this equation by $J$ gives

$$\frac{d^2\theta}{dt^2} + \frac{D}{J}\frac{d\theta}{dt} + \frac{S}{J}\theta = \frac{EG}{JR} \tag{3-16}$$

The solution of this equation depends upon the relative magnitude of $D/J$ and $S/J$.

### 3-4. THE UNDERDAMPED MOTION OF A GALVANOMETER [1,2,3]

The motion of a galvanometer is underdamped when

$$\frac{D^2}{4J^2} < \frac{S}{J} \quad \text{or} \quad D^2 < 4JS$$

The solution of Eq. (3-16), under these conditions, is

$$\theta = \theta_p[1 - K\epsilon^{-at}\sin(\omega t + \phi)] \tag{3-17}$$

where $\theta_p$ is the angle of the movement measured from its zero current position to its steady-state position. Then from eq. (3-16)

$$\theta_p = \frac{EG}{RS} \tag{3-18}$$

as $\dfrac{d^2\theta}{dt^2}$ and $\dfrac{d\theta}{dt}$ become zero as $t$ approaches infinity

The other constants in this equation are

$$a = \frac{D}{2J} \tag{3-19}$$

$$\omega = \sqrt{\frac{S}{J} - \frac{D^2}{4J^2}} \tag{3-20}$$

$$\phi = \tan^{-1} \frac{2J\omega}{D} \tag{3-21}$$

$$K = \frac{1}{\omega}\sqrt{\frac{S}{J}} \tag{3-22}$$

An underdamped galvanometer would start from its zero current position, which is usually its zero position, when a sudden emf is applied. Then it would oscillate about its final position $\theta_p$. This oscillation would be an attenuated sinusoidal motion. The angular velocity of the sinusoidal component of this motion is $\omega$. The frequency of this sinusoidal component is

$$f = \frac{\omega}{2\pi} \tag{3-23}$$

and the period is

$$T = \frac{1}{f} = \frac{2\pi}{\omega} \tag{3-24}$$

Further analysis of this motion will be made later in this chapter.

## 3-5. THE UNDAMPED MOTION OF A GALVANOMETER [1,2,4]

The undamped motion of a galvanometer movement is obtained when the damping $D$ is zero. This is not realized in a galvanometer, but the properties of the undamped galvanometer are used in expressing its motion under operating conditions. From Eq. (3-19), $a = 0$ when $D = 0$ and

$$\epsilon^{-at} = 1$$

Then, from Eq. (3-20), the angular velocity is

$$\omega_0 = \sqrt{\frac{S}{J}} \tag{3-25}$$

and

$$K = \frac{\omega_0}{\omega} = 1 \tag{3-26}$$

The frequency of the undamped oscillation is

$$f_o = \frac{\omega_o}{2\pi} = \frac{1}{2\pi}\sqrt{\frac{S}{J}}$$ (3-27)

and the *free period* of this oscillation is

$$T_o = \frac{1}{f_o} = 2\pi\sqrt{\frac{J}{S}}$$ (3-28)

and

$$\phi_o = \tan^{-1}\infty = 90°$$

Substituting these values in Eq. (3-17) gives

$$\theta_o = \theta_p[1 - \sin(\omega_o t + 90°)]$$
$$= \theta_p(1 - \cos\omega_o t)$$ (3-29)

The motion of the undamped galvanometer is an oscillation around the $\theta_p$ angle with a constant amplitude $\theta_p$ and a frequency $f_o$.

### 3-6. CRITICAL DAMPED MOTION OF A GALVANOMETER [1,4,5]

The critical damped motion of a galvanometer is obtained when

$$\frac{D^2}{4J^2} - \frac{S}{J} = 0$$ (3-30)

The value of the damping $D$ that produces critical damped motion of a given galvanometer is defined as the critical damping $D_c$. Then

$$D_c = 2J\sqrt{\frac{S}{J}} = 2J\omega_o$$ (3-31)

and the motion of the critical damped galvanometer is

$$\theta = \theta_p[1 - (1 + \omega_o t)\epsilon^{-\omega_o t}]$$ (3-32)

In this equation, $\omega_o t$ is the smallest exponent $\epsilon$ can have without becoming imaginary, and the galvanometer comes to rest in the minimum time without overshoot.

### 3-7. RELATIVE DAMPING [1,2,4,5]

The relative damping of a galvanometer $\gamma$ is defined as the ratio of the damping $D$ to the critical damping $D_c$. Then

$$\gamma = \frac{D}{D_c}$$ (3-33)

From Eq. (3-20) and (3-25),

$$D^2 = 4J^2 \left( \frac{S}{J} - \omega^2 \right)$$

$$= 4J^2(\omega_0{}^2 - \omega^2) \tag{3-34}$$

From Eq. (3-31),

$$D_c{}^2 = 4J^2\omega_0{}^2 \tag{3-35}$$

Dividing Eq. (3-34) by Eq. (3-35) gives

$$\gamma^2 = \frac{\omega_0{}^2 - \omega^2}{\omega_0{}^2} = 1 - \frac{\omega^2}{\omega_0{}^2}$$

or

$$\frac{\omega}{\omega_0} = \sqrt{1 - \gamma^2}$$

Then

$$\omega = \omega_0\sqrt{1 - \gamma^2} \tag{3-36}$$

From Eq. (3-26),

$$K = \frac{\omega_0}{\omega} = \frac{1}{\sqrt{1 - \gamma^2}} \tag{3-37}$$

From Eq. (3-19),

$$a = \frac{D}{2J} = \frac{D\omega_0}{2J\omega_0}$$

Substituting Eq. (3-35) in this equation gives

$$a = \frac{D}{D_c} \omega_0 = \gamma\omega_0 \tag{3-38}$$

From Eq. (3-21),

$$\phi = \tan^{-1}\frac{2J\omega}{D}$$

But from Eq. (3-35),

$$2J = \frac{D_c}{\omega_0}$$

Then

$$\phi = \tan^{-1}\frac{D_c\omega}{D\omega_0}$$

Substituting Eq. (3-33) for $D_c/D$ and Eq. (3-36) for $\omega/\omega_0$ gives

$$\phi = \tan^{-1}\frac{\sqrt{1 - \gamma^2}}{\gamma}$$

A triangle having a base $\gamma$ and an altitude $\sqrt{1 - \gamma^2}$ will have a hypotenuse of 1. Then

$$\phi = \sin^{-1}\sqrt{1 - \gamma^2} \tag{3-39}$$

Using the values of $K$, $a$, $\omega$, and $\phi$, given in Eqs. (3-37), (3-38), (3-36), and (3-39), respectively, in Eq. (3-17) gives the motion of an underdamped galvanometer in terms of $\omega_o$ and $\gamma$. Then

$$\theta = \theta_p \left\{ 1 - \frac{1}{\sqrt{1 - \gamma^2}} \epsilon^{-\gamma\omega_o t} \sin \left[ (\omega_o \sqrt{1 - \gamma^2})t + \sin^{-1} \sqrt{1 - \gamma^2} \right] \right\} \quad (3\text{-}40)$$

## 3-8. LOGARITHMIC DECREMENT [1,2]

The logarithmic decrement of a galvanometer is defined as the Napierian logarithm of the ratio of successive swings of the oscillating system.[1] This can be determined by computing the times at which the angle $\theta$ is a maximum, and solving for $\theta$ using these values of $t$. These computations will now be made. Differentiating Eq. (3-40) with respect to $t$ and equating to zero gives

$$\omega_o t_m \sqrt{1 - \gamma^2} = \tan^{-1} \frac{\sqrt{1 - \gamma^2}}{\gamma} - \sin^{-1} \sqrt{1 - \gamma^2} \quad (3\text{-}41)$$

where $t_m$ is the time at which $\theta$ is either a maximum or minimum. It will be noted that at $t = 0$, $\theta$ is a minimum position of the galvanometer movement; therefore, $t_m$ must have zero as its first minimum value. Substituting $t_m = 0$ into Eq. (3-41) gives

$$\tan^{-1} \frac{\sqrt{1 - \gamma^2}}{\gamma} - \sin^{-1} \sqrt{1 - \gamma^2} = 0 \quad (3\text{-}42)$$

But $\gamma$ for any given galvanometer circuit is a constant. Therefore, the $\tan^{-1} \frac{\sqrt{1 - \gamma^2}}{\gamma}$ and $\sin^{-1} \sqrt{1 - \gamma^2}$ are angles such that the tangent of the first is a constant and the sine of the second is a constant. Then the angle defined by Eq. (3-42) must be $N\pi$, where $N$ is an integer including zero and

$$\omega t = \omega_o t_m \sqrt{1 - \gamma^2} = N\pi$$

or

$$t_m = \frac{N\pi}{\omega_o \sqrt{1 - \gamma^2}} \quad (3\text{-}43)$$

The minimum values of $\theta$ will occur at even values of $N$, and the maximum values of $\theta$ will be at the odd values of $N$. The first maximum will be at $N = 1$, $t_m = t_1$, and $\theta = \theta_1$, or

$$t_1 = \frac{\pi}{\omega_o \sqrt{1 - \gamma^2}}$$

and substituting in Eq. (3-40) gives

$$\theta_1 = \theta_p \left[ 1 + \epsilon^{-\frac{\pi\gamma}{\sqrt{1-\gamma^2}}} \right]$$

The deviation of $\theta$ from the steady-state position is

$$\theta_{m1} = \theta_1 - \theta_p$$

$$= \theta_p \epsilon^{-\frac{\pi\gamma}{\sqrt{1-\gamma^2}}} \tag{3-44}$$

Similarly, the second maximum is

$$\theta_{m2} = \theta_p \epsilon^{-\frac{3\pi\gamma}{\sqrt{1-\gamma^2}}} \tag{3-45}$$

etc.

By definition, the logarithmic decrement is

$$\lambda = \ln \frac{\theta_{m1}}{\theta_{m2}} = \ln \frac{\theta_{m2}}{\theta_{m3}} \qquad \text{etc.}$$

$$= \ln \frac{\theta_p \epsilon^{-\frac{\pi\gamma}{\sqrt{1-\gamma^2}}}}{\theta_p \epsilon^{-\frac{3\pi\gamma}{\sqrt{1-\gamma^2}}}} = \ln \epsilon^{\frac{2\pi\gamma}{\sqrt{1-\gamma^2}}}$$

$$= \frac{2\pi\gamma}{\sqrt{1-\gamma^2}} \tag{3-46}$$

Solving Eq. (3-46) for $\gamma$ in terms of $\lambda$ gives

$$\gamma = \frac{\lambda}{\sqrt{4\pi^2 + \lambda^2}} \tag{3-47}$$

Also

$$\phi = \tan^{-1} \frac{\sqrt{1-\gamma^2}}{\gamma}$$

$$= \tan^{-1} \frac{2\pi}{\lambda} \tag{3-48}$$

$$a = \gamma\omega_o = \frac{\omega\lambda}{2\pi} \tag{3-49}$$

and, from Eq. (3-37),

$$K = \frac{\omega_o}{\omega}$$

Then the motion of the movement of the galvanometer, given in Eq. (3-17), expressed in terms of $\lambda$, $\omega$, and $\omega_o$, is

$$\theta = \theta_p \left[ 1 - \frac{\omega_o}{\omega} \epsilon^{-\frac{\omega\lambda}{2\pi}t} \sin\left(\omega t + \tan^{-1}\frac{2\pi}{\lambda}\right) \right] \tag{3-50}$$

## 3-9. OVERDAMPED MOTION OF A GALVANOMETER [1,2,4,5]

The overdamped motion of a galvanometer is nonoscillatory and is obtained when

$$\frac{D^2}{4J^2} > \frac{S}{J} \quad \text{or} \quad D^2 > 4JS$$

A solution of Eq. (3-16), under these conditions, is

$$\theta = \theta_p(1 - K_1\epsilon^{-a_1 t} + K_2\epsilon^{-a_2 t}) \tag{3-51}$$

where

$$K_1 = \frac{\dfrac{D}{2J} + \sqrt{\dfrac{D^2}{4J^2} - \dfrac{S}{J}}}{2\sqrt{\dfrac{D^2}{4J^2} - \dfrac{S}{J}}}$$

$$= \frac{\gamma + \sqrt{\gamma^2 - 1}}{2\sqrt{\gamma^2 - 1}} \tag{3-52}$$

$$K_2 = \frac{\dfrac{D}{2J} - \sqrt{\dfrac{D^2}{4J^2} - \dfrac{S}{J}}}{2\sqrt{\dfrac{D^2}{4J^2} - \dfrac{S}{J}}}$$

$$= \frac{\gamma - \sqrt{\gamma^2 - 1}}{2\sqrt{\gamma^2 - 1}} \tag{3-53}$$

$$a_1 = \frac{D}{2J} - \sqrt{\frac{D^2}{4J^2} - \frac{S}{J}}$$

$$= \omega_o(\gamma - \sqrt{\gamma^2 - 1})$$

$$a_2 = \frac{D}{2J} + \sqrt{\frac{D^2}{4J^2} - \frac{S}{J}}$$

$$= \omega_o(\gamma + \sqrt{\gamma^2 - 1}) \tag{3-54}$$

It will be noted that $\gamma = D/D_c$ for the overdamped motion of a galvanometer movement is greater than 1, so the radical terms $a_1$ and $a_2$ are real. Then the motion of the galvanometer is a simple decay curve without overshoot, but this motion is usually slow and is not desirable in indicating instruments.

## 3-10. NONDIMENSIONAL CURVES OF A GALVANOMETER MOTION[1]

It is often advantageous to plot curves in terms of nondimensional functions, as these curves are not limited to a given set of data but are general and represent a function to which the constants may be inserted to obtain a particular solution. There are many ways to present damped sinusoidal functions in nondimensional form. One form is shown in Fig. 3-3

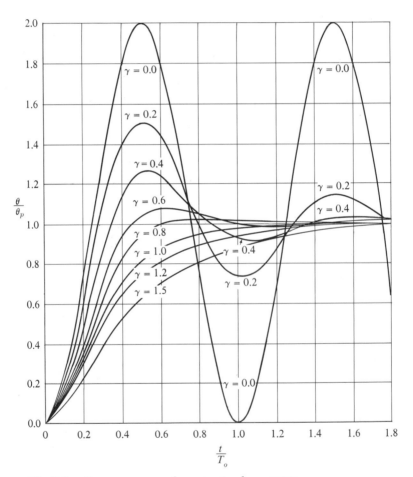

**Fig. 3-3.** *Response curve of a current galvanometer*

where $\theta/\theta_p$ is plotted as a function of $t/T_o$. These functions are nondimensional and the curves are plotted for a series of values of relative damping which is also a nondimensional function. This family of curves will apply to any galvanometer. To obtain the motion of a given galvanometer $\theta$ as a function of time, the ordinate $\theta/\theta_p$ is multiplied by $\theta_p$ and the abscissa $t/T_o$ is multiplied by $T_o$. These curves show that: (1) the period increases with increases in damping until critical damping is obtained; (2) as critical damping is approached, the amplitude of the oscillations is small; and (3) with damping greater than the critical damping, the movement is very sluggish.

A summary of the equations for a current galvanometer is given in Table 3-1.

## 3-11. GALVANOMETER SENSITIVITY [3]

Most manufacturers give both the sensitivity and the inverse sensitivity in specifying the sensitivity of a galvanometer. There are several ways of expressing the sensitivity of a galvanometer. The *current sensitivity* is defined as the ratio of the deflection of the galvanometer to the current which produced it. This is usually given in millimeters per microampere. Then the current sensitivity is

$$S_i = \frac{d}{I} \tag{3-55}$$

where

$I =$ galvanometer current, in microamperes

$d =$ deflection of the galvanometer in scale divisions, usually in millimeters

The *voltage sensitivity* of a galvanometer is the ratio of the deflection of the galvanometer by the voltage which produces it. It is usually given in millimeters per microvolt. Then the voltage sensitivity is

$$S_e = \frac{d}{e} \tag{3-56}$$

where

$e =$ microvolts applied to the galvanometer

$d =$ deflection of the galvanometer in scale divisions, usually in millimeters

The National Bureau of Standards defines the voltage used in determining voltage sensitivity as the voltage across the galvanometer and a resistance which is equal to its critical damping resistance in series. Most manufacturers omit the critical damping resistance in their definition of voltage sensitivity.

The *megohm sensitivity* of a galvanometer is defined as the resistance in megohms that must be inserted in series with the galvanometer so that a deflection of one scale division will be produced when 1 volt is applied to the

## Table 3-1
## Motion of a Current Galvanometer

| Damping | $\theta$ | $\theta_p$ | $K$ | $a$ | $\omega$ | $\phi$ |
|---|---|---|---|---|---|---|
| **Underdamped** $\dfrac{D^2}{4J^2} < \dfrac{S}{J}$ | $\theta = \theta_p[1 - K\epsilon^{-at}\sin(\omega t + \phi)]$ | $\dfrac{EG}{RS}$ | $\dfrac{1}{\omega}\sqrt{\dfrac{S}{J}}$ <br> $\dfrac{1}{\sqrt{1-\gamma^2}}$ <br> $\dfrac{\omega_o}{\omega}$ | $\dfrac{D}{2J}$ <br> $\gamma\omega_o$ <br> $\dfrac{\omega\lambda}{\pi}$ | $\sqrt{\dfrac{S}{J} - \dfrac{D^2}{4J^2}}$ <br> $\omega_o\sqrt{1-\gamma^2}$ | $\tan^{-1}\dfrac{2J\omega}{D}$ <br> $\sin^{-1}\sqrt{1-\gamma^2}$ <br> $\tan^{-1}\dfrac{\pi}{\lambda}$ |
| **Undamped** $D = 0$ | $\theta_o = \theta_p(1 - \cos\omega t)$ | $\dfrac{EG}{RS}$ | $1$ | $0$ | $\omega_o$ <br> $\sqrt{\dfrac{S}{J}}$ | $90°$ |
| **Critical damped** $\dfrac{D^2}{4J^2} = \dfrac{S}{J}$ $D = D_c$ | $\theta = \theta_p[1 - (1 + \omega_o t)\epsilon^{-\omega_o t}]$ | $\dfrac{EG}{RS}$ | — | — | $\omega_o$ <br> $\sqrt{\dfrac{S}{J}}$ | — |
| **Overdamped** $\dfrac{D^2}{4J^2} > \dfrac{S}{J}$ | $\theta = \theta_p(1 - K_1\epsilon^{-a_1 t} + K_2\epsilon^{-a_2 t})$ | $\dfrac{EG}{RS}$ | $K_1$ <br> $\dfrac{\dfrac{D}{2J} + \sqrt{\dfrac{D^2}{4J^2} - \dfrac{S}{J}}}{2\sqrt{\dfrac{D^2}{4J^2} - \dfrac{S}{J}}}$ <br> $\dfrac{\gamma + \sqrt{\gamma^2 - 1}}{2\sqrt{\gamma^2 - 1}}$ | $K_2$ <br> $\dfrac{\dfrac{D}{2J} - \sqrt{\dfrac{D^2}{4J^2} - \dfrac{S}{J}}}{2\sqrt{\dfrac{D^2}{4J^2} - \dfrac{S}{J}}}$ <br> $\dfrac{\gamma - \sqrt{\gamma^2 - 1}}{2\sqrt{\gamma^2 - 1}}$ | $a_1$ <br> $\dfrac{D}{2J} - \sqrt{\dfrac{D^2}{4J^2} - \dfrac{S}{J}}$ <br> $\omega_o(\gamma - \sqrt{\gamma^2 - 1})$ | $a_2$ <br> $\dfrac{D}{2J} + \sqrt{\dfrac{D^2}{4J^2} - \dfrac{S}{J}}$ <br> $\omega_o(\gamma + \sqrt{\gamma^2 - 1})$ |

circuit.[4,5]   This sensitivity is the equivalent of the current sensitivity when the resistance of the galvanometer is neglected. Then the megohm sensitivity is

$$S_R = \frac{d}{I} = S_i \qquad (3\text{-}57)$$

where

$d$ = deflection in scale divisions, usually in millimeters
$I$ = galvanometer current, in microamperes

The *ballistic sensitivity* of a galvanometer is defined as the ratio of maximum deflection $d_m$ of a galvanometer to the quantity $Q$ of electricity in a single pulse of electricity which produces this deflection. It is usually expressed in millimeters per microcoulomb. Then

$$S_Q = \frac{d_m}{Q} \qquad (3\text{-}58)$$

where

$Q$ = quantity of electricity, in microcoulombs
$d_m$ = maximum deflection in scale divisions, usually in millimeters

The application of ballistic galvanometers will be discussed later in this chapter.

### 3-12.  MEASURING THE GALVANOMETER CURRENT[3]

The current passing through a galvanometer is usually very small and, therefore, generally is not measured with standard laboratory equipment. The circuit in Fig. 3-4 is used to measure the current in terms of the voltage

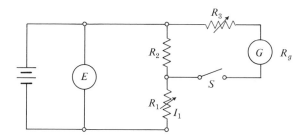

**Fig. 3-4.**   *Galvanometer current and resistance measurements*

$E$; the resistances $R_1$, $R_2$, $R_3$; and the resistance $R_g$ of the galvanometer itself. The resistance $R_1$ is very large compared with $R_2$. This is necessary to reduce the voltage across the galvanometer to a value which will not damage the galvanometer. Usually, $R_2$ is in the neighborhood of 1 ohm. $R_g$ and $R_3$ are generally much larger than $R_2$, and $R_1$ is larger than $R_g$ and $R_3$. The current through $R_1$ is

$$I_1 = \frac{E}{R_1 + \dfrac{R_2(R_3 + R_g)}{R_2 + R_3 + R_g}} \qquad (3\text{-}59)$$

Then the current passing through the galvanometer is

$$I_g = I_1 \frac{R_2}{R_2 + R_3 + R_g} = \left(\frac{E}{R_1 + \dfrac{R_2(R_3 + R_g)}{R_2 + R_3 + R_g}}\right)\left(\frac{R_2}{R_2 + R_3 + R_g}\right)$$

$$= \frac{ER_2}{R_1(R_2 + R_3 + R_g) + R_2(R_3 + R_g)} \qquad (3\text{-}60)$$

when

$$R_3 + R_g \gg R_2$$

$$I_g \approx \frac{ER_2}{(R_1 + R_2)(R_3 + R_g)} \qquad (3\text{-}61)$$

This equation gives the current in amperes when the resistances are expressed in ohms and the applied voltage is given in volts. Usually, this is converted into microamperes for galvanometer computations.

### 3-13. MEASURING THE RESISTANCE OF THE GALVANOMETER[3]

The suspension of a standard galvanometer is usually very small. Some galvanometers use a wire, 1 mm in diameter, which has been rolled flat into a ribbon. The current-carrying capacity of this wire suspension is very small, which prevents even the use of a Wheatstone bridge in measuring the resistance of the galvanometer unless special precautions are taken; therefore, the circuit shown in Fig. 3-4 is used to measure the resistance of the galvanometer. It must be kept in mind that the accuracy of measuring the resistance of the galvanometer is not of prime importance, inasmuch as the galvanometer circuit is usually composed of copper and the temperature coefficient of copper is such that there is a 1 percent change in the resistance of copper wire for each 2.5°C change in temperature.[4] Thus a 1 percent accuracy in determining the resistance of a galvanometer is sufficient. As stated above, $R_1$ is very much greater than $R_2$, and, as a rule, $R_3 + R_g$ is very much larger than $R_2$.

Then

$$I_1 \approx \frac{E}{R_1 + \dfrac{R_2(R_3 + R_g)}{R_3 + R_g}} = \frac{E}{R_1 + R_2} \tag{3-62}$$

$R_1$, $R_2$, and the applied voltage are constant. Therefore, $I_1$ will be assumed to be constant.

Let $R_1$ and $R_2$ be adjusted to the desired value and, then held constant, and let $R_3$ be set at a value $R_{3-1}$ such that

$$I_g = I_{g-1}$$

$I_{g-1}$ is usually set at the full-scale reading of the galvanometer, and the value of $R_{3-1}$ is recorded. Then $R_3$ is varied until

$$I_g = 0.5 I_{g-1}$$

This value of $R_3$ is defined as $R_{3-2}$. Then, by Eq. (3-61),

$$I_g = I_1 \frac{R_2}{R_2 + R_{3-1} + R_g} = 2I_1 \frac{R_2}{R_2 + R_{3-2} + R_g}$$

Solving for $R_g$,

$$R_g = R_{3-2} - 2R_{3-1} - R_2 \tag{3-63}$$

Although a slight approximation is made in assuming that $I_1$ remains constant in the two circuits in this computation, it is more than sufficiently accurate for the normal computation of the resistance of the galvanometer.

### 3-14. MEASURING THE CURRENT SENSITIVITY OF A GALVANOMETER[3]

The current sensitivity of a galvanometer can be obtained by using the circuits shown in Fig. 3-4. With a reasonable value of $R_1$ and $R_3$, the deflection of the galvanometer is measured. Then, by Eq. (3-61), the current in the galvanometer is computed. The current sensitivity of the galvanometer is computed by Eq. (3-55).

$$S_i = \frac{d}{I_g} \text{ mm}/\mu\text{a}$$

In measuring the current sensitivity of a galvanometer it is well to take several readings with different magnitudes of deflection, and then compare the readings. Sometimes it is advisable to plot the current sensitivity, as obtained by Eqs. (3-60) or (3-61), as a function of the deflection of the galvanometer, to determine if the galvanometer has a uniform sensitivity throughout its range.

## 3-15. MEASUREMENT OF THE VOLTAGE SENSITIVITY OF A GALVANOMETER

The voltage sensitivity of a galvanometer is obtained using Fig. 3-4 and for a particular deflection of the galvanometer. The current through the galvanometer is computed by Eq. (3-61), and the resistance of the galvanometer is computed by Eq. (3-63). Using these values of current and resistance, the voltage across the galvanometer can be determined. Then the voltage sensitivity is

$$S_e = \frac{d}{I_g R_g} \text{ mm/}\mu\text{v} \tag{3-64}$$

where

$I_g$ = galvanometer current, in microamperes

$R_g$ = resistance of galvanometer, in ohms

$d$ = deflection, in millimeters

The voltage sensitivity of the instrument may be determined for several magnitudes of deflection and plotted as a function of the galvanometer deflection. It should have characteristics similar to those obtained for the current sensitivity of the instrument, as the voltage sensitivity is the product of the current sensitivity and the reciprocal of the galvanometer resistance.

## 3-16. MEASUREMENT OF THE MEGOHM SENSITIVITY OF A GALVANOMETER

In defining the megohm sensitivity of a galvanometer, it was observed that the megohm sensitivity is equivalent to the current sensitivity. Thus

$$S_i = \text{millimeters/microampere}$$
$$= \text{millimeters/volt/megohm}$$

Then, when the volts equal 1,

$$S_i = S_R \tag{3-65}$$

where

$S_R$ = megohm sensitivity

$S_i$ = current sensitivity

Thus the megohm sensitivity can also be determined by applying the above computations, using the emf and resistances obtained from the circuit given in Fig. 3-4.

## 3-17. MEASUREMENT OF THE BALLISTIC SENSITIVITY OF A GALVANOMETER

The ballistic sensitivity of a galvanometer, as defined above, is the ratio of the maximum deflection of the galvanometer, in millimeters, to the charge, in microcoulombs, producing it. The circuit in Fig. 3-5 is used to determine

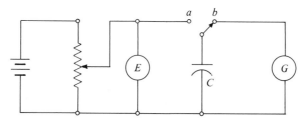

**Fig. 3-5.** *Ballistic-sensitivity measurements*

the charge supplied to the galvanometer. With $E$ volts across the capacitor $C$, the charge on the capacitor is given by

$$Q = CE$$

where

$Q$ = charge, in microcoulombs
$E$ = emf, in volts
$C$ = capacitance of capacitor, in microfarads

This charge on the capacitor is obtained when switch $S$ is thrown to $a$. When switch $S$ is thrown to $b$, this charge is supplied to the galvanometer and the maximum deflection of the galvanometer is observed. Ballistic sensitivity of the galvanometer, given by Eq. (3-58),

$$S_Q = \frac{d_m}{Q}$$

The value of the ballistic sensitivity can be obtained for several different charges giving the sensitivity for several deflections of the galvanometer. To determine whether the sensitivity of the galvanometer is uniform throughout the range of the instrument, the ballistic sensitivity can be plotted as a function of the maximum deflection.

### 3-18. MEASURING THE LOGARITHMIC DECREMENT OF A GALVANOMETER [1,5]

The logarithmic decrement can be determined using the circuit shown in Fig. 3-4. Knowing the value of $R_1$, $R_3$, and $R_g$, and the applied voltage, the value of $R_2$ can be computed to obtain about half-scale deflection on the galvanometer. The resistance of the galvanometer circuit is

$$R = R_2 + R_3 + R_g \qquad (3\text{-}66)$$

as the resistance $R_1$ is very large compared with $R_2$. The resistance $R$ determines the $G^2/R$ component of the damping when the galvanometer circuit is closed. The logarithmic decrement of the galvanometer with the circuit closed can be determined by observing the maximum deviations from the position $\theta_p$ at which the galvanometer comes to rest. Before the galvanometer circuit is closed, the angle $\theta$ is zero. Then the logarithmic decrement can be obtained by observing the first, second, and third maximum values of the galvanometer movement $\theta_1$, $\theta_2$, and $\theta_3$ after the galvanometer circuit is closed and the position $\theta_p$ at which the galvanometer comes to rest. Then, from Sec. 3-8,

$$\lambda = \ln \frac{\theta_1 - \theta_p}{\theta_2 - \theta_p} = \ln \frac{\theta_2 - \theta_p}{\theta_3 - \theta_p} \qquad (3\text{-}67)$$

Thus the logarithmic decrement can be determined for any damping as determined by the resistance $R$ of the galvanometer circuit.

When the switch $S$ is opened, the galvanometer will have no electromagnetic damping as $G^2/R$ is zero. The open-circuit logarithmic damping is determined by observing the first and second maximum deflections $\theta_1$ and $\theta_2$ of the galvanometer after the switch $S$ is opened. It will be noted that the position at which the galvanometer comes to rest after switch $S$ was opened is zero, which is $\theta_p$ from the position of the galvanometer before switch $S$ was opened. Then the open-circuit logarithmic decrement is

$$\lambda_2 = \ln \frac{\theta_p}{\theta_1} = \ln \frac{\theta_1}{\theta_2} \qquad (3\text{-}68)$$

where $\theta_p$ is the position of the galvanometer before the switch was opened, and the zero position is the open steady-state position of the galvanometer.

### 3-19. COMPUTING RELATIVE DAMPING [1]

The relationship between resistance in the galvanometer circuit $R$ and the relative damping can be determined as follows:

At open circuit there is no electromagnetic damping, and the total damping is $D_m$. The relative damping at open circuit is

$$\gamma_2 = \frac{D_m}{D_c} \tag{3-69}$$

With a closed circuit having a total resistance $R$, the relative damping of the galvanometer is

$$\gamma = \frac{D}{D_c} = \frac{D_m}{D_c} + \frac{G^2}{RD_c}$$

$$= \gamma_2 + \frac{G^2}{RD_c} \tag{3-70}$$

or

$$\gamma - \gamma_2 = \frac{G^2}{RD_c} \tag{3-71}$$

Similarly, when the resistance of the galvanometer circuit is $R_x$, and the relative damping is $\gamma_x$, then

$$\gamma_x - \gamma_2 = \frac{G^2}{R_x D_c} \tag{3-72}$$

Dividing Eq. (3-71) by Eq. (3-72) gives

$$\frac{\gamma - \gamma_2}{\gamma_x - \gamma_2} = \frac{R_x}{R}$$

where

$\gamma$ = relative damping with the resistance of the galvanometer circuit equal to $R$

$\gamma_x$ = relative damping with the resistance of the galvanometer circuit equal to $R_x$

or

$$R_x = R \frac{\gamma - \gamma_2}{\gamma_x - \gamma_2} \tag{3-73}$$

The relative damping at open circuit and with a galvanometer circuit resistance $R$ can be computed from the logarithmic decrement, which can be found by using the method outlined in Sec. 3-18. Knowing the values of $\gamma$ and $\gamma_2$, the total resistance $R_x$ of the galvanometer circuit can be computed for a desired relative damping $\gamma_x$ by Eq. (3-73).

**3-20. CRITICAL DAMPING RESISTANCE EXTERNAL** [1]

The critical damping resistance external, abbreviated CDRX, is defined as the resistance that must be added to the galvanometer circuit in order to produce critical damping. It is usually given by the manufacturer, but it must be appreciated that the damping depends upon the stiffness of the suspension, so when the suspension is changed, the damping is also changed. The critical damping can be obtained by varying the external resistance in the galvanometer circuit and observing the magnitude of this resistance when the galvanometer comes to rest in the minimum time without overshoot. The CDRX can also be determined by solving for the total resistance of the galvanometer circuit at critical damping $R_c$. At critical damping the relative damping is

$$\gamma_c = 1$$

Substituting this value of $\gamma_c$ into Eq. (3-73) for $\gamma_x$ gives

$$R_c = R\frac{\gamma - \gamma_2}{1 - \gamma_2} \tag{3-74}$$

Then

$$\text{CDRX} = R_c - R_g$$

$$= R\frac{\gamma - \gamma_2}{1 - \gamma_2} - R_g \tag{3-75}$$

The most effective damping is usually obtained when the galvanometer is slightly underdamped or the external resistance is slightly greater than the CDRX.

### 3-21. GALVANOMETER PROTECTION[3]

It is often necessary to provide protection of the galvanometer during the preliminary adjustment of a bridge circuit, and yet preserve the proper damping. This can be done by using a variable series resistor and a variable shunt resistor, as shown in Fig. 3-6 (a). In the unprotected condition,

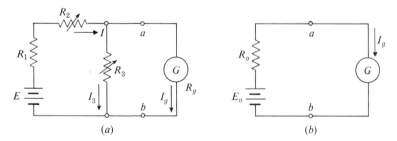

(a)                           (b)

**Fig. 3-6.** *Galvanometer circuit and its equivalent circuit*

$R_2 = 0$ and $R_3 = $ infinity. Now replace the circuit to the left of $a$ and $b$, in Fig. 3-6(a), by a Thévenin generator. The equivalent applied voltage $E_o$ in the Thévenin circuit is reduced, thus reducing $I_g$, and the resistance of the Thévenin generator $R$ is held constant by using the proper values of $R_2$ and $R_3$, thus retaining the same damping of the galvanometer. The ratio of galvanometer current under the unprotected conditions $I_{g^1}$ to the galvanometer current $I_g$ with $R_2$ and $R_3$ in the circuit is

$$K_i = \frac{I_{g^1}}{I_g} \qquad (3\text{-}76)$$

Knowing the factor $K_i$, the resistance $R_1$ and the galvanometer resistance $R_g$, it is necessary to determine the magnitude of $R_2$ and $R_3$. From the unprotected conditions

$$I_{g^1} = \frac{E}{R_1 + R_g}$$

and with the protective network

$$I_g = \frac{I_{g^1}}{K_i} = \frac{E}{K_i(R_1 + R_g)} \qquad (3\text{-}77)$$

also

$$I = I_3 + I_g$$

and

$$I_3 R_3 = I_g R_g$$

or

$$I_3 = I_g \frac{R_g}{R_3}$$

Then

$$I = I_g \frac{R_g}{R_3} + I_g = I_g \frac{(R_3 + R_g)}{R_3} \qquad (3\text{-}78)$$

Substituting Eq. (3-77) in Eq. (3-78) gives

$$I = \frac{E(R_3 + R_g)}{K_i R_3 (R_1 + R_g)} \qquad (3\text{-}79)$$

Solving for this current from the circuit in Fig. 3-6($a$) gives

$$I = \frac{E}{R_1 + R_2 + \dfrac{R_3 R_g}{R_3 + R_g}} = \frac{E(R_3 + R_g)}{(R_1 + R_2)(R_3 + R_g) + R_3 R_g} \qquad (3\text{-}80)$$

Equating these two expressions for the current $I$ gives

$$K_i R_3 (R_1 + R_g) = (R_1 + R_2)(R_3 + R_g) + R_3 R_g$$

Then

$$(R_1 + R_2)R_g = K_i R_3 (R_1 + R_g) - R_3(R_1 + R_2) - R_3 R_g$$
$$= R_3[(R_1 + R_g)(K_i - 1) - R_2] \qquad (3\text{-}81)$$

Solving for $R_o$ in the equivalent Thévenin circuit in Fig. 3-6($b$) and noting that it is necessary that $R_o = R_1$ to keep the damping of the galvanometer the same, then

$$R_o = R_1 = \frac{(R_1 + R_2)R_3}{R_1 + R_2 + R_3}$$

Solving for $R_3$,

$$R_3 \approx \frac{R_1(R_1 + R_2)}{R_2} \tag{3-82}$$

Substituting this value of $R_3$ into Eq. (3-81) and solving for $R_2$ gives

$$R_2 = R_1(K_i - 1) \tag{3-83}$$

Substituting this expression for $R_2$ in Eq. (3-82) gives

$$R_3 = \frac{R_1[R_1 + R_1(K_i - 1)]}{R_1(K_i - 1)}$$

$$= R_1 \frac{K_i}{K_i - 1} \tag{3-84}$$

Thus, knowing the resistance $R_1$ which will give the desired damping, and the ratio of the galvanometer current under unprotected conditions to the desired galvanometer current $K_i$, the values of $R_2$ and $R_3$ can be determined. Usually, a two-pole rotary switch is used to decrease $R_3$ and increase $R_2$ to give the desired sensitivity and maintain the correct damping.

### 3-22. THE AYRTON SHUNT[3]

In bridge circuits the resistance of the equivalent Thévenin generator looking into the bridge from the galvanometer circuit is large, and the current $I$ to the galvanometer circuit may be considered constant. This assumption is employed in the design of the Ayrton shunt for reducing the sensitivity of the galvanometer circuit shown in Fig. 3-7. The shunt has a total resistance $R_1$, approximately equal to the CDRX of the galvanometer, and is tapped at values of the resistance which will reduce the current through the galvanometer circuit by the factor marked on the tapped position. In this case these factors are 1, 0.1, 0.01, and 0.001. In position 1 the galvanometer current is

$$I_{g^1} = I \frac{R_1}{R_1 + R_g} \tag{3-85}$$

At position 0.1, the shunting resistance is $R_{0.1}$, the resistance of the galvanometer branch is $R_1 - R_{0.1} + R_g$, and the current through the galvanometer is

$$I_{g^{0.1}} = 0.1 \, I_{g^1} = I \frac{R_{0.1}}{R_1 + R_g} \qquad (3\text{-}86)$$

Then, dividing Eq. (3-85) by Eq. (3-86) gives

$$\frac{I_{g^1}}{I_{g^{0.1}}} = 10 = \frac{R_1}{R_{0.1}}$$

or

$$R_{0.1} = 0.1 R_1 \qquad (3\text{-}87)$$

Similarly,

$$R_{0.01} = 0.01 R_1 \qquad (3\text{-}88)$$

and

$$R_{0.001} = 0.001 R_1 \qquad (3\text{-}89)$$

etc.

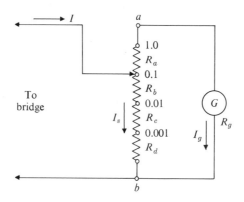

**Fig. 3-7.** *Ayrton shunt*

Where $R_{0.1}$, $R_{0.01}$, $R_{0.001}$, etc., are the resistances from the junction $b$ to the switch contacts 1, 0.1, 0.01, 0.001, etc., respectively, then the resistance $R_a$ is

$$R_a = R_1 - R_{0.1}$$
$$= R_1 - 0.1 R_1 = 0.9 R_1$$

Also

$$R_b = R_{0.1} - R_{0.001}$$
$$= 0.1 R_1 - 0.01 R_1 = 0.09 R_1$$
$$R_c = R_{0.01} - R_{0.001}$$
$$= 0.01 R_1 = 0.001 R_1 = 0.009 R_1$$
$$R_d = R_{0.001} = 0.001 R_1$$

Then

$$R_a + R_b + R_c + R_d = (0.9 + 0.09 + 0.009 + 0.001)R_1 = R_1$$

Thus the sensitivity of the galvanometer circuit can be decreased while the damping remains nearly constant. It will be noted that the values of 0.1, 0.01, 0.001, etc., were arbitrarily chosen in this example. Any other desired values may be used.

### 3-23. THE BALLISTIC GALVANOMETER[1]

The ballistic galvanometer is designed to respond to a single short-time impulse. The impulse is measured by the first swing of the galvanometer; therefore, the period of the galvanometer must be sufficiently long to allow an accurate observation of the maximum deflection. It is also advantageous to have no movement of the galvanometer during the impressed impulse, which requires that the period of the galvanometer be much greater than the duration of the impulse. Thus the name "ballistic" is applied to this galvanometer where an impulse impressed upon the movement for a comparatively short period of time stores sufficient energy in the galvanometer movement to carry it through its trajectory of motion.

### 3-24. MEASUREMENT OF THE QUANTITY OF ELECTRICITY

The measurement of the quantity of electricity

$$Q = \int i\, dt$$

with a galvanometer requires that the resistance of the galvanometer circuit be sufficiently small and the period of the galvanometer be sufficiently large that the charge $Q$ will pass through the galvanometer before the galvanometer deflects from its initial zero current position. This instant of time in which the charge $Q$ passes through the galvanometer will be defined as the time between $t = t_o = 0$ and $t = t_1$. Between $t_o$ and $t_1$, there is no motion of the galvanometer, and the equation of the torque exerted on the galvanometer is

$$\frac{d^2\theta}{dt^2} + \frac{D}{J}\frac{d\theta}{dt} + \frac{S}{J}\theta = \frac{G}{J}\frac{dQ}{dt}$$

Integrating gives

$$\left.\frac{d\theta}{dt}\right|_{t_o=0}^{t_1} + \frac{D}{J}\theta\Big|_{t_o=0}^{t_1} + \frac{S}{J}\int_o^{t_1}\theta\, dt = \frac{G}{J}Q$$

But $\theta$ remains at zero during the time $t_o$ to $t_1$. Then the above equation becomes

$$\frac{d\theta}{dt} = \frac{G}{J} Q$$

After $t_1$, no driving force is applied to the galvanometer, and the motion of the galvanometer can be obtained from the equation of the torques acting upon the movement. This is

$$\frac{d^2\theta}{dt^2} + \frac{D}{J} \frac{d\theta}{dt} + \frac{S}{J} \theta = 0 \tag{3-90}$$

Using the initial conditions that

(1) $$\theta = 0 \tag{3-91}$$

(2) $$\frac{d\theta}{dt} = \frac{G}{J} Q \tag{3-92}$$

at $t = 0$, a solution of Eq. (3-90) for the underdamped condition which requires that $D^2 < 4JS$ or $\gamma < 1$ is

$$\theta = QK_3\epsilon^{-a_3 t} \sin \omega t \tag{3-93}$$

where

$$K_3 = \left(\frac{\theta_p}{I}\right)\left(\frac{\dfrac{S}{J}}{\sqrt{\dfrac{S}{J} - \dfrac{D^2}{4J^2}}}\right) = \left(\frac{\theta_p}{I}\right)\frac{\omega_o^2}{\omega}$$

$$= \left(\frac{\theta_p}{I}\right)\frac{\omega_o}{\sqrt{1 - \dfrac{D^2}{4JS}}} = \left(\frac{\theta_p}{I}\right)\frac{\omega_o}{\sqrt{1 - \gamma^2}}$$

$$a_3 = \sqrt{\frac{D^2}{4J^2}} = \omega_o\gamma$$

$$\omega = \sqrt{\frac{S}{J} - \frac{D^2}{4J^2}} = \omega_o\sqrt{1 - \gamma^2}$$

and $I$ is the steady-state current that will produce the steady-state deflection $\theta_p$. Then the current sensitivity of this galvanometer is

$$S_i = \frac{\theta_p}{I}$$

It will be observed that $\theta$ becomes zero after $t$ becomes large as the steady-state term of Eq. (3-93) is zero. The measurement of $Q$ as a function of $\theta$ is obtained from the maximum value of $\theta$. The value of $\theta$ is computed by differentiating Eq. (3-93) and equating it to zero to obtain the time

$t_{m1}$ at which $\theta$ is its first maximum value, $\theta_{m1}$. Then the value of $t_{m1}$ is substituted in Eq. (3-93) to obtain $\theta_{m1}$. This computation yields

$$\theta_{m1} = Q\omega_o S_i \epsilon^{-a_3 t_{m1}} \qquad (3\text{-}94)$$

where $S_i$ is the current sensitivity in radians per microamperes and

$$t_{m1} = \frac{2J}{\sqrt{4JS - D^2}} \tan^{-1} \sqrt{\frac{4JS - D^2}{D^2}}$$

$$= \frac{1}{\omega} \tan^{-1} \frac{\omega}{\sqrt{\omega_o^2 - \omega^2}}$$

$$= \frac{1}{\omega_o\sqrt{1 - \gamma^2}} \tan^{-1} \frac{\sqrt{1 - \gamma^2}}{\gamma}$$

The ballistic sensitivity, by Eq. (3-58), is

$$S_Q = \frac{d_{m1}}{Q} = \frac{\theta_{m1}}{Q}$$

$$= \omega_o S_i \epsilon^{-a_3 t_{m1}} \qquad (3\text{-}95)$$

in radians per microcoulomb.

It will be observed that, for a given galvanometer circuit, $\gamma$ and $\omega_o$ are constant. Therefore $a_3 t_{m1}$ is a constant and $S_Q$ is constant. Thus $S_Q$ can be determined with a known $Q$, as described in Sec. 3-17, and will remain constant as long as the circuit is unchanged. The equations for $\theta_{m1}$ and $t_{m1}$, for underdamped, critical damped, and overdamped conditions, are obtained by using the criteria for these conditions and the initial conditions given in Eq. (3-91) and (3-92). A summary of these equations and conditions is listed in Table 3-2 for the response of a ballistic galvanometer to a charge $Q$. This response, in terms of $\theta/\theta_{m1}$ as a function of $t/T_o$, is given in Fig. 3-8.

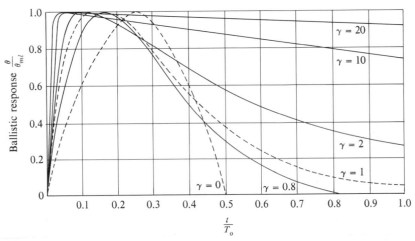

**Fig. 3-8.** *Response of a ballistic galvanometer*

## Table 3-2

| | $t_{m1}$ | $\theta_{m1}$ | $S_Q$ in radians per microcoulomb |
|---|---|---|---|
| Over-damped $\gamma > 1$ | $\dfrac{1}{\omega_0\sqrt{\gamma^2-1}}\tanh^{-1}\dfrac{\sqrt{\gamma^2-1}}{\gamma}$ | $Q\omega_0 S_i \epsilon^{-\left\{\frac{\gamma}{\sqrt{\gamma^2-1}}\tanh^{-1}\frac{\sqrt{\gamma^2-1}}{\gamma}\right\}}$ | $\omega_0 S_i \epsilon^{-\left\{\frac{\gamma}{\sqrt{\gamma^2-1}}\tanh^{-1}\frac{\sqrt{\gamma^2-1}}{\gamma}\right\}}$ |
| Critical damped $\gamma = 1$ | $\dfrac{1}{\omega_0}$ | $Q\omega_0 S_i \epsilon^{-1}$ | $\omega_0 S_i \epsilon^{-1}$ |
| Under-damped $\gamma < 1$ | $\dfrac{1}{\omega_0\sqrt{1-\gamma^2}}\tan^{-1}\left(\dfrac{\sqrt{1-\gamma^2}}{\gamma}\right)$ | $Q\omega_0 S_i \epsilon^{-\left\{\frac{\gamma}{\sqrt{1-\gamma^2}}\tan^{-1}\left(\frac{\sqrt{1-\gamma^2}}{\gamma}\right)\right\}}$ | $\omega_0 S_i \epsilon^{-\left\{\frac{\gamma}{\sqrt{1-\gamma^2}}\tan^{-1}\left(\frac{\sqrt{1-\gamma^2}}{\gamma}\right)\right\}}$ |
| Un-damped $\gamma = 0$ | $\dfrac{\pi}{2\omega_0}$ | $Q\omega_0 S_i$ | $\omega_0 S_i$ |

### 3-25. MEASUREMENT OF THE TIME INTEGRAL OF THE EMF [1]

In this section the characteristics of a ballistic galvanometer will be analyzed in terms of the integral of an "instantaneous" pulse of emf. This emf will be generated by reversing the flux in a magnetic circuit similar to the circuit shown in Fig. 3-9. The integral of emf is equal to the flux linkage, for, by Lenz's law,

$$e = -N \frac{d\phi}{dt}$$

Then

$$\int e \, dt = -N\Delta\phi \qquad (3\text{-}96)$$

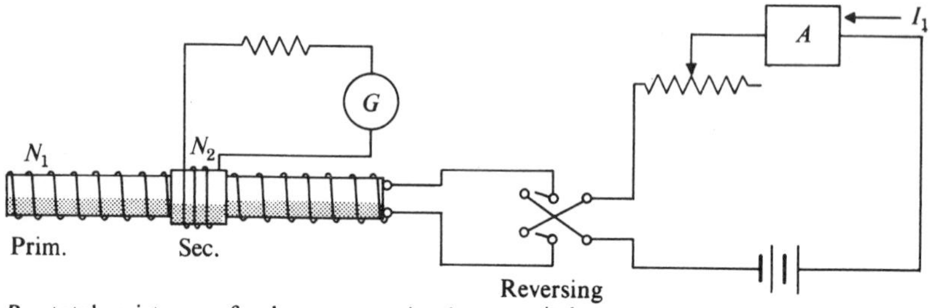

**Fig. 3-9.** *Measuring the flux-linkage sensitivity of a ballistic galvanometer*

The *flux-linkage sensitivity* is defined as the ratio of the maximum deflection of the galvanometer to the time integral of the emf. It is

$$S_{\phi N} = \frac{\theta_1}{\int e \, dt} \qquad (3\text{-}97)$$

where

$S_{\phi N}$ = flux-linkage sensitivity in maximum deflection/flux linkages (usually in millimeters/weber-turns)

$\phi$ = flux, in webers

$N$ = turns

$\theta_1$ = maximum deflection of the galvanometer

The general form of the equation of the torque on the galvanometer is

$$\frac{d^2\theta}{dt^2} + \frac{D}{J} \frac{d\theta}{dt} + \frac{S}{J} \theta = \frac{Ge}{JR} \qquad (3\text{-}98)$$

during the period from $t = 0$ to $t = t_1$, when the flux $\phi$ is linking the coil. This time interval is very short compared with the period of the ballistic galvanometer. Then the angular displacement, the movement during this period, is zero. The equation of the torque on the galvanometer movement after $t_1$ is

$$\frac{d^2\theta}{dt^2} + \frac{D}{J}\frac{d\theta}{dt} + \frac{S}{J}\theta = 0 \tag{3-99}$$

The initial conditions required for the solution of this equation are obtained by integrating Eq. (3-98) between the limits of $t = 0$ and $t = t_1$, giving

$$\frac{d\theta}{dt}\Big|_o^{t_1} + \frac{D}{J}\theta\Big|_o^{t_1} + \frac{S}{J}\int_o^t \theta\, dt = \frac{G}{JR}\int e\, dt$$

But $\theta = 0$ during the interval $t = 0$ to $t = t_1$. Then the initial conditions are

(1) $$\theta = 0 \tag{3-100}$$

(2) $$\frac{d\theta}{dt} = \frac{G}{JR}\int e\, dt \tag{3-101}$$

Solving Eq. (3-99) for $\theta$ using the initial conditions given in Eq. (3-100) and (3-101) for the underdamped movement when

$$D^2 < 4JS \quad \text{or} \quad \gamma < 1$$

gives

$$\theta = K_4 \int e\, dt\, \epsilon^{-a_4 t} \sin \omega t \tag{3-102}$$

where

$$K_4 = \frac{2\omega_o(\gamma - \gamma_2)}{G\omega_o\sqrt{1 - \gamma^2}}$$

$$= \frac{G}{JR\omega} = \frac{2\omega_o(\gamma - \gamma_2)}{G\omega_o\sqrt{1 - \gamma^2}}$$

$$= \frac{2(\gamma - \gamma_2)}{G\sqrt{1 - \gamma^2}}$$

$$a_4 = \sqrt{\frac{D^2}{4J^2}} = \sqrt{\omega_o{}^2 - \omega^2}$$

$$= \omega_o\gamma$$

$$\omega = \sqrt{\frac{S}{J} - \frac{D^2}{4J^2}} = \omega_o\sqrt{1 - \gamma^2}$$

where $\gamma_2 = D_m/D_c$, as given in Eq. (3-69).

The magnitude of $\theta_{m1}$ at the first maximum deflection of the galvanometer is determined by equating the first derivative of $\theta$ with respect to $t$ to zero and solving for the time $t_{m1}$ at which $\theta$ is $\theta_{m1}$. Then $t_{m1}$ is substituted into Eq. (3-102) to obtain the magnitude of $\theta_{m1}$. This computation yields

$$\theta_{m1} = \left( K_4 \int e \, dt \right)\left( \epsilon^{-a_4 t_{m1}} \sin \omega t_{m1} \right)$$

where

$$t_{m1} = \frac{1}{\sqrt{\dfrac{S}{J} - \dfrac{D^2}{4J^2}}} \tan^{-1} \sqrt{\frac{4JS - D^2}{D^2}}$$

$$= \frac{1}{\omega} \tan^{-1} \frac{\omega}{\sqrt{\omega_o{}^2 - \omega^2}}$$

$$= \frac{1}{\omega_o\sqrt{1 - \gamma^2}} \tan^{-1} \frac{\sqrt{1 - \gamma^2}}{\gamma}$$

For a given circuit, $\gamma$, $\omega_o$, and $\omega$ are constants. Then

$$\theta_{m1} = S_{\phi N} \int e \, dt$$

where

$$S_{\theta N} = \frac{2(\gamma - \gamma_2)}{G} \epsilon^{-\left\{ \frac{\gamma}{1 - \gamma^2} \tan^{-1} \frac{\sqrt{1 - \gamma^2}}{\gamma} \right\}}$$

$$= \frac{\theta_{m1}}{\int e \, dt} \tag{3-103}$$

This constant $S_{\phi N}$, by definition, is the *emf-time* or *flux-linkage sensitivity*. It is used in determining the hysteresis loops of magnetic materials.

The values of $\theta$, $\theta_m$, $t_m$, and $S_{\phi N}$ for the critical damped and overdamped ballistic galvanometers are given in Table 3-3.

### 3-26. MEASURING THE EMF-TIME OR FLUX-LINKAGE SENSITIVITY OF A GALVANOMETER

The circuit in Fig. 3-9 is used to determine the flux-linkage sensitivity of a ballistic galvanometer. The flux in the center of the long, closely wound, air-core, primary coil is

$$\phi = \frac{4\pi N_1 I_1 A}{L} \times 10^{-7} \text{ webers}$$

where

$L$ = length of the coil, in meters
$N_1$ = turns of the primary winding
$I_1$ = current in the primary winding, in amperes
$A$ = cross-sectional area of the coil, in square meters

**Table 3-3**

| | Underdamped $\gamma < 1$ | Critical damped $\gamma = 1$ | Overdamped $\gamma > 1$ |
|---|---|---|---|
| $\theta$ | $\dfrac{2(\gamma - \gamma_2)\int e\,dt}{G\sqrt{1-\gamma^2}}\,\epsilon^{-\omega_0\gamma t}\sin(\omega t\sqrt{1-\gamma^2})$ | $\dfrac{2\omega_0(1-\gamma_2)\int e\,dt}{G}\,t\epsilon^{-\omega_0 t}$ | $\dfrac{2(\gamma - \gamma_2)\int e\,dt}{G\sqrt{\gamma^2-1}}\,\epsilon^{-\omega_0\gamma t}\sinh(\omega_0 t\sqrt{\gamma^2-1})$ |
| $t_{m1}$ | $\dfrac{\omega_0}{\sqrt{1-\gamma^2}}\tan^{-1}\dfrac{\sqrt{1-\gamma^2}}{\gamma}$ | $\dfrac{1}{\omega_0}$ | $\dfrac{1}{\omega_0\sqrt{\gamma^2-1}}\tanh^{-1}\dfrac{\sqrt{\gamma^2-1}}{\gamma}$ |
| $\theta_{m1}$ | $\dfrac{2(\gamma - \gamma_2)}{G}\int e\,dt\,\epsilon^{-\left\{\frac{\gamma}{\sqrt{1-\gamma^2}}\tan^{-1}\frac{\sqrt{1-\gamma^2}}{\gamma}\right\}}$ | $\dfrac{2(1-\gamma_2)\int e\,dt}{G}\epsilon^{-1}$ | $\dfrac{2(\gamma - \gamma_2)}{G}\int e\,dt\,\epsilon^{-\left\{\frac{\gamma}{\sqrt{\gamma^2-1}}\tanh^{-1}\left(\frac{\sqrt{\gamma^2-1}}{\gamma}\right)\right\}}$ |
| $S_{\phi N}$ | $\dfrac{2(\gamma - \gamma_2)}{G}\epsilon^{-\left\{\frac{\gamma}{\sqrt{1-\gamma^2}}\tan^{-1}\frac{\sqrt{1-\gamma^2}}{\gamma}\right\}}$ | $\dfrac{2(1-\gamma_2)}{G}\epsilon^{-1}$ | $\dfrac{2(\gamma - \gamma_2)}{G}\epsilon^{-\left\{\frac{\gamma}{\sqrt{\gamma^2-1}}\tanh^{-1}\frac{\sqrt{\gamma^2-1}}{\gamma}\right\}}$ |

The flux linkage in the secondary circuit when the current in the primary is reversed is

$$-\Delta\phi N = \frac{8\pi N_1 N_2 A}{L} (\Delta I \times 10^{-7}) = \int e \, dt \qquad (3\text{-}104)$$

where

$\Delta\phi N$ = total flux linkage, in weber-turns
$N_2$ = total number of turns in the secondary winding

Then the flux-linkage sensitivity is the ratio of the first maximum deflection of the galvanometer $d_{m1}$ to the flux linkages computed from Eq. (3-104). Thus

$$S_{\phi N} = \frac{d_{m1}}{\Delta\phi \, N}$$

$$= \frac{d_{m1}}{\int e \, dt}$$

It will be noted that the flux-linkage sensitivity is a function of the resistance of the galvanometer circuit, and therefore the resistance of the circuit must remain constant.

## PROBLEMS

**3-1.** A current galvanometer has the following parameters:

$B = 100 \times 10^{-4}$ weber/sq m
$N = 200$ turns
$b = 1.6 \times 10^{-2}$ m
$L = 1.6 \times 10^{-2}$ m
$R = 120$ ohms
$S = 1.2 \times 10^{-8}$ newton-m/radian
$J = 5 \times 10^{-8}$ kg-m squared
$D = 5 \times 10^{-9}$ newton-m/radian/sec

Determine: (*a*) the deflection of the galvanometer in radians and in centimeters when a current of 1 $\mu$a is flowing through the galvanometer; (*b*) the current sensitivity; (*c*) the voltage sensitivity; (*d*) the megohm sensitivity; (*e*) the frequency of oscillation; (*f*) the undamped angular velocity $\omega_o$; (*g*) the relative damping; (*h*) the first maximum deflection; (*i*) the logarithmic decrement.

**3-2.** A galvanometer has the following parameters:

$B = 80 \times 10^{-4}$ weber/sq m
$N = 300$ turns
$b = 3 \times 10^{-2}$ m
$L = 1.5 \times 10^{-2}$ m
$J = 1 \times 10^{-8}$ kg-m squared
$S = 2.5 \times 10^{-9}$ newton-m/radian
$D = 2 \times 10^{-8}$ newton-m/radian/sec
$R = 80$ ohms

(a) An emf of $10^{-5}$ volt is applied to the galvanometer. Determine the deflection in radians and in centimeters. (b) Determine the undamped period of the galvanometer. (c) Determine the CDRX of the galvanometer. (d) Determine the frequency of oscillation of the galvanometer when the resistance of the galvanometer circuit is increased to 500 ohms.

**3-3.** The deflection of a galvanometer is zero with no current and 7.5 cm with a steady-state current of 5.6 $\mu$a. Its first maximum deflection, after a step function of voltage which produces a steady-state current of 5.6 $\mu$a is applied, is 11.2 cm. The maximum deflection of the next cycle is 8.4 cm. Determine: (a) the current sensitivity; (b) the logarithmic decrement; (c) the relative damping.

**3-4.** In Fig. 3-4 the emf is 1.5 volts, $R_1$ is 6,900 ohms, $R_2$ is 2 ohms, $R_3$ is 1,240 ohms when the galvanometer deflection is 15 cm, and $R_3$ is 420 ohms when the deflection is 30 cm. Determine: (a) the resistance of the galvanometer; (b) the current in the galvanometer when the deflection is 15 cm; (c) the current sensitivity of the galvanometer; (d) the voltage sensitivity of the galvanometer; (e) the megohm sensitivity of the galvanometer.

**3-5.** In Fig. 3-4 $R_1$ is 5,000 ohms and $R_2$ is 4 ohms. The deflection of the galvanometer is 10 cm when $R_3$ is 1,500 ohms and 16 cm when $R_3$ is 860 ohms. Determine: (a) the resistance of the galvanometer; (b) the current through the galvanometer when the deflection is 10 cm.

**3-6.** A galvanometer has a logarithmic decrement of 2.2 with the galvanometer circuit resistance of 1,500 ohms. With the galvanometer circuit open, the relative damping is 0.11. Determine: (a) the relative damping of the galvanometer with 1,500 ohms in the galvanometer circuit; (b) the resistance of the galvanometer circuit that will produce a relative damping of 0.5; (c) the logarithmic decrement when the relative damping is 0.5.

**3-7.** The CDRX of the galvanometer is a 1,200-ohm resistance. The resistance of the galvanometer is 450 ohms. Determine the resistance of $R_2$ and $R_3$, in Fig. 3-6, to reduce the sensitivity to 0.1 of its sensitivity without $R_2$ and $R_3$ in the circuit. $R_1$ is 1,200 ohms.

**3-8.** An Ayrton shunt, as shown in Fig. 3-7, has a total resistance of 2,000 ohms. The resistance of the galvanometer is 420 ohms. The Ayrton shunt has a sensitivity of 1.0, 0.5, 0.05, and 0.005. Determine: (a) the resistance of $R_a$, $R_b$, $R_c$, and $R_d$; (b) the ratio of the current $I$ to the galvanometer current $I_g$ at each setting of the Ayrton shunt.

**3-9.** A galvanometer has a resistance of 150 ohms and an undamped period of 7.5 sec. A steady emf of 0.0035 volt produces a deflection of 21 cm. Determine the quantity of electricity discharged from a capacitor when the deflection of the galvanometer is 7.5 cm. The relative damping is 0.8.

**3-10.** The discharge of a capacitor through a ballistic galvanometer produces a frequency of 0.125 cycles per second and maximum deflections of 12, 9.6, and 7.68 cm. Determine: (a) the logarithmic decrement; (b) the frequency of the undamped system.

**3-11.** A 1.2-$\mu$f capacitor is charged with a 10-volt source. It is then discharged through a ballistic galvanometer. The maximum deflection of the galvanometer is 15 cm. Determine the coulomb sensitivity of the galvanometer.

**3-12.** The primary coil in Fig. 3-9 has 1,200 turns and the secondary coil has 45 turns. The current $I_1$ is 1.35 amp. The first maximum deflection of the galvanometer is 13.5 cm. Determine the flux-linkage sensitivity of the galvanometer circuit. The diameter of the primary winding is 0.12 m. The length of the primary coil is 1 m.

**3-13.** The frequency of oscillation is 0.37 cps and the logarithmic decrement is 1.2. Determine (*a*) the relative damping, (*b*) the natural undamped frequency, and (*c*) the free undamped period of oscillation.

**3-14.** A ballistic galvanometer has a natural undamped free period of 8.7 sec and a relative damping of 0.8. Determine the time required for the galvanometer to pass through zero after the application of the initial charge of electricity.

**3-15.** A ballistic galvanometer coil has an effective length of 2.5 cm, a width of 5 cm, and 350 turns. The average flux density is $80 \times 10^{-4}$ Webers per square meter. The relative damping is unity. The spring coefficient is $1.2 \times 10^{-7}$ newton-m per radian. The current is $10^{-5}$ amp. The undamped angular velocity is 0.23 radian per second. Plot the angular displacement $\theta$ as a function of time.

REFERENCES

1. F. K. Harris, *Electrical Measurements*, John Wiley & Sons, Inc., New York, 1952.

2. S. Fich, *Transient Analysis in Electrical Engineering*, Prentice-Hall, Inc., Englewood Cliffs, N.J., 1951, Chap. 2.

3. M. B. Stout, *Basic Electrical Measurements*, 2nd ed., Prentice-Hall, Inc., Englewood Cliffs, N.J., 1960, Chap. 5.

4. Ernest Frank, *Electrical Measurement Analysis*, McGraw-Hill Book Company, Inc., New York, 1959.

5. I. F. Kinnard, *Applied Electrical Measurements*, John Wiley & Sons, Inc., New York, 1956, p. 37.

# Chapter 4

# INDICATING

**4-1. CONSTRUCTION OF A D'ARSONVAL MOVEMENT**[1,2,3,4,5]

Most d-c indicating instruments use some form of the d'Arsonval movement, consisting of a magnetic field supplied by a permanent magnet and a rotating coil. In these instruments the coil has small bearing supports glued to the core frame, as shown in Fig. 4-1. The bearings consist of small pins of hard steel inserted in the bearing support. The pinpoint sits in a stationary jeweled cup, as shown in Fig. 4-2. It will be noted, in Fig. 4-2, that there are two types of jeweled cups and pinpoints. One pin is very sharp and sits in a small jeweled cup. This type of bearing is used for very sensitive, delicate movements and must be handled carefully to preserve the bearing mounting. In portable equipment which may receive comparatively rough usage, the pinpoints are made flatter on the end and the cup is arranged so that the bearing has a much larger contact surface to absorb shock. This type of bearing is rugged and will stand comparatively rough usage. Wearing of the bearings or improper adjustment of the jewel cups may produce errors in the instrument and increase the drag torque, causing an increase in the dead zone.

Figure 4-3 shows the complete assembly of a permanent magnet and a coil in a d-Arsonval movement. The permanent magnet is usually of alnico. The pole faces and the core that sits inside the moving coil are of soft iron.

70

# DIRECT-CURRENT

# INSTRUMENTS

Nonmagnetic material is used to support the bearings and the coil. Thus the coil is free to move in the uniform gap between the solid core and the pole pieces.

Figure 4-4 shows the arrangement of the pointer and springs mounted on the coil. The pointer is dynamically and statically balanced by counterweights on the arm opposite to the pointer and on bars which extend at right angles from the pointer at the bearing position. These weights are adjusted until the center of gyration of the movement lies on a line through the bearing points. The two springs, one at each end of the coil, apply the correct amount of restoring force to the moving mechanism and supply the current to the moving coil.

On delicate instruments the coils are mounted on nonconducting material, usually of noncorrosive plastic rosin which holds the coils in their proper form. Some moving coils in d'Arsonval movements are wound on light aluminum frames. Electrically, this metal frame is a one-turn shorted coil. It will have approximately the same length $L$ and width $b$ as the coil wound on it. From Eq. (3-12) the emf induced in the frame is

$$e_f = -BLb\frac{d\theta}{dt}$$

$$= -G_f\frac{d\theta}{dt} \tag{4-1}$$

71

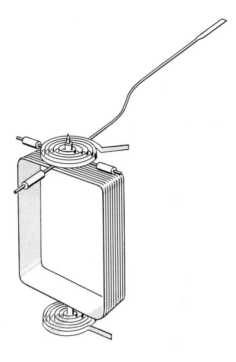

**Fig. 4-1.** *Coil assembly and pointer of a d'Arsonval movement (courtesy of the Weston Electrical Instrument Corporation)*

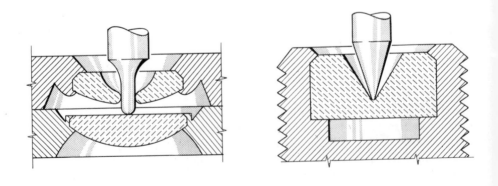

**Fig. 4-2.** *Bearings for a d'Arsonval movement (courtesy of the Weston Electrical Instrument Corporation)*

 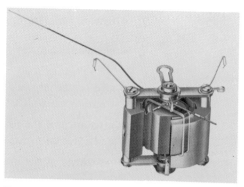

**Fig. 4-3.** *The complete assembly of a d'Arsonval movement with magnet (courtesy of the Weston Electrical Instrument Corporation)*

**Fig. 4-4.** *A d'Arsonval movement without the magnet (courtesy of the Weston Electrical Instrument Corporation)*

where $\theta$ is the angular movement of the coil and $G_f = BLb$ corresponding to $G = NBLb$ for the winding supported by the frame, as given in Eqs. (3-4) and (3-13). Then

$$\frac{G_f}{G} = \frac{1}{N}$$

or

$$G_f = \frac{G}{N} \tag{4-2}$$

Also, the torque produced by the current $I_f$ induced in the frame is

$$\tau_f = i_f BLb$$

$$= G_f i_f = G_f \frac{e_f}{R_f}$$

$$= \frac{G_f{}^2}{R_f} \frac{d\theta}{dt}$$

$$= \frac{G^2}{N^2 R_f} \frac{d\theta}{dt} \tag{4-3}$$

Then, referring to Eq. (3-15), the corresponding equation for the damping with the winding on a metal frame is

$$D = \text{total damping}$$

$$= D_m + \frac{G^2}{R} + \frac{G^2}{NR_f} \tag{4-4}$$

where

$D_m$ = mechanical damping or open-circuit damping

$\dfrac{G^2}{R}$ = electromechanical damping due to the moving coil

$\dfrac{G^2}{NR_f}$ = electromechanical damping produced by the moving mutual frame upon which the coil is wound

$R$ = resistance of the total meter circuit, or the sum of internal and external resistance in the circuit

$R_f$ = resistance of the metal frame

$N$ = number of turns in the moving coil

Thus the metal frame produces additional damping of the movement.

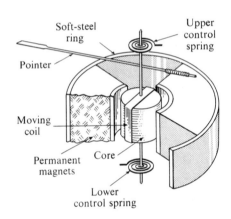

Fig. 4-5. *A concentric-magnet movement (courtesy of the General Electric Company)*

The accuracy of the instrument will depend on the uniformity of the flux throughout the gap in which the coil moves. Any variation in the flux will produce a nonlinearity of the displacement of the pointer as a function of the current in the coil. The flux must be constant with respect to time; otherwise, a reliable output could not be obtained from the instrument. Great care is taken to "cure" the permanent magnets so that the flux will remain constant and will not deteriorate with time or rough usage.

In order to obtain a longer movement of the pointer and a longer angular swing of the coil, a concentric magnet with radial flux has been developed. This is shown in Fig. 4-5, where the magnet is of the concentric type producing a flux radially from the magnet itself. This will allow a movement of 250 deg or more and is used on many panel-type instruments and some portable instruments.

## 4-2. CURRENT MEASUREMENTS[1,2,3]

Essentially all d'Arsonval movements are current-measuring devices, as the displacement torque produced in the coil is

$$\tau_d = BNAI$$

In the figure labels:

Soft-steel ring

Upper control spring

Pointer

Moving coil

Permanent magnets

Core

Lower control spring

where

$\tau_d$ = displacement torque
$B$ = flux density of the air gap
$N$ = number of turns on the coil
$A$ = cross-sectional area of the coil—the product of the length times the width of the coil
$I$ = current in the coil

This displacement torque is in equilibrium with the restoring torque which is a function of the spring and is equal to the product of the spring constant $S$ and the angular displacement of the coil $\theta$. Then

$$\tau_r = S\theta$$

where

$\tau_r$ = restoring torque

At rest

$$\tau_d = \tau_r$$

or

$$BNAI = S\theta$$

Then

$$I = \frac{S\theta}{BNA} \tag{4-5}$$

In most instruments $B$ may be assumed to be constant, $N$ is constant, and $A$ is constant. Then

$$I = K_i\theta \tag{4-6}$$

where $K_i$ is a constant and the displacement of the coil will be directly proportional to the currents in the coil. The dynamic characteristics of this instrument will be the same as the dynamic characteristics for the current galvanometer; in fact, this instrument is essentially the same as that of a current galvanometer in all respects, except that in this instrument it is essential that the flux density remain constant in the air gap through which the coil moves. Commercial ammeters are made to consume about 25 $\mu$w to produce full-scale reading for small instruments, and large instruments will require about 200 $\mu$w to produce a full-scale reading. Direct-current ammeters are commercially available in ranges from 20 $\mu$a to several amperes full scale. They usually have a uniform scale. For precision work, these instruments may be accompanied with a calibration chart or they may have very accurately hand-calibrated scales.

This instrument is always connected in series with the load, as shown in Fig. 4-6, because the ammeter has low resistance and would draw damaging current unless

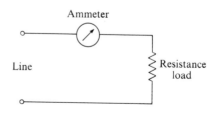

Fig. 4-6. *Ammeter circuit*

there were a limiting resistance or load in series with it. *Never connect an ammeter across a steady source of emf, and be sure there is sufficient resistance in series with the ammeter to limit the current to the range of the meter.*

### 4-3. AMMETER SHUNTS AND MULTIRANGE AMMETERS[1,2,3]

When a d'Arsonval movement is used as a current-measuring instrument, the current passes through the coil winding. This coil winding is very small and will carry only low currents. To measure high currents, part of the current is shunted around the d'Arsonval movement through a resistance, as shown in Fig. 4-7,

where

$I$ = load current to be measured

$I_m$ = current in the d'Arsonval movement

$I_s$ = current in the shunt

$R_m$ = resistance of the meter

$R_s$ = resistance of the shunt

The voltage across the shunt is

$$V_m = I_m R_m \qquad (4\text{-}7)$$

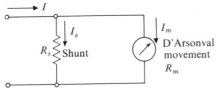

The current through the shunt is

$$I_s = I - I_m \qquad (4\text{-}8)$$

Then the resistance of the shunt is

**Fig. 4-7.** *D'Arsonval movement with shunt*

$$R_s = \frac{V_m}{I_s} = \frac{V_m}{I - I_m} \qquad (4\text{-}9)$$

Substituting Eq. (4-7) for $V_m$ gives

$$R_s = \frac{I_m R_m}{I - I_m}$$

$$= \frac{R_m}{\dfrac{I}{I_m} - 1} \qquad (4\text{-}10)$$

The shunt resistance used with a d'Arsonval movement may consist of a coil of resistance wire within the case of the instrument, or it may be an external shunt having a very low resistance.

An external shunt is shown in Fig. 4-8. It consists of evenly spaced sheets of resistive material welded into a large block of heavy copper on each end of the sheets. The resistance material has a very low temperature coefficient and a low thermal electric effect between the resistance material and the copper. The heavy lugs on each end of the shunt carry the load current, while the binding posts on each end of the shunt are used to connect

**Fig. 4-8.** *Ammeter shunt (courtesy of the Leeds and Northrup Company)*

the ammeter to the shunt and carry only the current which passes through the meter. Meters using external shunts are usually designed to operate at a certain full-scale voltage rating. These ratings are usually 50, 75, or 100 mv. This is the voltage across the small terminals of the shunt when full-scale current flows through the load. Inasmuch as the current producing the meter deflection is a function of the voltage drop across the small terminals of the shunt and the resistance of the instrument, including the leads, the millivoltmeter used with external shunts must have leads with a specified resistance to accompany the meter. Never cut off any portion of the leads or exchange the leads which are supplied with a millivoltmeter that is to be used with a shunt.

A multirange-ammeter circuit is shown in Fig. 4-9. This circuit has four shunts, $S_1$, $S_2$, $S_3$, and $S_4$, to give the ammeter ranges of $I_1$, $I_2$, $I_3$, and $I_4$.

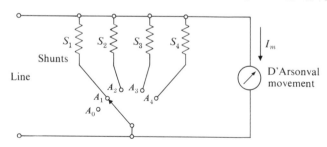

**Fig. 4-9.** *Multirange ammeter*

Many low-range ammeters use a multiposition make-before-break switch, included in the case of the instrument, when changing from one current range to another. When larger currents are used, the connections are brought out to binding posts and the leads are connected directly to the binding post which is identified with the desired range. These instruments are used for ranges from 1 to 50 amp. When using a multirange ammeter, first use the largest current range, then decrease the current range until a good up-scale reading is obtained.

## 4-4. VOLTMETERS [1,2,3]

The basic current-measuring d'Arsonval movement is adapted to voltage measurement by inserting a resistance in series with a d'Arsonval movement, as shown in Fig. 4-10. The voltage across the terminals $a$ and $b$ will be the product of the current and the total resistance of the circuit. Thus

$$V = I_m(R_1 + R_m) \tag{4-11}$$

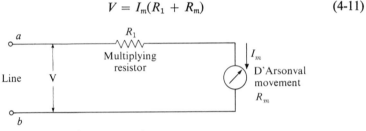

**Fig. 4-10.** *Voltmeter circuit*

Solving for the value of $R_1$ gives

$$R_1 = \frac{V - I_m R_m}{I_m}$$

$$= \frac{V}{I_m} - R_m \tag{4-12}$$

Figure 4-11($a$) shows a multirange voltmeter using a tap-changing switch with resistances $R_1$, $R_2$, $R_3$, and $R_4$ for voltage ranges $V_1$, $V_2$, $V_3$, and

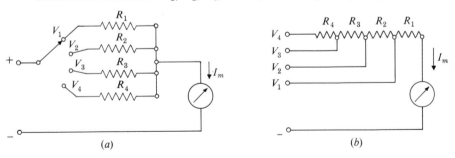

(a)                    (b)

**Fig. 4-11.** *Multirange voltmeter*

$V_4$, respectively. The values of $R_1$, $R_2$, $R_3$, and $R_4$ can be computed by using Eq. (4-12). Another multirange-meter circuit is shown in Fig. 4-11($b$) in which the connections are made at the junctions of resistances $R_1$, $R_2$, $R_3$, and $R_4$ in series to obtain the voltage ranges $V_1$, $V_2$, $V_3$, and $V_4$ and are brought out to binding posts on the instrument, and the instrument is connected to the proper binding post for the desired voltage range. The series resistance for the voltage ranges of $V_1$, $V_2$, $V_3$, and $V_4$ can be computed as follows:

$$R_1 = \frac{V_1}{I_m} - R_m$$

$$R_2 = \frac{V_2}{I_m} - (R_m + R_1)$$

$$R_3 = \frac{V_3}{I_m} - (R_m + R_1 + R_2)$$

$$R_4 = \frac{V_4}{I_m} - (R_m + R_1 + R_2 + R_3) \qquad (4\text{-}13)$$

etc.

These instruments are very effective for moderate-range voltages. For higher-range voltages it is often desirable to use external resistances in connection with a given voltmeter. The value of the external resistance can be computed in the same manner as is done in Eqs. (4-12) or (4-13). These series resistances are defined as multipliers or multiplying resistors, as compared with shunts or shunt resistors for the resistances used in ammeter circuits. The only precaution necessary in the average use of a voltmeter is to be sure that the voltmeter has sufficient range to measure the applied voltage. Therefore, in using a multirange instrument, it is the usual procedure first to connect the instrument to the highest voltage-range terminal or set the switch to the highest voltage which the instrument will read. Then connect the meter to the circuit and measure the voltage. Then decrease the ranges of the instrument until a good up-scale reading is obtained on the voltmeter. In changing terminals it is necessary first to disconnect the voltmeter leads from the source of power. Then change the connection at the binding post; otherwise, it is possible to short the voltmeter leads and damage the circuit being measured, or badly burn the terminals on the voltmeter leads.

## 4-5. VOLTMETER-AMMETER MEASUREMENTS

In Fig. 4-12(a) a voltmeter connected across the source of emf and an ammeter connected in series with the load are shown. This is a common method of connecting a voltmeter and ammeter to measure the current and the voltage of the load. The ammeter measures the true current supplied to the loads, but the voltmeter has an error. It measures the voltage across the load plus the voltage across the ammeter. The voltage across the ammeter will be equal to the current times the meter resistance. Therefore, it is desirable in this circuit to have an ammeter with as low an internal resistance

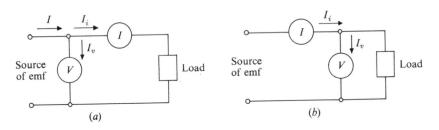

**Fig. 4-12.** *Voltmeter-ammeter measurements*

as possible. As an example of the resistance of ammeters, a large manufacturer of portable d-c meters lists the resistance of a few typical current-measuring instruments as follows:

| Full scale current | Resistance |
|:---:|:---:|
| 30 μa | 490–23,000 Ohms |
| 200 μa | 15–200 Ohms |
| 1 ma | 43 Ohms |
| 15 ma | 1 Ohm |

Thus, although the normal power-measurement error may be small, when small currents are being measured, such as in electronic circuits, the resistance of the meter may produce very large errors in the circuit.

In Fig. 4-12(*b*) the ammeter is connected ahead of the voltmeter to measure the current and the voltage supplied to the load. In this circuit the voltmeter reads the true voltage across the load, while the ammeter reads the current supplied to the load and the current supplied to the voltmeter. The error will depend on the current drawn by the voltmeter. The current drawn by the voltmeter is indicated by the ohms per volt of the voltmeter. In power-measuring equipment where the current is large, voltmeters are usually 100 ohms per volt. For laboratory use in power circuits, 1,000 ohms per volt is in common use. For radio service work the common multimeters have 20,000 ohms per volt, while vacuum-tube voltmeters are usually rated in input resistance, which is usually 10 megohms or more. When the ohms-per-volt rating of a given instrument is known, the error in the current reading can be computed by dividing the voltage read by the product of the ohms per volt and the full-scale voltage of the instrument.

Having determined the current and the voltage supplied to a load, the resistance of the circuit and the power supplied to the circuit can be computed.

## 4-6.  SERIES-TYPE OHMMETER[1]

A circuit of a series-type ohmmeter is given in Fig. 4-13. It consists of a galvanometer movement with an adjustable shunting resistor $R_2$. This parallel circuit is in series with a resistance $R_1$ and a battery having an emf $E$. This series circuit is connected to the terminals $a$ and $b$ of the unknown resistance. It will be observed that, when the unknown resistance $R_x$ is 0, the maximum emf will be applied to the galvanometer. Under this condition $R_2$ is adjusted until the galvanometer has its full-scale current reading. Thus the meter reads full-scale current when the unknown resistance $R_x$ is zero. Similarly, when $R_x$ is removed from the circuit, that is, when the circuit $a$-$b$ is open, the resistance between $a$-$b$ is infinity, and no emf is applied to the galvanometer circuit. Thus the galvanometer will read infinite resistance at the zero current position and zero resistance at full-scale current position.

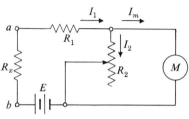

**Fig. 4-13.**  *Series-type ohmmeter*

In order to obtain a consistent idea of the resistance scale, the midpoint of the pointer movement is taken as a reference. At this position the resistance across the terminals $a$-$b$ will be defined as $R_x = R_H$, or the half-scale position resistance. The analysis of this circuit is as follows:

At

$$R_x = R_H$$
$$I_m = 0.5 I_{FS}$$

where

$I_m$ = current in the meter
$I_{FS}$ = full-scale current through the meter

Also

$$I_1 = I_m + I_2 = I_m + \frac{I_m R_m}{R_2} = I_m \left(1 + \frac{R_m}{R_2}\right)$$

$$= 0.5 I_{FS} \left(1 + \frac{R_m}{R_2}\right) = \frac{E}{R_H + R_1 + \dfrac{R_2 R_m}{R_2 + R_m}} \tag{4-14}$$

At $R_x = 0$, the current in the meter is $I_{FS}$. Then

$$I_1 = I_{FS} \left(1 + \frac{R_m}{R_2}\right) = \frac{E}{R_1 + \dfrac{R_2 R_m}{R_2 + R_m}} \tag{4-15}$$

Dividing Eq. (4-15) by Eq. (4-14) gives

$$\frac{R_H + R_1 + \dfrac{R_2 R_m}{R_2 + R_m}}{R_1 + \dfrac{R_2 R_m}{R_2 + R_m}} = 2$$

Solving for $R_H$ gives

$$R_H + R_1 + \frac{R_2 R_m}{R_2 + R_m} = 2\left(R_1 + \frac{R_2 R_m}{R_2 + R_m}\right)$$

or

$$R_H = R_1 + \frac{R_2 R_m}{R_2 + R_m} \qquad (4\text{-}16)$$

Thus the resistance $R_H$ is equal to the resistance of the ohmmeter circuit. Substituting $R_H$ for the resistance of the ohmmeter circuit in Eq. (4-15) gives

$$\frac{E}{R_H} = I_{FS}\left(1 + \frac{R_m}{R_2}\right) \qquad (4\text{-}17)$$

Solving for $R_2$,

$$\frac{R_m}{R_2} = \frac{E}{I_{FS} R_H} - 1$$

or

$$R_2 = \frac{R_m}{\dfrac{E}{I_{FS} R_H} - 1} = \frac{I_{FS} R_m R_H}{E - I_{FS} R_H} \qquad (4\text{-}18)$$

It will be noted that as $I_{FS} R_H$ approaches $E$, $R_2$ approaches infinity. If $R_2$ is to have a finite limit, say 500,000 ohms, then solving Eq. (4-17) for $R_H$ gives

$$R_H = \frac{E}{I_{FS}\left(1 + \dfrac{R_m}{R_2}\right)} = \frac{E R_2}{I_{FS}(R_2 + R_m)}$$

$$= \frac{500{,}000 E}{I_{FS}(500{,}000 + R_m)}$$

If $R_2$ is to compensate for a 10 percent drop in the battery voltage, then the maximum value of $R_H$ will be

$$R_H = \frac{(500{,}000)(0.9)E}{I_{FS}(500{,}000 + R_m)} = \frac{0.9E}{I_{FS}} \qquad (4\text{-}19)$$

If the resistance $R_H$ is to be increased beyond this value, a battery with a higher emf must be used.

Solving Eq. (4-16) for $R_1$,

$$R_1 = R_H - \frac{R_2 R_m}{R_2 + R_m}$$

Substituting Eq. (4-18) for $R_2$ in this equation gives

$$R_1 = R_H - \frac{R_m(I_{FS}R_mR_H)/(E - I_{FS}R_H)}{I_{FS}R_mR_H/(E - I_{FS}R_H) + R_m}$$

$$= R_H - \frac{R_m(I_{FS}R_mR_H)}{I_{FS}R_mR_H + ER_m - I_{FS}R_mR_H}$$

$$= R_H - \frac{I_{FS}R_mR_H}{E} \tag{4-20}$$

Thus, in terms of the full-scale meter current, the resistance of the meter, the battery voltage, and the measured resistance at half scale, the resistance of $R_1$ and of $R_2$ can be determined and the maximum value of $R_H$ for a given battery emf can be computed.

The meter current $I_m$ at any unknown resistance $R_x$ is

$$I_m = I_1 \frac{R_2}{R_2 + R_m} = \frac{ER_2}{(R_2 + R_m)\left(R_x + R_1 + \dfrac{R_2R_m}{R_2 + R_m}\right)}$$

Substituting $R_H$ for its equivalent, given in Eq. (4-16), gives

$$I_m = \frac{ER_2}{(R_2 + R_m)(R_x + R_H)} \tag{4-21}$$

At $R_x = 0$

$$I_m = I_{FS}$$

and

$$I_{FS} = I_1 \frac{R_2}{R_2 + R_m} = \frac{ER_2}{(R_2 + R_m)\left(R_1 + \dfrac{R_2R_m}{R_2 + R_m}\right)}$$

$$= \frac{ER_2}{(R_2 + R_m)R_H} \tag{4-22}$$

Dividing Eq. (4-21) by Eq. (4-22) gives

$$s = \frac{I_m}{I_{FS}} = \frac{R_H}{R_x + R_H} \tag{4-23}$$

where $s$ is the fraction of full-scale reading when measuring an unknown resistance $R_x$. Thus the scale of the ohmmeter for a given $R_H$ can be calibrated either by direct calibration, using known values of $R_x$, or it can be calculated in terms of the fraction of the full-scale readings, which can be computed from the resistance to be measured $R_x$ and the half-scale resistance $R_H$. This type of ohmmeter is very popular in portable instruments, as it measures the usual ranges of resistance required in service work.

## 4-7.  SHUNT-TYPE OHMMETER[1]

A circuit of a shunt-type ohmmeter is shown in Fig. 4-14. It consists of a battery in series with an adjustable resistance $R_1$ and a galvanometer. The

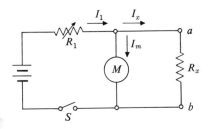

galvanometer is shunted by the unknown resistance $R_x$. It will be noted, in this circuit, that it is necessary to have an off-and-on switch $S$ to disconnect the battery from the circuit when the instrument is not in use. Otherwise, there would be a continual drain upon the battery.

**Fig. 4-14.**  *Shunt-type ohmmeter*

The analysis of the shunt-type ohmmeter is similar to that of a series-type ohmmeter. From the circuit shown in Fig. 4-14, the full-scale meter current will flow when the circuit from $a$ to $b$ is open or $R_x$ is infinite. The full-scale current will be

$$I_{FS} = \frac{E}{R_1 + R_m} \tag{4-24}$$

Solving for $R_1$,

$$R_1 = \frac{E}{I_{FS}} - R_m \tag{4-25}$$

With any resistance $R_x$ to be measured, the meter current $I_m$ will be

$$I_m = \left( \frac{E}{R_1 + \dfrac{R_m R_x}{R_m + R_x}} \right) \left( \frac{R_x}{R_m + R_x} \right)$$

$$= \frac{E R_x}{R_1 R_m + R_x(R_1 + R_m)} \tag{4-26}$$

At half-scale reading of the meter,

$$I_m = 0.5 I_{FS}$$

and

$$R_x = R_H$$

Then

$$0.5 I_{FS} = \frac{E R_H}{R_1 R_m + R_H(R_1 + R_m)} \tag{4-27}$$

Dividing Eq. (4-26) by Eq. (4-24) gives

$$s = \frac{I_m}{I_{FS}} = \frac{R_x(R_1 + R_m)}{R_1 R_m + R_x(R_1 + R_m)}$$

Usually, $R_1$ is very much larger than $R_m$. Then

$$s = \frac{R_x}{R_m + R_x} \qquad (4\text{-}28)$$

Thus the meter can be calibrated by computing the fraction of full-scale $s$ for a given resistance $R_x$ in terms of $R_x$ and the meter resistance $R_m$.

In order to determine the relative scales, for a given value of $R_1$, the half-scale reading $R_H$ can be determined by dividing Eq. (4-24) by Eq. (4-27), and solving for $R_H$.

$$R_H = \frac{R_1 R_m}{R_1 + R_m} \qquad (4\text{-}29)$$

From the above analysis it is shown that: (1) the battery emf $E$, the meter full-scale current $I_{FS}$, and the meter resistance $R_m$ determine the resistance $R_1$; (2) this resistance $R_1$ and the meter resistance $R_m$ determine the half-scale resistance $R_H$ of the meter. Therefore, the meter-resistance scale depends only upon the meter and the battery voltage used. Usually, the battery emf is 1.5 to 15 volts, while the full-scale current may vary from 0.25 ma to 1 amp or more, depending upon the meter and battery used. Then $R_1$ will vary from 5 to 12,000 ohms. As $R_1$ decreases, the current rating of the meter increases and the resistance of the meter decreases. Usually, $R_1$ is very much larger than $R_m$. Then

$$R_1 + R_m \approx R_1 \qquad (4\text{-}30)$$

Substituting Eq. (4-30) in Eq. (4-29) gives

$$R_H = R_m \qquad (4\text{-}31)$$

Assuming that a meter has a 10-ma movement with a resistance of 5 ohms, the half-scale resistance would be

$$R_{H1} = 5 \text{ ohms}$$

If this movement were to be converted to a 50-ma meter by using the proper shunt, the resistance of the movement and the shunt would be 1 ohm, and the half-scale resistance would be

$$R_{H2} = 1 \text{ ohm}$$

Now if this milliammeter movement were shunted to convert the meter to 250 ma full-scale, the combined resistance of the movement and the shunt would be 0.2 ohm. Then the half-scale resistance would be

$$R_{H3} = 0.2 \text{ ohm}$$

Similarly, if the meter were converted to 1 amp full-scale, the resistance of the movement and the shunt would be 0.05 ohm and

$$R_{H4} = 0.05 \text{ ohm}$$

Thus, using the proper meter and shunts, low values of resistances can be measured. This ohmmeter is not in common use, but it is very effective in measuring low resistances. An ammeter which will draw an appreciable current can be used in this circuit. The advantage of this arrangement is that a high-reading ammeter usually has a very low resistance, and this arrangement is used for measuring resistances comparable to the resistance of the ammeter. In these measurements the battery must supply the required current without appreciable internal drop, and $R_1$ and $R_x$ must be capable of carrying the required current without appreciable temperature rise.

### 4-8. CROSS-COIL OHMMETERS[1]

There are two types of cross-coil ohmmeters. One type has two moving coils arranged in a manner very similar to the d'Arsonval movement, except that the core is set off center from the center of the pole pieces, thus giving a varying air-gap flux. This arrangement is shown in Fig. 4-15. The current to the two coils is supplied from the same battery. The circuit from one

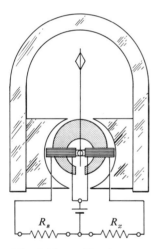

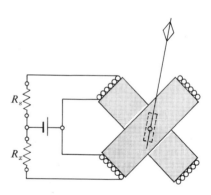

**Fig. 4-15.** *Fixed-magnet moving-coil ohmmeter*

**Fig. 4-16.** *Crossed-coil moving-magnet ohmmeter*

coil to the battery is connected through a known resistance $R_s$, and the circuit from the other coil to the battery is connected through an unknown resistance $R_x$. The current flowing through the two coils will be inversely proportional to the resistance in series with the respective coils. The coils will seek an equilibrium position where the product of the current and the flux density of one coil will equal the product of the current and the flux density of the other coil. Thus the pointer will indicate the ratio of the unknown resistance to the known resistance, and the scale can be calibrated to read the resistance being measured.

Another type uses two fixed stationary coils set 90 deg from each other, with a magnet suspended at the center of these coils. The flux produced at the center of the coils will be the vector sum of the flux produced by the two coils. One coil is connected through a known resistance $R_s$ to the source of emf, while the other coil is connected through an unknown resistance $R_x$. Thus the current through the two coils will be inversely proportional to the resistances connected in series with the respective coils. The pointer will assume a position in line with the resultant field, which will depend on the ratio of the two resistances. The scale is then calibrated to give the value of the unknown resistance. The arrangement of this instrument is shown in Fig. 4-16.

### 4-9. MEGGER [1]

Although there are several instruments designed to measure a high resistance in the neighborhood of a megohm, most of these circuits use a bridge method which will be included in a later chapter. The most common indicating-type high-resistance measuring unit is the megger, made by the

**Fig. 4-17.** *The megger (courtesy of the James G. Biddle Company)*

James G. Biddle Company. This instrument is shown in Fig. 4-17. It will be seen that this indicating instrument is operated with a crank. The crank turns a generator through a clutch which keeps the generator at a nearly constant speed. The voltage generated is in the neighborhood of 500 volts and supplies the voltage for a cross-coil ohmmeter movement, one coil being connected to a standard resistance and the other coil to the resistance to be measured, as shown in the circuit diagram in Fig. 4-18. The movement has no restoring

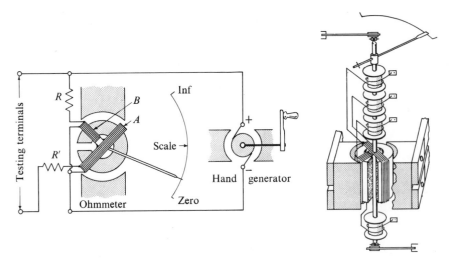

**Fig. 4-18.** *The megger circuit* (*courtesy of the James G. Biddle Company*)

torque; therefore, the position of the coils is determined entirely by the flux density and the current in the coils. Care must be taken that the leads to the coils produce no torsional effect upon the movement. An arrangement to ensure this is shown in Fig. 4-18. This instrument is used extensively in testing low-voltage insulation. Some models of the megger operate from an a-c supply which is rectified to supply voltages of 100, 500, 1,000, 3,500, and 5,000 volts. This makes a very versatile instrument. Not only can these voltages be used to extend the range of the ohmmeter; in addition, the value of $R$ can be changed to provide the desired range. Its basic scale is in megohms, and it is used to measure insulation resistance.

#### 4-10. VOLT-OHM-MILLIAMMETER [4]

It will be observed that the shunt-type ohmmeter, the voltmeter, and the ammeter utilize a simple d'Arsonval movement. The only difference between these instruments is the circuit used with the basic movement. Therefore, a meter can be designed, using the proper circuits, which will measure volts, ohms, and amperes or milliamperes. The Simpson Model 260 volt-ohm-milliammeter is such a meter. These meters are often called *multimeters*.

A volt-ohm-milliammeter is shown in Fig. 4-19, and the circuit diagram of this meter is given in Fig. 4-20. This meter is a combination of a d-c milliammeter, an ammeter, a d-c voltmeter, an a-c voltmeter, a multirange ohmmeter, and an output meter. The circuits of the a-c voltmeter and output meter will be discussed in the next chapter.

**Fig. 4-19.** *The Simpson volt-ohmmilliammeter (courtesy of the Simpson Electric Company)*

The circuit for the multirange d-c voltmeter is shown in Fig. 4-21. For voltmeter measurements, the common input terminals are used for ranges from 0–1.5 volts to 0–1,000 volts, and the voltage jack on the right of the meter is used for the 0–5,000-volt range. This circuit has been described in section 4-4 on voltmeters. Its operation should be apparent from this discussion. The basic movement of the meter has a full-scale current reading of 50 $\mu$a and a resistance of 2,000 ohms. The values of the resistances used with this circuit are given in the figure. With this circuit, full-scale voltages of 2.5, 10, 50, 250, 1,000, and 5,000 volts can be obtained. This is a very useful instrument for service work, especially in the electronic field. Care should be taken to have the lead wires of this instrument connected to the proper jack, the switch on the left should be set to DC, and the range switch set to 1,000 before connecting the instrument to the circuit to be measured. After the

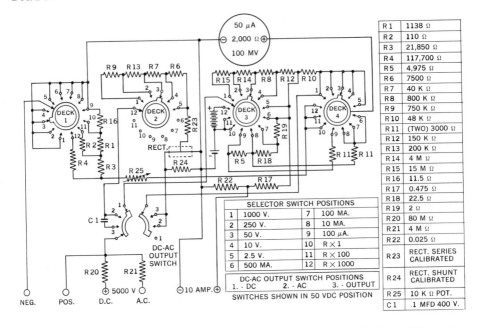

| R 1 | 1138 Ω |
|---|---|
| R 2 | 110 Ω |
| R 3 | 21,850 Ω |
| R 4 | 117,700 Ω |
| R 5 | 4,975 Ω |
| R 6 | 7500 Ω |
| R 7 | 40 K Ω |
| R 8 | 800 K Ω |
| R 9 | 750 K Ω |
| R 10 | 48 K Ω |
| R 11 | (TWO) 3000 Ω |
| R 12 | 150 K Ω |
| R 13 | 200 K Ω |
| R 14 | 4 M Ω |
| R 15 | 15 M Ω |
| R 16 | 11.5 Ω |
| R 17 | 0.475 Ω |
| R 18 | 22.5 Ω |
| R 19 | 2 Ω |
| R 20 | 80 M Ω |
| R 21 | 4 M Ω |
| R 22 | 0.025 Ω |
| R 23 | RECT. SERIES CALIBRATED |
| R 24 | RECT. SHUNT CALIBRATED |
| R 25 | 10 K Ω POT. |
| C 1 | .1 MFD 400 V. |

**SELECTOR SWITCH POSITIONS**

| 1 | 1000 V. | 7 | 100 MA. |
|---|---|---|---|
| 2 | 250 V. | 8 | 10 MA. |
| 3 | 50 V. | 9 | 100 μA. |
| 4 | 10 V. | 10 | R × 1 |
| 5 | 2.5 V. | 11 | R × 100 |
| 6 | 500 MA. | 12 | R × 1000 |

DC-AC OUTPUT SWITCH POSITIONS
1. - DC      2. - AC      3. - OUTPUT
SWITCHES SHOWN IN 50 VDC POSITION

**Fig. 4-20.** *A schematic diagram of the circuit of a Simpson volt-ohm-milliammeter (courtesy of the Simpson Electric Company)*

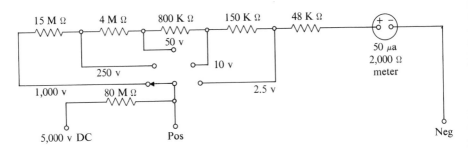

**Fig. 4-21.** *Multirange voltmeter circuit of a Simpson volt-ohm-milliammeter (courtesy of the Simpson Electric Company)*

meter is connected to the circuit to be measured, the range should be reduced until a good up-scale reading is obtained.

The circuit for measuring milliamperes and amperes is given in Fig. 4-22. For d-c measurements the switch to the left is set to DC, and the multi-range switch is set to the proper current range. When using this instrument, be sure that there is sufficient resistance between the instrument and the source of the emf to limit the current to the value set on the meter. The common ($+$) and ($-$) terminals are used for ranges up to 0–500 ma. The jacks marked $-10A$ and $+10A$ are used for the 0–10-amp range.

The resistance measurements are obtained by setting the range-scale switch to the resistance scale desired, and the switch to the left to the DC position. The circuits showing the operation of the ohmmeter ranges are

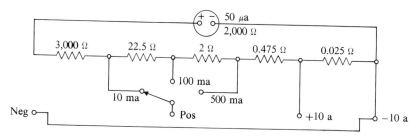

**Fig. 4-22.** *Multirange milliammeter circuit of a Simpson volt-ohm-milliammeter (courtesy of the Simpson Electric Company)*

given in Fig. 4-23. The circuit shown in Fig. 4-23(*a*) gives the ohmmeter circuit for a scale multiplication of 1. Before connecting the meter to the resistance to be measured, the instrument is short-circuited and the dial on the right is adjusted until the instrument reads zero resistance. Then the unknown resistance is connected between the common input terminals. The meter will read the resistance directly on the resistance scale. In Fig. 4-23(*b*) the circuit for measuring resistances using a scale multiplication of 100 is given. The procedure is the same as described above. Similarly, when a scale multiplier of 10,000 is desired, the circuit is altered to that shown in Fig. 4-23(*c*). Thus, by changing the range switch, a scale multiplication of 1, 100, or 10,000 can be obtained.

The a-c voltmeter readings are obtained by setting the switch to the left to the AC position. The circuit for measuring alternating current uses a rectifier unit which rectifies the alternating current and supplies direct current to the meter. The operation of this circuit and the errors it incurs will be discussed in Chap. 5.

## 4-11. DIRECT-CURRENT WATTHOUR METER

In d-c measurement, the power consumed is equal to the product of the current and the voltage. Thus it is not necessary to have a wattmeter in d-c circuits, but it is necessary to use a d-c watthour meter to measure the energy consumed. An early type of watthour meter was developed by Elihu Thompson in 1889. This meter consists of an armature and field similar to a d-c motor, except that no ferromagnetic materials are used. The armature current is supplied through a resistance connected in series with the armature.

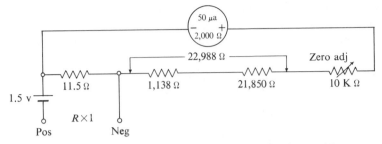

(a) Ohmmeter circuit for a scale-multiplying factor of 1

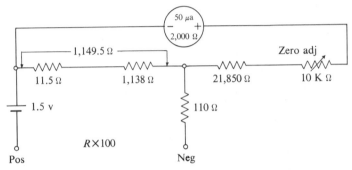

(b) Ohmmeter circuit for a scale-multiplying factor of 100

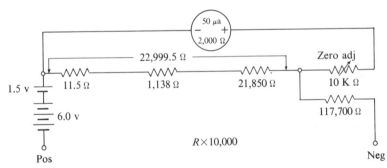

(c) Ohmmeter circuit for a scale-multiplying factor of 10,000

**Fig. 4-23.** *Ohmmeter circuits of a Simpson volt-ohm-milliammeter (courtesy of the Simpson Electric Company)*

This circuit is connected across the line and functions as a voltage-measuring device. The field of this motor is connected in series with the load. Thus the field current is the current being consumed by the load. The torque of the motor is opposed by viscous damping created by the field of two permanent magnets which cut a rotating disk. The emf generated in the disk produces a circulating current which in turn produces a torque that opposes the rotation of the disk. The circuit showing this arrangement is given in Fig. 4-24.

The torque in the armature of the watthour meter is

$$\tau_a = K_a I_a \phi_f \qquad (4\text{-}32)$$

where the flux $\phi_f$ through the armature is produced by the current $I$ supplied to the load. Then

$$\phi_f = K_\phi I \qquad (4\text{-}33)$$

The armature current $I_a$ is

$$I_a = \frac{E + e_c}{R_a} \qquad (4\text{-}34)$$

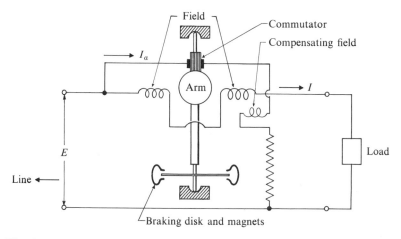

**Fig. 4-24.** *Direct-current watthour meter*

where

    $E$ = line voltage

    $R_a$ = resistance of the armature circuit, including the external resistor

    $e_c$ = counter emf in the armature generated by its conductors cutting the magnetic field

But the counter emf is

$$e_c = -K_c \phi_f n \qquad (4\text{-}35)$$

where

    $K_c$ = a constant

    $n$ = revolutions per minute of the meter

The counter emf is reduced to a minimum by keeping the revolutions per minute small. Then

$$\tau_a = K_a \frac{E}{R_a} K_\phi I$$
$$= K_a' EI \tag{4-36}$$

where

$$K_a' = \frac{K_a K_\phi}{R_a}$$

The torque produced by the braking action on the disk due to the rotation of the disk in the field of the permanent magnets is

$$\tau_b = K_b \phi_b \frac{e_b}{R_b} r$$

But

$$e_b = K_{\phi b} n \phi_b$$

Then

$$\tau_b = K_b K_{\phi b} \phi_b{}^2 nr/R$$
$$= K_b' n \tag{4-37}$$

where

$\tau_b$ = braking torque
$e_b$ = voltage generated in the disk
$n$ = revolutions per minute of disk
$R_b$ = effective resistance of the path of the current in the disk
$r$ = effective radius of the disk
$K_\phi$, $K_b$, and $K_b'$ = constants for this particular meter as the flux, resistance, and radius are constant

At equilibrium

$$K_a' EI = K_b' n \tag{4-38}$$

Integrating this equation,

$$K_a' \int EI \, dt = K_b' \int n \, dt$$

or

$(K_a')$ (energy delivered to the load) = $(K_b')$ (total number of revolutions).

Then

$$\text{Energy in kilowatthour} = K \text{ (number of revolutions)} \tag{4-39}$$

where

$$K = \frac{K_b}{K_a'}$$

The linking gears between the meter shaft and the indicating counter insert the proper constant $K$. The adjustment of the position of the permanent magnets relative to the disk is made to obtain the correct value of $K$ for the meter movement.

In this meter, the friction of the bearings and brushes produces an almost constant torque. This retarding torque may be as great as 10 percent of the torque at low loads. To compensate for this, a compensating field winding is added in series with the armature winding, producing an additional field proportional to the applied voltage, which is nearly constant. Thus a nearly constant torque will be produced in the armature to overcome the friction of the meter.

This instrument is calibrated by setting the power consumed at full load and adjusting the disk until the meter reads the proper energy. This can be done by using the constant factor $K$, in Eq. (4-34), to determine the number of revolutions per minute to measure the kilowatthours. Then, by keeping the power supplied to the load constant and counting the revolutions per minute of the disk, the calibration of the watthour meter can be determined. This method is used to find the power at full load and at light load, which is usually taken at 5 to 10 percent of the full load. It is assumed that, if the power is correct at these two values, the meter will have good calibration. Usually, between these two values the power delivered to the load may be a little less than the power measured, and below the light load the measuring point of the meter will read less than the power delivered to the load. Although this instrument is used at the present time for d-c power measurements only, it will also measure a-c power if calibrated correctly. There are other types of watthour meters which are more efficient and more accurate for a-c measurements. These will be discussed in the following chapter.

## 4-12. DIRECT-CURRENT RECORDING INSTRUMENTS[5]

There are many d-c strip-chart and circular-chart recording instruments. These may have ranges from a few milliamperes to several amperes or from a few millivolts to several hundred volts. Basically, they have a d'Arsonval movement, and the pointer is equipped with a recording-pen mechanism which records the analog value of the quantity being measured on a moving strip chart or circular chart. These charts are driven either by a spring or by an electric motor. The movement of the instrument requires appreciable torque. To obtain this torque, the movement consists of a large moving coil in a strong magnetic field. For small current measurements it is often necessary to insert a linear electronic amplifier between the input of the instrument and the driving element. The required torque is obtained by making the coil long, with a large number of turns, and increasing the flux density by decreasing the air gap. This instrument is critically damped or nearly critically damped; thus it will have very little overshoot, but its time response will be comparatively slow—from $\frac{3}{4}$ to $1\frac{1}{2}$ sec. Therefore, it is designed for average current reading and not for recording fast variations in either current or voltage. The meters are commonly used in recording currents, voltages, and power in power applications where the average value is desired. A strip-chart d-c voltmeter is shown in Figs. 4-25 and 4-26.

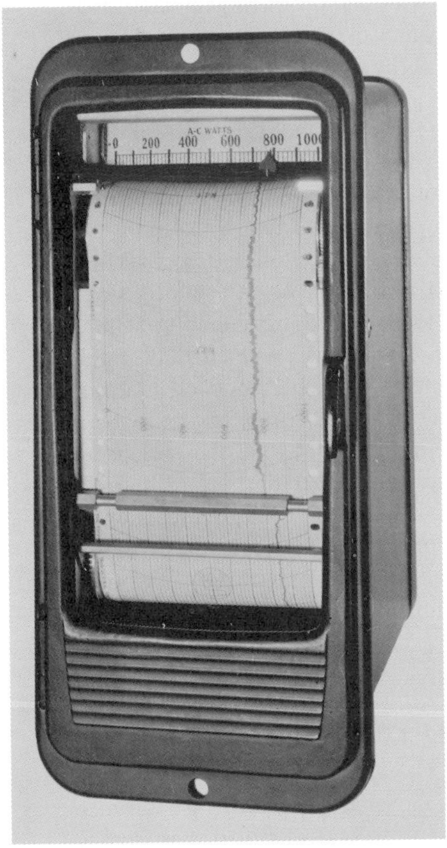

When the pen moves in a circular arc, the chart must be designed to record this movement, and the scale is drawn in circular form. A circular-type recorder is shown in Fig. 4-27. This instrument is very effective in recording a 12- or 24-hr period of line voltage or current in power systems. In these recorders the bearings must be substantially larger than those in an indicator instrument, because of the mass of the large moving coil and the recording pen. Thus the friction becomes a factor that must be considered.

The analysis of the motion of a galvanometer movement in Chap. 3 neglected the *sliding friction* which is also defined as *coulomb friction*. This friction is constant and is not a function of the angular velocity as is the viscous friction which produces the mechanical damping. When the coulomb friction is considered, the equation of motion becomes

**Fig. 4-25.** *A strip-chart recorder (courtesy of the Westinghouse Electric Corporation)*

$$J\frac{d^2\theta}{dt^2} + D\frac{d\theta}{dt} + S\theta + F = Gi \quad (4\text{-}40)$$

where $F$ is the torque due to coulomb friction.

The solution of this equation, after the transient effect is reduced to zero, is

$$S\theta + F = Gi$$

or

$$S\theta = Gi - F$$

Then

$$\theta = \frac{G}{S}i - \frac{F}{S} \qquad (4\text{-}41)$$

The deflection of the recording pen is proportional to the product of the constant $G/S$ and the current $i$, less a constant $F/S$. This $F/S$ is the error term which produces the dead zone, as the instrument will fail to reach the desired

**Fig. 4-26.** *A strip-chart recorder with cover removed (courtesy of the Westinghouse Electric Corporation)*

reading $(G/S)i$ by $F/S$. Care must be taken to reduce the coulomb friction to a minimum and to produce a large driving torque so that $F/S$ will be very small compared to $Gi/S$. Referring to Eq. (3-3),

$$G = BNLb$$

Therefore, a large moving coil with many turns will produce a large $G$ resulting in a large driving torque. Also, the flux density $B$ can be increased by decreasing the air gap. Recording instruments are designed to produce an accuracy of 2 percent or better.

**Fig. 4-27.** *A circular-chart recorder* (*courtesy of the Westinghouse Electric Corporation*)

## PROBLEMS

**4-1.** Design a multirange ammeter with ranges of 0–1, 0–10, 0–50, and 0–150 amp, using a 0–15 ma movement with 47 ohms internal resistance.

**4-2.** Design a multirange voltmeter with ranges of 0–3, 0–10, 0–50, and 0–150 volts, using a 50-$\mu$a movement with 1,200 ohms resistance, and determine the efficiency of this meter in ohms per volt.

**98** CHAPTER 4

**4-3.** Design a series-type ohmmeter, using a 100-$\mu$a movement with a resistance of 620 ohms. The half-scale reading of the ohmmeter shall be: (a) 10 ohms; (b) 1,000 ohms; (c) 100,000 ohms.

**4-4.** Design a shunt-type ohmmeter with a half-scale reading of 0.5 ohm, using an ammeter with a 0–1-amp range and 0.1 ohm resistance.

**4-5.** Design a d-c volt-ohm-milliammeter with the following ranges:

0–3, 0–15, 0–150, 0–750 volts

0–10, 0–100, 0–1,000 ma and 0–10 amp

15-ohm, 1,500-ohm, 150,000-ohm half-scale readings

The movement used in this instrument has a 0–50-$\mu$a range and 1,500 ohms resistance.

**4-6.** Determine the driving torque in dyne-centimeters and in inch-ounces on the movement of a recording galvanometer with a full-scale current of 100 ma. The effective length of the coil is 5 cm, and the width of the coil is 1.50 cm. The flux density of the air gap is 1,500 gauss. The coil has 500 turns.

**4-7.** Describe the difference between the bearing of a sensitive standard d'Arsonval meter and a portable meter. Explain why there is a difference.

**4-8.** A d'Arsonval movement has a constant flux density of $2.5 \times 10^{-3}$ Webers per square meter. The cross-sectional area of the coil is $2.5 \times 10^{-4}$ square meters, and the coil has 120 turns. The spring constant is $28 \times 10^{-8}$ newton-m per radian. Determine the current required to produce a deflection of 57 deg.

**4-9.** A d'Arsonval movement has a coil 1.5 cm wide and 1.2 cm long. The flux density of the air gap is $1.8 \times 10^{-3}$ Webers per square meter, and the spring constant is $1.4 \times 10^{-7}$ newton-m per radian. Determine the number of turns required to produce an angular deflection of 90 deg when a current of 5.0 ma is flowing through the coil.

**4-10.** Determine the resistance of the shunts in Fig. 4-9 when the meter has a resistance of 730 ohms and the full-scale current of the movement is 5 ma. The meter has a full-scale reading of 1 amp in position $A_1$, 5 amp in position $A_2$, 25 amp in position $A_3$, and 125 amp in position $A_4$.

**4-11.** The movement in Fig. 4-11(a) has a full-scale reading of 50 $\mu$a and a resistance of 1,800 ohms. The full-scale meter reading is 1.0 v with the switch connected to $V_1$, 5.0 v with the switch connected to $V_2$, 25 v with the switch connected to $V_3$, and 125 v with the switch connected to $V_4$. Determine (a) the resistance of the multiplier resistors $R_1$, $R_2$, $R_3$, and $R_4$ and (b) the ohms per volt of the meter.

**4-12.** The voltmeter in Fig. 4-12(b) has 1,000 ohms per volt. The full-scale reading of the voltmeter is 150 v. The voltage across the load is 123 v. Determine the error in measuring the power by the voltmeter–ammeter method when the measured current is (a) 50 ma, (b) 1 amp, and (c) 10 amp.

**4-13.** A shunt is rated at 100 amp and 50 mv. Determine (a) the approximate resistance of the shunt. (b) If this shunt were designed for a given meter, what precautions should be taken in connecting the meter to the shunt?

**4-14.** Which of the two meters shown in Figs. 4-15 and 4-16 would be most affected by stray magnetic fields?

**4-15.** Design an ohmmeter with a center-scale reading of 100 ohms using a 3-volt battery and a 100-$\mu$a meter with 760 ohms resistance.

**4-16.** Design an ohmmeter with a center reading of 1 ohm using a 5-ma meter with a resistance of 83 ohms and a 6-v lead battery.

**4-17.** There are three rods *A*, *B*, and *C* driven in the ground several feet apart. The resistances between the respective rods are as follows: *A* to *B*, 15.6 ohms; *B* to *C*, 24.0 ohms; *C* to *A* 12.0 ohms. Determine the ground resistance of each rod.

**4-18.** List the sources of error in a dc watthour meter.

**4-19.** The coil of a recording ammeter movement is 6.5 cm long and 2.5 cm wide. The rated current of the coil is 10 ma. The flux density in the air gap is $4.6 \times 10^{-3}$ Webers per square meter. The damping is $8 \times 10^{-3}$ newton-m per radian per second. The moment of inertia is $8 \times 10^{-3}$ kg-m squared. The spring constant is $16 \times 10^{-3}$ newton-m per radian. The coulomb friction is $2 \times 10^{-7}$ newton-m. (*a*) Determine if the meter is underdamped, critically damped, or overdamped. (*b*) Determine the number of turns on the coil to produce a deflection of 100 deg at rated current. (*c*) Determine the current required to overcome the coulomb friction. (*d*) Determine the percent error produced by the coulomb friction based on rated current.

**4-20.** (*a*) List the features of a d'Arsonval movement that would produce a precise instrument. (*b*) List the additional requirements that would make the instrument accurate.

## REFERENCES

1. M. B. Stout, *Basic Electrical Measurements*, 2nd ed., Prentice-Hall, Inc., Englewood Cliffs, N.J., 1960.

2. I. F. Kinnard, *Applied Electrical Measurements*, John Wiley & Sons, Inc., New York, 1956.

3. W. C. Michels, *Electrical Measurements and Their Applications*, D. Van Nostrand Company, Inc., Princeton, N.J., 1957.

4. *Operators Manual, Model 260, Volt-Ohm-Milliammeter*, Simpson Electric Co., Chicago, Illinois.

5. F. K. Harris, *Electrical Measurements*, John Wiley & Sons, Inc., New York, 1952.

# Chapter 5

# INDICATOR

## 5-1. INTRODUCTION[1,2,3]

The d'Arsonval movement, described in Chap. 4, measures the average current flowing through the movement. If the current varied sinusoidally with respect to time, this instrument would have a torque in one direction during one half of a cycle and in the opposite direction during the other half of the cycle, and it would vibrate about the zero position. When alternating current is measured, it is necessary to devise some means of obtaining a undirectional force which will not reverse each half cycle. The a-c instruments read the rms value of the current, except for some special applications where the peak values of the alternating current are required.

Implements used for measuring alternating current include rectifier-type, thermocouple, electrodynamic, and vane-type instruments. The operation of these instruments, with their advantages and limitations, will be given in this chapter.

## 5-2. RECTIFIER-TYPE A-C INSTRUMENTS[1]

A rectifier-type a-c instrument uses the d'Arsonval movement. A rectifier is used to convert the alternating current to direct current or unidirectional

# ALTERNATING-CURRENT

# INSTRUMENTS

current before it flows through the meter. Rectifier-type instruments use copper oxide, selenium, doped germanium, and silicon $P-N$ crystal-diode rectifiers. The copper oxide elements have an inverse peak voltage in the order of 2 volts, and the selenium elements have an inverse peak voltage in the order of 10 volts. These elements are becoming obsolete, since germanium diodes have an inverse peak voltage in the order of 50 volts and a current range in the order of 10 ma, and silicon diodes have inverse peak voltages up to 600 volts and current ranges up to 750 ma. These elements conduct currents with low resistance in one direction and with high resistance in the other direction. This characteristic is shown in Fig. 5-1.

The rectifier may have a half-wave circuit, as shown in Fig. 5-2 where the current flows through the movement during every other half cycle while the proper polarity is applied to the movement, or a full-wave circuit, such as the bridge rectifier shown in Fig. 5-3, where the current flows through the movement during each half of the cycle.

Normally, these instruments read the average current and are calibrated in terms of the rms value of a sinusoidal input where the ratio of the rms current to the average current is 1.11. If the wave form is not sinusoidal, errors in the rms reading may be introduced. In a full-wave rectifier, a 50 percent second harmonic may introduce a 0 to 10 percent error, while a 50 percent third harmonic produces an error of − 10 to + 16 percent, depending on its phase relation.

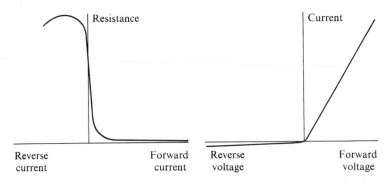

**Fig. 5-1.** *Characteristic curves of a rectifier*

The resistance of the rectifier changes with temperature. A copper oxide rectifier reverse resistance decreases 3 percent per degree centigrade rise in

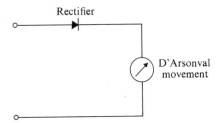

**Fig. 5-2.** *Half-wave rectifier circuit*

temperature, while the forward resistance decreases about 1 percent per degree centigrade rise, resulting in a decrease in the meter reading with temperature rise.

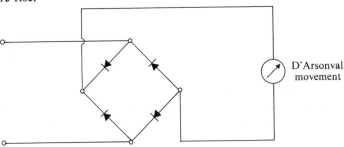

**Fig. 5-3.** *Full-wave rectifier circuit*

Rectifiers have the property of an imperfect capacitor, which bypasses the higher frequencies, and the decrease in the meter reading may be as large as 0.5 percent/kc rise in frequency. By decreasing the size of disks and by other refinements, however, this error can be decreased to less than 1 percent/ 100 kc.

The current range of these rectifiers is approximately 0 to 15 ma. The instrument range of the meter may be expanded by the use of shunts, multipliers, or current or potential instrument transformers.

Some rectifier-type instruments use a filter, consisting of resistances and capacitors, to smooth the flow of current. In these instruments the current in the movement is a function of the peak current being measured, and there is an appreciable delay in the response of the instrument. These circuits are often used in volt-ohm-milliammeters and, under normal operation, have an accuracy of $\pm 5$ percent of full scale.

## 5-3. THERMOCOUPLE INSTRUMENTS[1,2,3]

When two metals having different work functions are placed together, a voltage is generated at the junction which is nearly proportional to the temperature. This junction, called a *thermocouple*, will be discussed more fully in a later chapter. This principle is used to convert heat energy to electrical energy at the junction of two conductors, as shown in Fig. 5-4. The heat at

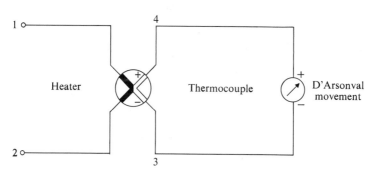

**Fig. 5-4.** *Circuit of a thermocouple instrument*

the junction is produced by the electrical current flowing from terminals 1 to 2, while the thermocouple produces an emf at terminals 3 and 4 which are connected to a d'Arsonval movement. The heat generated in the junction of the two metals, in joules, is equal to the current squared times the resistance, and the emf of the thermocouple is very nearly proportional to the temperature rise. Then the voltage generated at the junction will be approximately proportional to the square of the current flowing into the instrument, and the deflection of the instrument will be proportional to the square of the rms current input. If this instrument reads 100 volts at full scale, at one fourth of full scale it will read 50 volts. The lower readings are crowded closely together and are very inaccurate. This meter should be used only on the upper half of the scale.

The emf supplied to the movement is also a function of the temperature of the nonheated "cold" terminals 3 and 4 to the thermocouple. For most materials used in thermocouples, the voltage generated owing to a difference between the cold-junction and the hot-junction temperatures $\Delta t$ is

$$E = a \,\Delta t + b \,\Delta t^2$$

where

$\Delta t =$ difference in temperature between the junctions

$a =$ coefficient, which is usually between 40 and 50 $\mu v$ or more per degree difference in temperature

$b =$ another constant, usually in the order of a few microvolts per degree difference in temperature

The squared term of the temperature difference is usually small.

Another factor entering into measurements using thermocouples is the skin effect. At higher frequencies the current is forced to the outer surface of the conductor owing to the internal inductance in the wire. This increases the effective resistance of the conductor. To reduce this, the conductors are usually made very small, so that the ratio of surface area to cross-sectional area is small. By using copper wire 1 mil in diameter, the increase in resistance is approximately 1 percent at 20 megacycles, while in constantan wire of the same size the increase in resistance is only 0.0015 percent at 20 megacycles. Thus, using small high-resistance wire, the skin effect at moderate frequencies is not appreciable. The wires from terminals 1 and 2 to the hot junctions in Fig. 5-4 are very fine. The cold junctions are attached to large blocks of metal which have a large radiating area that keeps the temperature of the cold junctions near that of the surrounding medium. In this arrangement, comparatively high currents can be obtained in the galvanometer circuit. The General Electric Company, using eight thermocouple bridges as shown in Fig. 5-5, produces a thermocouple with a voltage of 25 mv and a heating current of 250 ma. These instruments are primarily designed for high-frequency measurements and are superior in this field. Other applications of thermocouple instruments will be given later in this book.

## 5-4. ELECTRODYNAMIC INSTRUMENTS [1,3,4]

Electrodynamic instruments use the current from the measured quantity to produce the stationary field and the current in the moving coil. No ferromagnetic material is used.

The flux density is

$$\beta = K_1 I$$

and the driving torque is

$$\tau_d = K_2 I \beta$$
$$= K I^2 \qquad\qquad (5\text{-}1)$$

where

$$K_1 \text{ and } K_2 = \text{constants}$$
$$K = K_1 K_2$$

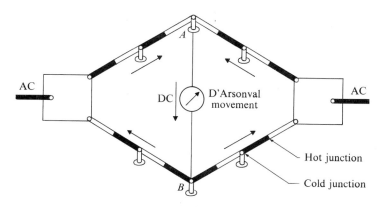

**Fig. 5-5.** *Bridge-type thermocouple instrument*

This torque is positive regardless of the sign of the current, as the sign of the current in the moving coil and the flux through the stationary coil are both reversed when the current is reversed. Thus this instrument will read alternating current as well as direct current. A diagram of this circuit is shown in Fig. 5-6(*a*). The deflection of an electrodynamic instrument is a function of the square of the current, and the voltmeter [Fig. 5-6(*c*)] and ammeter [Fig. 5-6(*b*)] using this movement will have a squared scale. The field in the moving coil is approximately 60 gauss, which is only 3 or 4 percent of the flux in a d'Arsonval movement. Stray fields may produce appreciable error, therefore laboratory instruments of this type should be shielded.

The current limit of the control springs on the moving coil is about 0.2 amp. This limits the range of the series circuit shown in Fig. 5-6. For large currents a shunt may be connected across the entire circuit, or current transformers may be used.

The electrodynamic voltmeter may use the circuit shown in Fig. 5-6(*c*) with resistances in series with each coil and the two circuits connected in parallel. The currents in the two coils must be in phase, and thus the power-factor angles of the circuits must be the same; care must, therefore, be taken to keep the ratio of $X/R$ equal in the two branches of this circuit.

Eddy currents in the metal parts of the instrument will produce a coupling between the metal and the moving coil, resulting in additional errors. Metal parts should be reduced to a minimum, and any metal used should have high resistance.

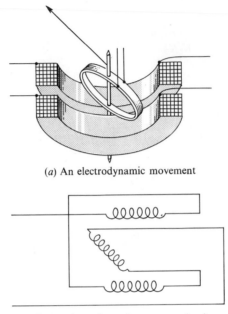

(*a*) An electrodynamic movement

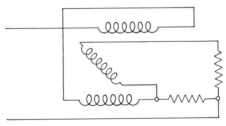

(*b*) An electrodynamic ammeter circuit

(*c*) An electrodynamic voltmeter circuit

**Fig. 5-6.** *Electrodynamic instrument* (*courtesy of the Weston Electrical Instrument Corporation*)

The reactance and the effective resistance of the coils increase with frequency. The coupling between the moving coils and the stationary coil varies with frequency. Thus the instrument has a limited frequency range, but at low frequencies it is very accurate. It can be calibrated with a potentiometer, using direct current, and then used for power frequencies as a secondary standard. Electrodynamic ammeters and voltmeters are used for very precise measurements. Other types of instruments are more adaptable for general use.

## 5-5. IRON-VANE INSTRUMENTS[1,2]

There are many kinds of iron-vane a-c instruments. The radial-vane repulsion instrument is among those more commonly used. It has a coil of many turns, as shown in Fig. 5-7. A stationary iron vane is attached to the coil, and a moving iron vane extends radially from the rotating shaft connected to one end of the stationary vane. The current in the coil magnetizes the vanes with the same polarity, creating a repelling force between the vanes. This force is

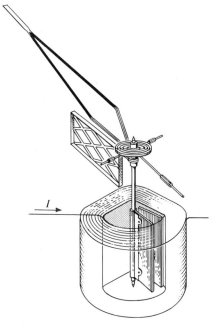

$$F = \frac{m_1 m_2}{d^2}$$

where

$m_1$ and $m_2$ = pole strength of the vanes
$d$ = effective distance between the poles

The strength of the poles $m_1$ and $m_2$ is nearly proportional to the current in the coil, and the product of $m_1$ and $m_2$ is nearly proportional to the current squared. The distance is proportional to the force between the two vanes. As the force increases, the distance $d$ increases, producing a force nearly proportional to the current in the coil, except for the demagnetizing effect that is produced when the vanes are close together. This

Fig. 5-7. *Radial-vane repulsion instrument (courtesy of the Weston Electrical Instrument Corporation)*

results in a compression of the scale of the meter at the very low end of the movement, but most of the scale is nearly linear.

Another vane-type instrument is shown in Fig. 5-8(a). It has a tapered concentric vane fixed to the coil with a moving bar which moves coaxially inside the stationary vane. The current in the coil magnetizes both the fixed vane and the moving vane with the same polarity. The thicker portion of the stationary vane produces the stronger repulsion force on the moving vane, and the vane moves in the direction of the taper with increase in the current in the coil. By using the proper taper, an almost linear scale can be produced. The practical limits of the deflection of these repulsion-type instruments is

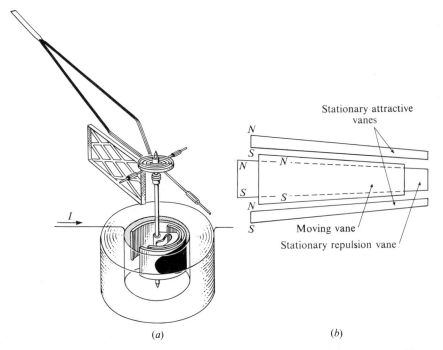

Stationary attractive vanes

Moving vane

Stationary repulsion vane

(a)

(b)

**Fig. 5-8.** *Tapered concentric-vane attraction instrument (courtesy of the Weston Electrical Instrument Corporation)*

about 90 deg. This range can be extended to 240 deg or more by combining the concentric-vane type of repulsion instrument with an attraction-type instrument by adding an outer vane to the vane as shown in Fig. 5-8(*b*). The outer vanes have the same polarity as the moving vane, and they attract it in the same direction as the repulsion of the inner vane. By properly designing the tapers, the required scale of the instrument can be obtained. On some instruments the two outside vanes can be moved at the upper end of the movement to obtain the correct reading at the upper end of the scale.

When these instruments operate at the lower end of the magnetization curve, the permeability of the iron increases with an increase in current. Therefore the peaks of alternating current will produce greater displacement per unit current than the average value. As a result, the meter a-c reading will be higher than the d-c reading at the lower end of the scale. For the larger readings, the iron will approach the knee of the magnetization curve, the permeability will decrease with increase in current, the peaks will produce less deflection per unit current, and the alternating current will read lower than the equivalent value of direct current.

The hysteresis in the iron will produce a higher reading for decreasing values of direct current than for increasing currents. This may produce a 2 or 3 percent error. With the use of nickel-iron alloys with very narrow hysteresis loops, this can be reduced to less than half of 1 percent.

Alternating current produces eddy currents in the vanes and in any metal parts of the instrument. These eddy currents produce a field which induces emfs in the coil. These emfs, in turn, cause a reduction in the current flowing through the coil, thus reducing the reading of the instrument. The inductance of the coil and the eddy currents both increase with frequency. By proper design, these effects can be reduced to 0.5 to 1 percent/kc.

The field in these instruments is small—60 to 75 gauss at full-scale current. Thus stray fields will produce errors in these instruments unless they are magnetically shielded.

For high currents these instruments can be shunted in a manner similar to a d'Arsonval movement. Also, resistance or impedance multipliers can be used in voltmeter circuits. In voltmeters the effect of increase in the reactance of the coil with frequency can be compensated over certain ranges by shunting a portion of the multiplying-series resistance with the proper capacitor.

Although these instruments will read direct current, they cannot be calibrated with direct current and used with alternating current. They must be calibrated at the frequencies for which they are to be used. Some of these meters have an accuracy of 0.5 percent of full scale for frequencies from 25 to 135 cycles per second, and 1 percent of full scale for direct current. They are very popular for laboratory work.

## 5-6. ELECTROSTATIC INSTRUMENTS[4]

There are several electrical instruments which use the reaction of two electrically charged bodies to measure electrical potential. The gold-leaf electroscope is an example of this type of instrument. The charge on the two leaves is the same and produces a repelling force, causing them to separate. The angle of separation is an indication of the quantity of electricity on the leaves. The string electrometer measures the deflection of a charged string suspended between two plates having a known charge. There are several other laboratory instruments which use this principle. These instruments are voltage-measuring devices and consume no power except during the brief period while the plates are receiving their charge.

The electrostatic voltmeter is the most common indicating electrostatic instrument. Figure 5-9 gives the circuit of this instrument. The plate $R$ attached to the pointer is the moving plate, while plate $S$ is stationary. The movement is supported by a shaft mounted in jeweled bearings, with a spiral spring supplying the restoring force. The charges on plates $R$ and $S$ are opposite in sign and produce an attractive force. The driving torque produced by the charge is

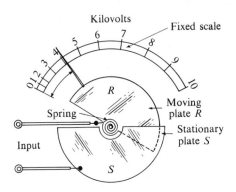

**Fig. 5-9.**   *Electrostatic voltmeter*

$$\tau_d = \frac{dU}{d\theta} = \frac{V^2}{2}\frac{dC}{d\theta}$$

where $U$ is the energy stored in the capacitance $C$ of the two plates. The restoring torque of the spring is

$$\tau_r = S\theta$$

where $S$ is the torque constant of the spring. Then

$$\theta = \frac{V^2}{2S}\frac{dC}{d\theta}$$

If the capacitance of the two plates were constant, the deflection $\theta$ would be proportional to the square of the applied voltage $V$, but the capacitance varies with the movement of plate $R$; therefore, the calibration of the voltmeter must be empirical. Variations of this instrument give voltage ranges from 0–120 to 0–60,000 volts and have a resistance of from $10^{10}$ to $10^{15}$ ohms.

When alternating current is applied to an electrostatic voltmeter, the angular displacement is

$$\theta_{ac} = \frac{1}{T}\int_o^T \frac{e^2}{2S}\frac{\partial C}{\partial \theta}\,dt$$

$$= \frac{1}{2S}\frac{\partial C}{\partial \theta}\frac{1}{T}\int_o^T e^2\,dt$$

$$= \frac{1}{2S}\frac{\partial C}{\partial \theta}E_{\text{rms}}^2$$

## 5-7.  POWER MEASUREMENTS

The a-c power supplied to a circuit is

$$P = VI\cos\theta$$

where

$V = $ voltage drop across the circuit

$I = $ current

$\theta = $ power factor angle between the voltage and the current

The electrodynamic-type instrument is very effective in measuring this power. The moving coil is connected across the line in series with a resistance, as shown in Fig. 5-10, so the current in the moving coil is proportional to the

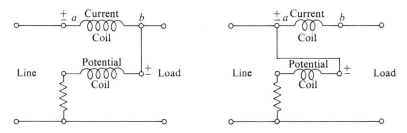

**Fig. 5-10.** *Wattmeter circuit*

line voltage. The stationary coil is connected in series with the load so the current in the coil is proportional to the load current. The driving torque produced in the moving coil is

$$\tau_d = \frac{\partial U}{\partial \theta} = \frac{\partial}{\partial \theta} \left[ \frac{1}{2} (i_1{}^2 L_1 + i_2{}^2 L_2) + i_1 i_2 M_{12} \right] = i_1 i_2 \frac{\partial M_{12}}{\partial \theta} \qquad (5\text{-}2)$$

where

$i_1$ = current in the moving potential coil
$i_2$ = current in the stationary current coil
$L_1$ = self-inductance of the moving potential coil
$L_2$ = self-inductance of the stationary current coil
$M_{12}$ = mutual inductance of the two coils

Then the average angular displacement of the movement is

$$\theta = \frac{\tau_d}{S} = \frac{1}{S} \frac{\partial M_{12}}{\partial \theta} \frac{1}{T} \int_0^T i_1 i_2 \, dt \qquad (5\text{-}3)$$

But $M_{12}$ varies with $\theta$. The coils can be designed so that $M_{12}/\theta$ is nearly constant and $i_1 = Ye_1$ where $e_1$ is the emf applied to the circuit of the potential coil and $Y$ is the admittance of this circuit. Then

$$\theta = \frac{K}{T} \int_0^T e_1 i_2 \, dt = KP \qquad (5\text{-}4)$$

where

$$K = \frac{Y}{S} \frac{\partial M_{12}}{\partial \theta}$$

and $P$ is the average power supplied to the load. $K$ is not constant, but the variation is small, and the scale of the wattmeter is nearly linear except at the lower and upper ends.

Wattmeters have one current terminal marked $\pm$ and one voltage terminal marked $\pm$ ; when the current terminal marked $\pm$ is connected to the incoming line and the other current is connected to the load, and the $\pm$ voltage terminal is connected to the current terminal $a$ or $b$, in Fig. 5-10, the wattmeter will read up scale when the power flows from the line to the load.

When the voltage $\pm$ terminal is connected to terminal $a$, the current in the current coil will be the same as the load current, and the voltage across the voltage coil will be the load voltage plus the drop across the current circuit of the wattmeter; when the $\pm$ terminal of the voltage circuit is connected to terminal $b$, however, the voltage across the voltage-measuring circuit is the same as the load voltage, but the current in the current coil is the sum of the load current and the current in the voltage-measuring circuit. To compensate for this error, the current winding is made with two windings, each having the same number of turns, as shown in Fig. 5-11. One winding uses large wire

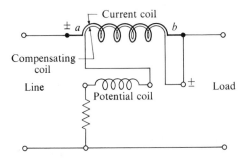

**Fig. 5-11.** *Compensated wattmeter circuit*

which carries the load current plus the current to the potential coils. The other winding uses small wire which carries the current to the potential-measuring circuit, but this current flows in a direction opposite to the current in the large winding. Thus the net current in the current coils is the load current. This is a compensated wattmeter.

### Measurement of Polyphase Power

The average power supplied to a polyphase is

$$P = \frac{1}{T} \int_o^T (V_{aO'}i_{Aa} + V_{bO'}i_{Bb} + \ldots + V_{nO'}i_{Nn})\, dt$$

where $T$ is the period of one cycle, and the currents and voltages are as shown in Fig. 5-12. But

$$V_{aO} = V_{aO'} - V_{OO'}$$

and

$$V_{bO} = V_{bO'} - V_{OO'}$$
$$V_{nO} = V_{nO'} - V_{OO'}$$

etc., and the algebraic sum of the wattmeter readings is

$$W = \frac{1}{T} \int_0^T (V_{ao}i_{Aa} + V_{bo}i_{Bb} + \ldots + V_{no}i_{Nn})\, dt$$

$$= \frac{1}{T} \int_0^T (V_{aO'}i_{Aa} + V_{bO'}i_{Bb} + \ldots + V_{nO'}i_{Nn})\, dt$$

$$+ \frac{1}{T} \int_0^T V_{OO'}(i_{Aa} + i_{Bb} + \ldots + i_{Nn})\, dt$$

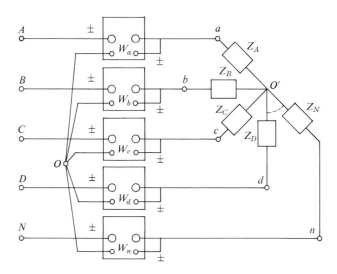

**Fig. 5-12.** *Polyphase wattmeter connections*

But from Kirchhoff's current law at point $O'$

$$i_{Aa} + i_{Bb} + \ldots + i_{Nn} = O$$

Then

$$W = P$$

and the algebraic sum of the power measured by the $N$ wattmeters is the power supplied to the polyphase load regardless of the magnitude of the power required of each phase or the angle between each phase. It is also applied to mesh-connected loads as well as to star-connected loads.

The common connection $O$ can be placed anywhere; for example, it can be connected to $N$. Then $W_n$ will read zero, and the algebraic sum of $N - 1$ wattmeters will read the total power supplied to the polyphase circuit. Thus wattmeter $W_n$ can be omitted, and the power of any $N$-phase circuit can be measured with $N - 1$ wattmeters. A neutral line is included in $N$.

### Reactive-Power Measurements

The reactive power supplied to a circuit is

$$P_x = EI \sin \theta = EI \cos (\theta - 90°)$$

where $\theta$ is the phase angle between the load current and the applied emf while the real power is

$$P_r = EI \cos \theta$$

which is measured by a wattmeter. If the voltage supplied to a wattmeter were rotated a negative 90 deg and then supplied to a wattmeter, as shown in Fig. 5-13, the wattmeter would read the reactive power supplied to the load in vars (volt-amperes-reactive).

In a balanced three-phase circuit this shift of the emf can be obtained by using two autotransformers connected in open delta, as shown in Fig. 5-14. The phase-$B$ line is connected to the common terminal of the two autotransformers, and the phase-$A$ and phase-$C$ lines are connected to the 100 percent tap of the winding which will produce 115.4 percent of line voltage across the total transformer windings. The wattmeters are connected from the center tap of one autotransformer to the end of the other autotransformer. This will supply an emf to the wattmeter $W_1$ which lags the emf $E_{AB}$ by 90 deg, and then the emf supplied to wattmeter $W_2$ lags the emf $E_{CB}$ by 90 deg. When wattmeter $W_1$ measures the current in line $A$ and $W_2$ measures the current in line $C$, the algebraic sum of the two wattmeter readings is the reactive power supplied to the three-phase load.

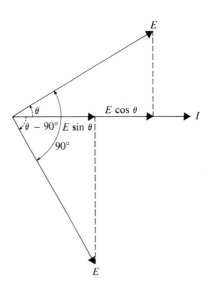

**Fig. 5-13.** *Diagram of the voltage vector when it is shifted clockwise 90 deg*

### Thermal Watt Converters

A very effective instrument which uses thermocouples to measure electrical power is the thermal watt converter. An elementary circuit of this converter is given in Fig. 5-15(*a*). The plain arrows show the direction of the current from the current transformer, and the flagged arrows show the direction of the current in the potential circuit at a given instant of time. The current in the insulated heater at thermocouple $A$ is the sum of the currents produced by the potential circuit and the current transformer. The current

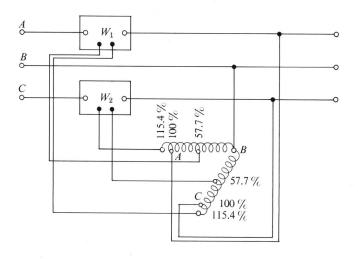

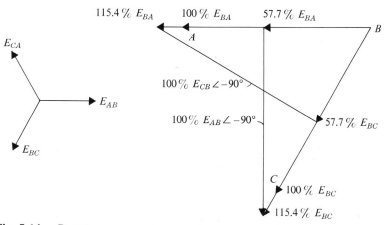

**Fig. 5-14.** *Reactive-power measurement*

in the insulated heater at thermocouple $B$ is the difference of these currents. The vector sum $S$ of the potential-circuit current $I_e$ and the current-transformer current $I_i$ can be determined from the geometric relation

$$S^2 = I_e{}^2 + I_i{}^2 + 2I_eI_i \cos \theta$$

and the difference $D$ is

$$D^2 = I_e{}^2 + I_i{}^2 - 2I_eI_i \cos \theta$$

Then

$$S^2 - D^2 = 4I_eI_i \cos \theta = 4W$$

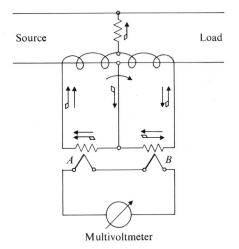

Multivoltmeter

(a) Elementary circuit of a thermal converter

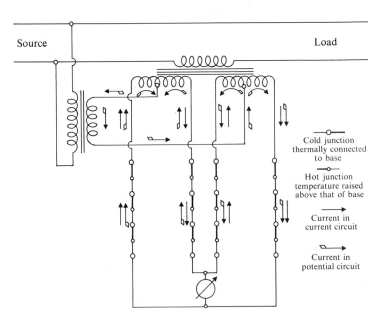

(b) Complete circuit of a thermal converter

**Fig. 5-15.** *The thermal converter (courtesy of the Weston Electrical Instrument Corporation)*

or

$$W = \frac{1}{4}(S^2 - D^2)$$

where

$W$ = power, in watts

$\theta$ = angle between $I_e$ and $I_i$

Now the heat generated in the thermocouples is proportional to the square of the current in the heater, and the emf is approximately proportional to the heat; then the emf produced by thermocouple $A$ is proportional to $S^2$, and the emf produced by thermocouple $B$ is proportional to $D^2$. The outputs of these thermocouples are connected so that they oppose each other. Then the emf measured by the multivoltmeter is

$$E = K(S^2 - D^2) = K'W$$

where $K$ and $K'$ are constants and the output of the meter is proportional to the power. A more practical circuit is shown in Fig. 5-15($b$).

Thermal convectors can be used to measure the power in several circuits, and the sum of their outputs can be applied to a recording potentiometer which will record the total power.

## 5-8. WATTHOUR METERS

Alternating-current energy is measured with a watthour meter which consists of a disk mounted in a field produced by a current coil and a field produced by a voltage coil. The fields produce an emf in the disk, causing eddy currents to flow in the disk. The reaction of the eddy current produced by the current coil and the field produced by the voltage coil creates a torque on the disk, causing it to rotate. The field of two permanent magnets cuts this disk as it rotates. This also produces eddy currents in the rotating disk which reacts with the field of the permanent magnets, damping the motion of the disk. The shaft supporting the disk is geared to a mechanism which operates the clocklike dials on the front of the meter that indicates the watthours. The disk, magnetic circuit, and permanent magnets are shown in Fig. 5-16.

The full-load calibration of a watthour meter is made with rated load on the meter; the permanent magnets are adjusted until the meter reads correctly. At light loads the voltage component of the field produces a torque that is not proportional to the load. This error is often compensated by inserting a shading coil or plate over a portion of the voltage pole. This adjustment is made at 10 percent of rated load. When these adjustments are made, the meter reads correctly at 10 percent and at 100 percent of full load, and the meter is usually satisfactory at other loads.

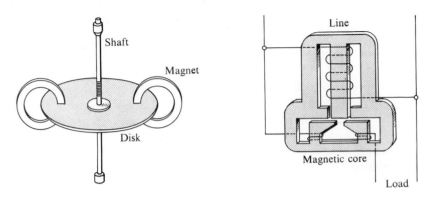

**Fig. 5-16.** *The circuit and components of a single-phase watthour meter*

Some watthour meters have a magnet at each end of the rotating shaft. The upper magnet is attracted to a magnet set in the bearing, while the lower magnet is repelled by a magnet set in the lower bearing, with the result that the whole movement floats without touching the bearing. This is called the floating-shaft watthour meter. The only contact made with this movement is that of the gear connecting the shaft with the gear train.

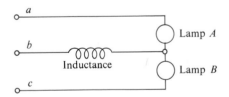

**Fig. 5-17.** *The watthour meter (courtesy of the Westinghouse Electric Corporation)*

**Fig. 5-18.** *Phase-sequence indicator*

Polyphase watthour meters employ current and voltage connections similar to those in the wattmeter. Each phase of a watthour meter has its own disk and magnetic circuit, yet all the disks are mounted on the same shaft to make the total revolutions per minute of the shaft proportional to the total three-phase energy. The units of a polyphase watthour meter may be connected as shown in Fig. 5-12, which would require $N - 1$ units, where $N$ is the number of lines supplying the load; or they may be connected to measure the energy supplied to each phase of the load, which would require $N$ units. A typical single-phase watthour meter is shown in Fig. 5-17.

### 5-9. PHASE-SEQUENCE MEASUREMENTS

The sequence of polyphase emfs is an important factor in determining the rotation of polyphase motors and synchronous motors. A simple method of determining the sequence of a three-phase circuit is shown in Fig. 5-18. Two lamps of proper voltage rating and inductance form a wye-connected load applied to the three-phase circuit. If lamp $A$ is brighter than lamp $B$, the phase sequence is $V_{ab}$, $V_{bc}$, and $V_{cd}$. If the lamp $B$ is brighter than lamp $A$, the phase sequence is $V_{ab}$, $V_{ca}$, and $V_{bc}$. Thus the sequence is from dim lamp to bright lamp. The proof of this rule is left to the reader. When capacitance can be used instead of an inductance in this circuit, the lamp $B$ will be brighter than lamp $A$ for a $V_{ab}$, $V_{bc}$, $V_{ca}$ sequence.

### 5-10. POWER-FACTOR MEASUREMENTS AND PHASEMETERS[1]

There are several types of power-factor meters and phasemeters. One kind of power-factor meter is shown in Fig. 5-19($a$). It has two stationary field coils producing a flux in the same direction, and two moving coils mounted on the same shaft at right angles to each other. When this instrument is used to measure single-phase power factors, the coils are connected as shown in Fig. 5-19($b$). When three-phase power factor is to be measured, the coils are connected as shown in Fig. 5-19($c$).

In Fig. 5-19($b$) the line current flows through the stationary coil. If the line voltage is $E_m \sin \omega t$ and the line current is

$$i_f = I_m \sin (\omega t + \phi) \tag{5-5}$$

the current in coils 1 and 2 is

$$i_1 = (E_m/R) \sin \omega t$$

$$i_2 = (E_m/X) \sin (\omega t - 90°) \tag{5-6}$$

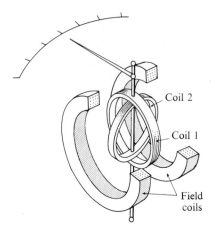

(*a*) Crossed-coil power-factor indicator mechanism

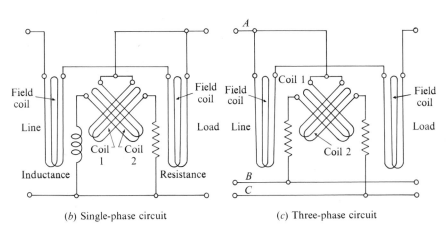

(*b*) Single-phase circuit          (*c*) Three-phase circuit

**Fig. 5-19.**   *Crossed-coil power-factor meter*

Then the average torques on coils 1 and 2 are

$$\tau_1 = \frac{1}{T} \int_{o}^{T} i_1 i_f \frac{dM_1}{d\theta}$$

$$\tau_2 = \frac{1}{T} \int_{o}^{T} i_2 i_f \frac{dM_2}{d\theta} \tag{5-7}$$

where

$M_1$ and $M_2$ = mutual inductances between the stationary coil and coils 1 and 2, respectively

$T$ = period of one cycle of the current

Also

$$\frac{dM_1}{d\theta} = K_1 \sin \theta$$

$$\frac{dM_2}{d\theta} = K_2 \sin (\theta + 90°) \tag{5-8}$$

where $\theta$ is measured from the position where the axis of coil 1 coincides with the axis of the field coil, and $K_1$ and $K_2$ are constants. When the coils are at rest

$$\tau_1 = \tau_2 \tag{5-9}$$

Substituting the values of $i_1$, $i_2$, and $i_f$ given in Eqs. (5-5) and (5-6) and the values of $dM_1/d\theta$ and $dM_2/d\theta$ into Eq. (5-7) and equating these values of $\tau_1$ and $\tau_2$ gives

$$\frac{K_1}{R} \sin \theta \int_o^T \sin \omega t \sin (\omega t + \phi) \, dt$$

$$= \frac{K_2}{X} \sin (\theta + 90°) \int_o^T \sin (\omega t - 90°)(\sin \omega t + \phi) \, dt$$

Integrating gives

$$\frac{K_1}{R} \sin \theta \cos \phi = \frac{K_2}{X} \cos \theta \sin \phi \tag{5-10}$$

Then the angular displacement $\theta$ is a function of the phase angle $\phi$, as $K_1/R$ and $K_2/X$ are constant for a given frequency. Then

$$\theta = K\phi$$

where $K$ is the constant of proportionality. If

$$K_1/R = K_2/X$$

then

$$\theta = \phi$$

There are other types of power-factor meters that use a different circuit but depend on a rotating flux to measure power factor. All power-factor meters that depend upon a rotating-field principle are limited to comparatively low frequency measurements.

There are several electronic phasemeters[5] which measure the phase angle between two voltages of the same frequency. A very common phasemeter uses two pulse generators, one in each input circuit, which produce a very sharp pulse at the instant the incoming wave passes through zero. The pulse from one generator triggers a multivibrator circuit, turning it on, and the pulse from the other generator turns the multivibrator circuit off. The average current output of the multivibrator is proportional to the phase angle between the two inputs and can be read on a d-c meter. A block diagram of this phasemeter is shown in Fig. 5-20.

Another phase-measuring circuit is shown in Fig. 5-21. The emf of input 1 is applied to the circuit through a two-winding transformer $T_1$ and

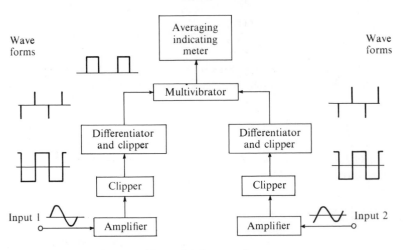

Fig. 5-20. *Block diagram of a multivibrator phasemeter*

input 2 is applied to the circuit through three-winding transformers such that the voltage $e_1$ is

$$e_1 = E_m \sin \omega t$$

and

$$e_2 = E_m \sin (\omega t + \phi)$$

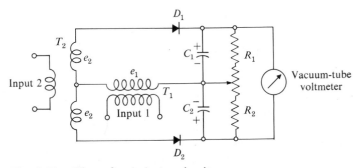

Fig. 5-21. *Phase-discriminator circuit*

When the magnitude of $e_1$ equals the magnitude of $e_2$. $D_1$ and $D_2$ are diode rectifiers; the voltage applied to $D_1$ is

$$e_1 + e_2 = E_m[\sin \omega t + \sin (\omega t + \phi)]$$

$$= 2E_m \left[ \sin \frac{1}{2} (2 \omega t + \phi) \cos \frac{1}{2} (-\phi) \right]$$

and the voltage applied to $D_2$ is

$$e_1 - e_2 = E_m[\sin \omega t - \sin (\omega t + \phi)]$$
$$= 2E_m \cos \frac{1}{2} (2\omega t + \phi) \sin \frac{1}{2} (-\phi)$$

The capacitors $C_1$ and $C_2$ are equal. If the values of $C_1$, $C_2$, $R_1$, and $R_2$ are such that the capacitors are charged to the peak value of the above voltages, the voltage across $C_1$ is

$$E_{C_1} = 2E_m \cos \frac{1}{2} (-\phi)$$

and the voltage across $C_2$ is

$$E_{C_2} = 2E_m \sin \frac{1}{2} (-\phi)$$

The voltage $V$ across the meter is

$$V = E_{C_1} - E_{C_2} = 2E_m \left[ \left| \cos \frac{1}{2} (-\phi) \right| - \left| \sin \frac{1}{2} (-\phi) \right| \right]$$

The voltage $V$ varies linearly as a function of $\phi$ from $+1$ at $\phi$ equals zero to $-1$ at $\phi$ equals 180 deg, which is a point of discontinuity. From this point it varies linearly to $+1$ at 360 deg. The function repeats itself as $\phi$ increases. This requires that the quadrant in which the frequencies occur be known.

### 5-11. SYNCHROSCOPES[1]

In power systems it is necessary to know if the voltage, sequence, frequency, and phase angle of an isolated portion of the system are equal to the voltage, sequence, frequency, and phase angle of the main system before the two systems can be connected together without the transfer of excessive currents. This process is defined as *synchronizing*. Usually, the sequence of the two systems is checked when the connecting switch is installed, and this sequence remains fixed for all subsequent normal switching operations. The voltage of each of the systems is checked with voltmeters on the control boards. The frequency and the phase are compared with a synchroscope. The appearance, construction, and circuit of one type of synchroscope are shown in Fig. 5-22. The two-phase stator winding is connected to the isolated system. It produces a rotating field which has the revolutions per minute and the phase angle determined by this system. The polarizing coil is connected to the corresponding phase of the main system which produces a pulsating flux in this coil and in the iron vane. The reaction between the stator field and the rotor field will produce a torque on the rotor which is a function of the difference between the frequency of the isolated system and the frequency of the main system. When the two frequencies are equal, there is no torque on the rotor, and the position of the rotor will depend on the difference of the phase angle of the two systems. If the phase angles of the two systems are equal, the pointer will be in the 12-o'clock position; if they are 180 deg, the pointer will be in the 6-o'clock position. If the frequency of the isolated system is greater

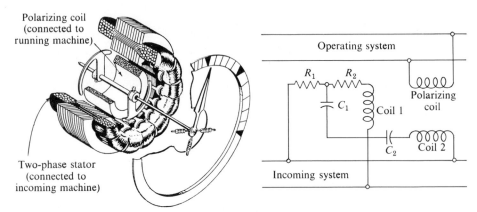

**Fig. 5-22.** *Synchroscope connections and construction* (*courtesy of the General Electric Company*)

than that of the main system, the pointer will rotate in the fast direction; if the frequency of the isolated system is less than the frequency of the main system, the pointer will rotate in the slow direction.

Extreme care should be taken to assure that the meter is connected correctly. If either of the two leads is reversed, the two systems will be 180 deg out of phase when the pointer is in the 12-o'clock position.

### 5-12. FREQUENCY MEASUREMENTS

There are several types of frequency-measuring meters. These meters use the effect of frequency upon mutual inductance, resonant circuits, mechanical resonance, and other quantities which are functions of frequency. An *electrodynamic-type frequency meter*, shown in Fig. 5-23, consists of two stationary field coils and a moving coil. One field coil is connected to a series resonance circuit having a resonant frequency of $f_1$, and a similar circuit is

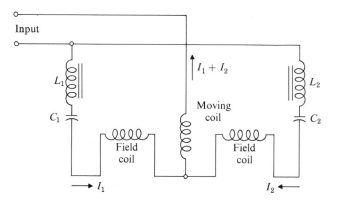

**Fig. 5-23.** *Electrodynamic-type frequency-meter circuit*

connected in series with the other field coil which has a resonant frequency of $f_2$. A small iron vane is mounted on the moving coil, providing the restoring torque. The torques produced by the two coils are in opposition. The resulting torque on the moving coil is a function of the frequency. The position of the coil is unique for each frequency within the range of the instrument. Usually, this instrument has a scale angle of 90 deg and a frequency range of only a few cycles. It is used for monitoring the frequency of power systems.

A *saturable-core frequency meter* is shown in Fig. 5-24. The input winding is wound around both of two cores, one core of nonmagnetic material and the

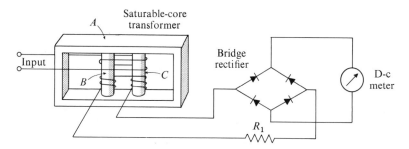

**Fig. 5-24.** *Saturable-core frequency-meter circuit*

other of magnetic material which saturates at a very low mmf. The yoke is of magnetic material with a cross section so large that it does not saturate. The secondary winding consists of a winding around the magnetic core in series with a winding around the nonmagnetic core. The emfs induced in these secondary windings oppose each other. When the magnetic core is saturated, the rate of increase of induced voltage in the magnetic-core winding will equal the rate of increase of induced voltage in the nonmagnetic-core winding. Thus the rate of increase in these two windings will cancel, and the secondary voltage will not be a function of the primary voltage but will be a function of the frequency only. Let $\phi$ be the difference between the flux in the magnetic core and the flux in the nonmagnetic core. Then the induced emf in the total secondary winding is

$$e = N \, d\phi/dt$$

and the average secondary voltage per half cycle is

$$E = (\omega/\pi) \int_0^{\pi/\omega} e \, dt = (\omega/\pi)N \int_{-\phi}^{+\phi_m} d\phi$$
$$= 4Nf\phi_m$$

or

$$f = \frac{E}{4N\phi_m} = KE$$

where $K$ is a constant as $\phi_m$ is constant after the magnetic core becomes saturated. The output of this circuit is rectified, and the current supplied to the d-c meter is

$$I = \frac{E}{R}$$

where $R$ includes the resistance of the bridge rectifier, the meter, and the resistance $R_1$. Then

$$f = KRI$$

and the deflection of the meter will be proportional to the frequency. This meter can measure a wide range of frequencies.

The *electronic counter*, which records pulses at an extremely rapid rate during a very accurately measured period of time, is used extensively in laboratory work for frequency measurements through the audio-frequency range to 100 kc and higher. These instruments will count the cycles during 0.1-sec to 10-sec timing periods with an accuracy of $\pm 1$ cycle.

Very high frequencies are often measured by comparing the frequency to be measured with a known frequency. One method of comparing two frequencies uses a cathode-ray oscilloscope. This method will be described in Chap. 7. Standard frequencies can be obtained from radio WWV in Washington, D.C., or WWV-H in Hawaii.

### 5-13. ALTERNATING-CURRENT RECORDING METERS

Alternating-current recording meters employ attraction-repulsion iron-vane-type movements for measuring currents and voltages giving nearly a linear scale. Also, rectifier-type meters with d'Arsonval movements are used to measure currents and voltages. They are well adapted for multirange instruments. Electrodynamic-type movements are used for measuring current and voltages, but their square scale is a disadvantage. The major use of electrodynamic instruments is in recording wattmeters which have a linear scale. The electrodynamic-type movement is also employed in recording frequency meters.

Power companies must know the peak loads and the power factors of their industrial customers. These quantities are usually measured with a recording demand meter that integrates and records the power used over a 15-min period. A similar meter is connected to the line, using a phase-shifting transformer to measure and record the reactive power over the same period of time. The power factor is

$$\text{Power factor} = \frac{P}{\sqrt{P^2 + Q^2}}$$

where

$P$ = power
$Q$ = reactive power

## PROBLEMS

**5-1.** Determine the reading of a d-c ammeter used with a full-wave rectifier circuit to measure a current having an instantaneous value of
$$i = 10 \sin 377t$$
Assume that the rectifier elements are perfect.

**5-2.** An ammeter uses copper oxide elements to read a-c current. The meter is correct at 20°C. What will the error be at 10°C?

**5-3.** A thermocouple instrument reads 10 amp at full scale. Determine the current when the meter reads one third of full scale.

**5-4.** What type of a-c instruments can be accurately calibrated with direct current and a potentiometer and used for a secondary standard for measuring currents and voltages in the power-frequency range?

**5-5.** What type of an a-c ammeter would be used to measure a current with an instantaneous value of
$$i = 10 \sin 377t + 5 \sin 754t + 3 \sin 1,508t$$

**5-6.** List the advantages and disadvantages of: (a) the radial-vane repulsion meter; (b) the tapered concentric-vane attraction meter; (c) the repulsion-attraction vane-type meter.

**5-7.** What precautions must be taken when an iron-vane-type meter is used to measure direct current?

**5-8.** What is the main advantage of an electrostatic voltmeter?

**5-9.** What type of meter would be used to measure radio-frequency currents?

**5-10.** What is the minimum number of wattmeters required to measure the three-phase power supplied to a balanced delta-connected load?

**5-11.** What is the minimum number of wattmeters required to measure the power to an unbalanced, four-wire, wye-connected load? Why?

**5-12.** What is the purpose of the magnets in a watthour meter?

**5-13.** What is the main advantage of a thermal watt converter?

**5-14.** How is the sequence of a three-phase line determined?

**5-15.** What type of phasemeter would be used to measure the phase angle of high-frequency voltages over a wide range of frequencies?

**5-16.** What is the function of a synchroscope, and how does it operate?

**5-17.** What instrument is used to measure frequencies through the audio-frequency range in general laboratory use?

**5-18.** What type of frequency meter is used to measure the frequency of a generator in a power plant?

**5-19.** What precautions should be taken when using a vane-type instrument?

**5-20.** What precautions should be taken when constructing a cross-coil power-factor meter?

**5-21.** What precautions should be taken when connecting a synchroscope to a system?

**5-22.** Describe how light-load and full-load adjustments of a watthour meter are made.

## REFERENCES

1. M. B. Stout, *Basic Electrical Measurements*, 2nd ed., Prentice-Hall, Inc., Englewood Cliffs, N.J., 1960.

2. F. K. Harris, *Electrical Measurements*, John Wiley & Sons, Inc., New York, 1952.

3. I. F. Kinnard, *Applied Electrical Measurements*, John Wiley & Sons, Inc., New York, 1956.

4. Ernest Frank, *Electrical Measurements Analysis*, McGraw-Hill Book Company, Inc., New York, 1959.

5. G. R. Partridge, *Principles of Electronic Instruments*, Prentice-Hall, Inc., Englewood Cliffs, N.J., 1958.

# Chapter 6

# INSTRUMENT

6-1. THE IDEAL TRANSFORMER [1]

The ideal transformer is a nonexistent theoretical transformer with a magnetic core which has no losses and requires negligible magnetizing current. All the flux produced by the mmf of the windings on the core flows in the core, and the windings and the core have no losses. A diagrammatic sketch of this transformer is shown in Fig. 6-1. The primary winding has $N_1$ turns, and the secondary winding has $N_2$ turns. The voltage applied to the primary circuit is $V_1$, and the voltage across the secondary is $V_2$. The emf induced by the flux $\phi_c$ in the core is

$$e_1 = N_1 \frac{d\phi_c}{dt} \tag{6-1}$$

Let

$$\phi_c = \phi_m \cos \omega t \tag{6-2}$$

Then

$$e_1 = -N_1 \omega \phi_m \sin \omega t = -2\pi f N_1 \phi_m \sin \omega t \tag{6-3}$$

where $\phi_m$ is the maximum value of the flux in the core. Comparing Eqs. (6-2) and (6-3), it will be observed that the cosine function lags the negative sine

132

# TRANSFORMERS

function by 90 deg, or the induced emf leads the flux by 90 deg. Converting $e_1$ to an rms phasor quantity gives

$$E_1 = j \frac{2\pi}{\sqrt{2}} f N_1 \phi_m = j4.44 f N_1 \phi_m \qquad (6\text{-}4)$$

There is no resistance loss or leakage reactance in the windings; then the voltage at the input terminals is

$$V_1 = E_1 = j4.44 f N_1 \phi_m \qquad (6\text{-}5)$$

Similarly, the emf induced in the secondary winding is

$$E_2 = j4.44 f N_2 \phi_m \qquad (6\text{-}6)$$

This is also the emf at the open terminals of the secondary. Then

$$V_2 = j4.44 f N_2 \phi_m \qquad (6\text{-}7)$$

The ratio of $V_1$ to $V_2$ is

$$\frac{V_1}{V_2} = \frac{N_1}{N_2} = a \qquad (6\text{-}8)$$

133

Now connect a load $Z_L$ across the secondary terminals. A current

$$I_2 = \frac{V_2}{Z_L}$$

will flow in the secondary, producing an mmf $I_2N_2$. If the total mmf on the core changes, the flux will change, and if the flux changes, the emf $E_1$ will

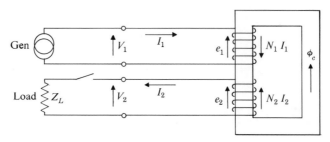

**Fig. 6-1.** *An ideal-transformer circuit*

change and the applied voltage $V_1$ will change. But $V_1$ is held constant. Therefore, the mmf must remain constant, and a current must flow in $\dot{N}_1$ such that

$$I_1N_1 = I_2N_2 \tag{6-9}$$

as the total magnetizing mmf is negligible for an ideal transformer.

Thus a converter has been produced that will change the voltage by a factor of $1/a$ and will change the current by a factor of $a$. Then

$$V_2 = \frac{1}{a} V_1 \tag{6-10}$$

and

$$I_2 = \frac{N_1}{N_2} I_1 = aI_1 \tag{6-11}$$

Multiplying Eq. (6-10) by Eq. (6-11) gives

$$V_1I_1 = V_2I_2 \tag{6-12}$$

Thus the volt-ampere output equals the volt-ampere input.

It will also be observed that in this ideal transformer the windings have no resistance and no leakage reactance; therefore, there is no phase shift, and the phase angle between the current and voltage into the transformer is the same as the phase angle between the current and voltage into the load.

## 6-2. LOSSES IN A TRANSFORMER[1]

The voltage drop and the power losses in an actual transformer are produced by (1) the resistance of the primary winding $R_1$ and the resistance of the secondary winding $R_2$; (2) the leakage reactance of the secondary winding $X_1$ and the leakage reactance of the secondary winding $X_2$, owing to the fact that some of the flux in one coil does not link all the windings of the other coil; and (3) the core losses, which include the hysteresis losses required to reorient the magnetic domains in the iron core and the eddy-current losses produced by the induced emfs in the core.

In addition to these losses, the transformer has a finite magnetizing current $I_m$, which is in phase with the flux and lags $E_1$ by 90 deg, and a core-loss current $I_c$ in phase with $E_1$. At no load, the primary current $I_o$ is the phasor sum of the magnetizing current $I_m$ and the current $I_c$. Then

$$I_o = I_m + I_c \tag{6-13}$$

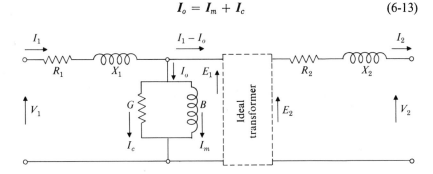

**Fig. 6-2.** *Equivalent circuit of a transformer*

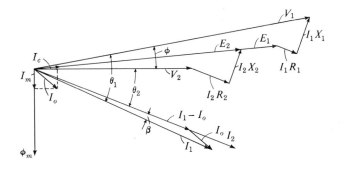

**Fig. 6-3.** *Phasor diagram of the currents and voltages in a transformer*

the equivalent circuit of a transformer is given in Fig. 6-2. The phasor diagram of this circuit is given in Fig. 6-3 with $V_2$ taken as the reference vector. With a given load voltage $V_2$, load current $I_2$, and load phase angle $\theta_2$, the induced secondary emf $E_2$ is

$$E_2 = V_2 + I_2 R_2 + I_2 X_2 \tag{6-14}$$

where $I_2R_2$ is in phase with $I_2$, and $I_2X_2$ leads $I_2$ by 90 deg, as shown in the vector diagram. The emf induced in the primary of the ideal transformer is

$$E_1 = \frac{N_1}{N_2} E_2 = aE_2 \qquad (6\text{-}15)$$

and the current in the primary of the ideal is

$$I_1 - I_o = \frac{N_2}{N_1} I_2 = \frac{1}{a} I_2 \qquad (6\text{-}16)$$

Then the primary current in the actual transformer is $I_1$. The primary input voltage $V_1$ is

$$V_1 = E_1 + I_1R_1 + I_1X_1 \qquad (6\text{-}17)$$

where $I_1R_1$ is in phase with $I_1$, and $I_1X_1$ leads $I_1$ by 90 deg.

### 6-3. IMPEDANCE TRANSFORMATION [1]

The circuit in Fig. 6-2 could be simplified if the impedance $R_2 + jX_2$ could be transferred to the primary side of the transformer. If this equivalent secondary impedance transferred to the primary were called $R_2' + jX_2'$, then the voltage drop across $R_2' + jX_2'$ in the primary would be equal to the voltage drop across $R_2 + jX_2$ in the secondary multiplied by $a$. Then

$$I_1(R_2' + jX_2') = aI_2(R_2 + jX_2)$$

But $I_2 = aI_1$. Then

$$I_1(R_2' + jX_2') = a^2I_1(R_2 + jX_2)$$

and

$$R_2' + jX_2' = a^2(R_2 + jX_2) \qquad (6\text{-}18)$$

Thus, to transfer an impedance from the secondary to the primary of a transformer, multiply the impedance by $a^2$; to transfer an impedance from the primary to the secondary of a transformer, divide the impedance by $a^2$.

This equivalent circuit of a transformer with the secondary impedance transferred to the primary is given in Fig. 6-4. The current in the primary ideal transformer is

$$I_1' = \frac{1}{a} I_2$$

and the actual primary current is

$$I_1 = I_1' + I_o \qquad (6\text{-}19)$$

The ideal current is

$$\frac{I_1'}{I_2} = \frac{1}{a}$$

while the actual ratio is

$$\frac{I_1}{I_2} = \frac{1}{a} + \frac{I_o}{I_2} \qquad (6\text{-}20)$$

Then $I_o/I_2$ is the ratio error of the transformer. It will be noted that $I_o$ is a function of the voltage. Thus the error will vary with the volt-ampere burden in a current.

Similarly, the ideal voltage ratio is

$$\frac{E_1}{E_2} = a \qquad (6\text{-}21)$$

and the actual voltage ratio is

$$\frac{V_1}{V_2} = a + \frac{I_1(R_1 + jX_1) + I_1'a^2(R_2 + jX_2)}{V_2} \qquad (6\text{-}22)$$

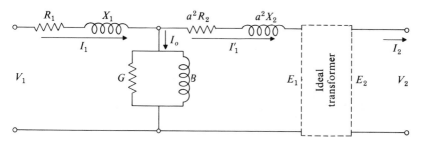

**Fig. 6-4.** *The equivalent circuit of a transformer with the secondary impedance transferred to the primary circuit*

It will be noted that the error in this ratio is a function of the load current. Therefore, this error will vary with the volt-ampere burden of the load on a potential transformer.

There is another error introduced in the actual transformer. Referring to the vector diagram in Fig. 6-3, it will be seen that the phase angle $\theta_1$ is not equal to the phase angle $\theta_2$. This error in phase angle is not important in voltage and current measurements, but it is very important in power measurements.

## 6-4. POTENTIAL TRANSFORMERS[1,2,3]

The potential transformer is usually employed to reduce the voltage to be measured to a safe voltage so that it can be measured with an ordinary meter. In power systems the voltage ratio is from the standard transmission-line voltage to 120 volts. Standard transmission-line voltages include 2,400

4,160, 7,200, 12,470, 13,800, 44,000, 66,000, 120,000, and 240,000 volts. There are some voltages in commercial use larger than 240,000, but they have not been considered standard. These transformers must have sufficient insulation to isolate completely and protect the secondary windings from the primary circuit. Portable potential transformers usually have primary taps of 2,400, 600, 440, and 220 volts, with sufficient insulation for the highest voltage and a secondary rating of 120 volts. On three-phase, four-wire systems the potential transformers are often connected from line to ground, whereas on three-phase, three-wire systems they are connected from line to line. The primary must have a sufficient number of turns to reduce the magnetizing current to a reasonably small value, yet the equivalent series resistance and reactance drop of the transformer must be small.

Figure 6-5 shows a high-voltage potential transformer with its line and meter connections. The dots marked on the transformer leads indicate the

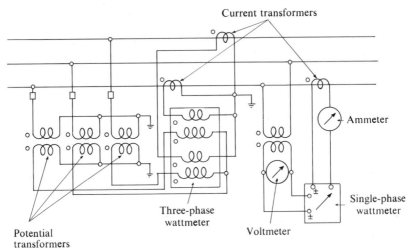

**Fig. 6-5.** *Potential-and current-transformer connections in metering circuits*

"polarity" of the transformer. During the a-c cycle, the marked terminals have the same polarity at a given instant of time. These transformers are used for potential and power measurements and for protective relaying. It is necessary to know the polarity of these transformers in order to make the correct connections for polyphase power measurements and protective relaying. Figure 6-6 shows a typical power-type potential transformer, a power-type current transformer, and a laboratory-type current transformer.

The ratios of potential transformers are marked on the transformer to indicate the ratio at a probable operating condition. This ratio is not the turns ratio of the transformer. The true ratio varies with load. The vector diagrams in Fig. 6-7(*a*), (*b*), and (*c*) show the effect of load upon the phase angle of the potential transformer. Figure 6-7(*d*) gives the *ratio corrective*

(a) *Potential transformer*  (b) *Current transformer*

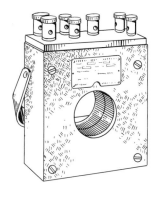

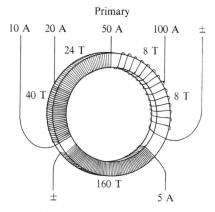

(c) *Laboratory-type current transformer and circuit*

**Fig. 6-6.** *Potential and current transformers*

*factor* (RCF) of a potential transformer as a function of the volt-ampere burden. Where the ratio corrective factor is

$$RCF = \frac{\text{true ratio}}{\text{marked ratio}}$$

Figure 6-7(e) gives the phase-angle error of a potential transformer as a function of the volt-ampere burden.

**Testing Potential Transformers[2]**

There are several methods for determining the ratio corrective factor and the phase-angle error of a potential transformer. Only one method will be

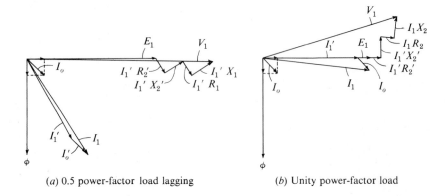

(a) 0.5 power-factor load lagging            (b) Unity power-factor load

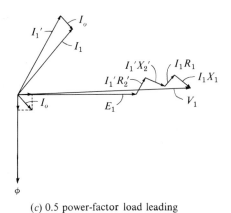

(c) 0.5 power-factor load leading

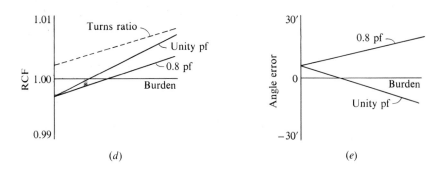

Fig. 6-7.   *Effects of the load on a potential transformer*

described to illustrate the principles involved in these tests. The circuit used for this test is shown in Fig. 6-8. The correct high voltage $V_1$ is supplied to the transformer under test. The voltage $V_1$ is also applied to a high-voltage potential divider $R_1$, consisting of the resistance from $H$ through $A$ and $B$ to $G$. From $H$ to $A$, the required number of resistors, each designed for 1,000

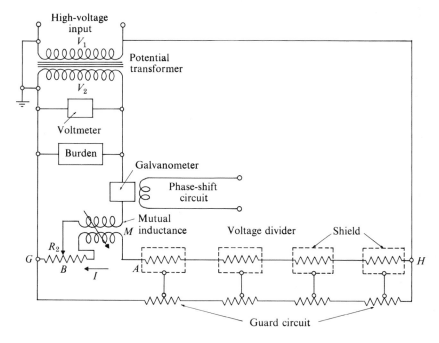

**Fig. 6-8.** *Circuit for testing potential transformers*

volts with 10,000 ohms resistance, are connected in series. The case of each of these resistors is connected to the center tap of a 20,000-ohm resistor. These 20,000-ohm resistors are connected across the voltage $V_1$ and from a guard circuit which reduces the capacitive effect between the resistors in the potential divider and ground. The bottom part of the resistance in the potential-divider circuit is the resistance $R_2$ from $B$ to $G$. The mutual inductance $M$ and the resistance $R_2$ are adjusted until a null is indicated on the galvanometer. An a-c galvanometer is used in this circuit. The field of this instrument is supplied from an a-c source through a phase-shifting circuit which is adjusted until the field current is in phase with the current to obtain maximum deflection. When a null is obtained,

$$V_1 = IR_1$$

and

$$V_2 = IR_2 + j\omega MI$$

Then the true ratio is

$$\frac{V_1}{V_2} = \frac{R_1}{R_2 + j\omega M}$$

or

$$\frac{V_1}{V_2} = \frac{R_1}{R_2} \cos \phi$$

where the phase angle $\phi$ between $V_1$ and $V_2$ is small. Then

$$\phi = \tan^{-1} \frac{\omega M}{R_2}$$

$$= \frac{\omega M}{R_2} \text{ radian}$$

$$= 3,438 \frac{\omega M}{R_2} \text{ min}$$

This method is effective in low- and medium-range potential transformers. Other methods are available for high-voltage potential transformers.

## 6-5. THE CURRENT TRANSFORMER [1,2,3]

The primary of a current transformer is connected in series with the load, as shown in Fig. 6-5, in contrast to the line-to-line connection for potential and power transformers. Often, this primary winding is a single conductor running through the core of the transformer. In circuits where large quantities of current are to be measured, this single conductor is large, and the core is built around it. The secondary has several turns and is usually designed for a current of 5 amp. For example, a 1,000/5-amp current transformer with a single-turn primary would have 200 turns on the secondary. The open-circuit voltage of this transformer is very high and could break down the insulation between the secondary windings. Therefore, the secondary windings are shorted, except when a meter or a relay coil is connected across the secondary. This is done not only to protect the insulation of the transformer but also to protect those who may be working with these circuits. *Remember, it is dangerous to work with current transformers when the secondary circuit is not shorted or connected to a low-impedance load.*

The secondary must be insulated from the potential of the primary circuit. The current transformers on high-voltage transformers, circuit breakers, and similar equipment may be included in the high-voltage bushings on this equipment. These are called *bushing-type current transformers.* Laboratory-type current transformers usually have a primary and secondary winding on a circular core, as shown in Fig. 6-6. For the highest current ratio, the primary conductor is run once through the hole in the core. Half of this turns ratio is obtained when the primary conductor is looped around the core and the primary conductor passes through the core twice in the same direction. Similarly, looping the primary conductor around the core so it goes four times through the core will reduce the current ratio to one fourth of its highest value. Other current ratios are obtained by conducting the primary winding on the core in series with the load and using the desired ratio as indicated by the tap-changing switch on the transformer. Note that this transformer has a shorting switch across the secondary terminals which should only be opened when a meter is connected to the transformer. It has been shown that there are ratio errors and phase-angle errors in a transformer.

Usually, the nominal ratio of the current transformer and not the turns ratio is given on the nameplate. This ratio is correct for a given load. The correct ratio varies with load. To reduce both the ratio error and the phase error of a current transformer, the no-load current $I_o$ must be reduced to a minimum by reducing the flux density in the core. This is done by increasing the cross section of the core. The no-load current $I_o$ is further reduced by increasing the permeability of the core. Permalloy and Hipernik have very high permeability at low flux densities and are frequently used for current transformers. Special current-compensating windings and shunts are also used to improve the operation and accuracy of current transformers.

**Measuring the Characteristics of a Current Transformer**[2,4]

There are several methods for measuring the true ratio and the phase-angle error of a current transformer. Only one method will be described to illustrate the basic principles involved in these tests. The testing circuit is shown in Fig. 6-9. The voltage drop across the resistor $R_1$ in the primary

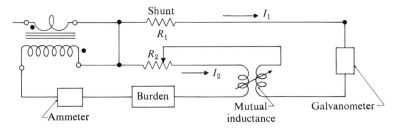

**Fig. 6-9.** *Circuit for testing current transformers*

circuit is balanced against the variable resistance $R_2$ in the secondary circuit. A mutual inductance $M$ is connected between the secondary circuit and the galvanometer circuit to produce the correct phase shift. Then the resistance $R_1$ and the mutual inductance $M$ are varied until the current in the a-c galvanometer is zero, and the voltage around the galvanometer circuit is

$$I_1 R_1 - I_2 R_2 - j\omega M I_2 = 0$$

Let the angle between $I_1$ and $I_2$ be $\phi$. Then, using $I_1$ as the reference current,

$$I_1 R_1 + I_2(\cos \phi + j \sin \phi)(-R_2 + j\omega M) = 0$$

Equating real and imaginary components gives

$$I_1 R_1 = I_2 R_2 \cos \phi - I_2 \omega M \sin \phi$$

and

$$I_2 \omega M \cos \phi = I_2 R_2 \sin \phi$$

Then

$$\tan \phi = \frac{\sin \phi}{\cos \phi} = \frac{\omega M}{R_1}$$

and

$$\frac{I_1}{I_2} = \frac{R_2 \cos \phi - M \sin \phi}{R_1}$$

But angle $\phi$ is very small, and the tangent is equal to the angle in radians. Then

$$\phi = \frac{\omega M}{R_1} \text{ radian} = 3{,}438 \frac{M}{R_1} \text{ min}$$

The sine and the cosine of the angle $\phi$ obtained from the above value of the $\tan \phi$ are

$$\sin \phi = \frac{\omega M}{\sqrt{R_2{}^2 + \omega^2 M^2}}$$

and

$$\cos \phi = \frac{R_2}{\sqrt{R_2{}^2 + \omega^2 M^2}}$$

Then

$$\frac{I_1}{I_2} = \frac{R_2{}^2 + \omega^2 M^2}{R_1 \sqrt{R_2{}^2 + \omega^2 M^2}}$$

$$= \frac{\sqrt{R_2{}^2 + \omega^2 M^2}}{R_1}$$

$$\cong \frac{R_2}{R_1}$$

as $R_2 \gg \omega M$ when angle $\phi$ is small.

## Clamp-on Ammeters

A current transformer with a single conductor is used in combination with a dry-type bridge rectifier and a d-c milliammeter to produce a very useful service meter. The core of the transformer opens so it can be clamped around the conductor to measure the current, thus avoiding the necessity of opening the circuit to the load. By changing the shunt resistance of the milliammeter, current ranges from 0–5 to 0–600 amp can be obtained. The same milliammeter and rectifier are used with two external binding posts and a range switch for a multirange a-c voltmeter. The circuit used in this *clamp-on ammeter* is shown in Fig. 6-10.

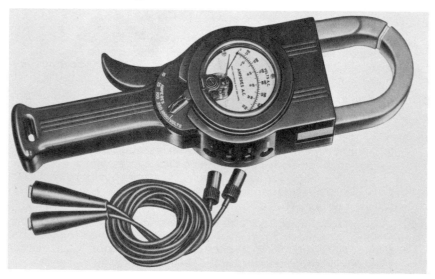

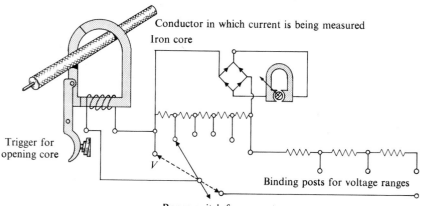

Conductor in which current is being measured
Iron core

Trigger for opening core

*V*

Binding posts for voltage ranges

Range switch for current ranges
Position "V" used for measuring voltage

**Fig. 6-10.** *Combined voltmeter and clamp-on ammeter circuit (courtesy of the Weston Electrical Instrument Corporation)*

This type of clamp-on transformer is used with recording ammeters. These transformers have 5,000-volt insulation between the primary and secondary. There are several variations of this clamp-on transformer which are used in measuring maximum current in a line, real and reactive power, and power factor supplied to a load.

## PROBLEMS

**6-1.** An ideal transformer has a primary voltage of 2,400 volts, and a 20:1 turns ratio. Determine the primary current, the secondary current, the secondary terminal voltage, and the primary power factor when the transformer is supplying a burden of 40 va at 0.8 lagging power factor.

**6-2.** A potential transformer has a primary resistance $R_1$ of 300 ohms, a primary leakage reactance $X_1$ of 600 ohms, a secondary resistance $R_2$ of 0.75 ohms, and a secondary reactance $X_2$ of 1.5 ohms. The primary-to-secondary turns ratio is 20:1. The primary voltage is 2,400 volts. Neglect the magnetizing and core-loss currents $I_o$. Determine the voltage-ratio correction factor and the phase-angle error when the burden on the secondary of the transformer is: (a) 40 va at 0.5 power factor, lagging; (b) 40 va at unity power factor; (c) 40 va at 0.5 power factor, leading; (d) 20 va at 0.5 power factor, lagging; (e) 20 va at unity power factor; (f) 20 va at 0.5 power factor, leading.

**6-3.** A current transformer has a 200:1 turns ratio and is rated at 1,000:5 amp and 40 va. The core-loss current is 0.8 amp and the magnetizing current is 1.4 amp. Determine the RCF and the phase-angle error, neglecting the resistance and leakage reactance of the windings, for the following loads: (a) 5 amp at 40 va and unity power factor; (b) 2 amp at 16 va and unity power factor; (c) 5 amp at 40 va and 0.8 power factor, lagging; (d) 2 amp at 16 va and 0.8 power factor lagging.

**6-4.** A potential transformer with a nominal ratio of 2,400:115 volts, an RCF of 0.99, and a phase angle ($V_2$ lags $V_1$) of $-22$ min is used with a current transformer with a nominal ratio of 100:5 amp, an RCF of 1.005, and a phase-angle error ($I_2$ leads $I_1$) of 10 min to measure the power to a single-phase induction load. The meters connected to these transformers give a corrected reading of 118 volts, 4.2 amp, and 390 watts. Determine the true values of the voltage, current, and power supplied to the load.

**6-5.** A clamp-on ammeter, as shown in Fig. 6-10, has 1,000 turns on the secondary winding. Determine the current in the secondary winding when the current in the conductor is 100 amp. Neglect the transformer losses.

**6-6.** The clamp-on ammeter in Prob. 6-5 has a d'Arsonval movement that has a full-scale reading of 25 ma (average current) and a resistance of 750 ohms. Determine the total resistance connected across the input to the rectifier when the current-range switch is in the right position (minimum-current position) and the current in the conductor is 10 amp. Neglect the losses in the transformer, and assume a perfect full-wave rectifier. Note that the d'Arsonval movement measures the average of the full-wave rectifier output.

**6-7.** Determine the resistance between the last two taps to the left of the current-range switch of the clamp-on ammeter in Prob. 6-6. Note that in the switch position shown in Fig. 6-10, the meter is on the 1,000 amp range.

**6-8.** Prove that there are 3,438 minutes in one radian.

**6-9.** Describe in your own words the operation of the circuit in Fig. 6-8.

**6-10.** Describe in your own words the operation of the circuit in Fig. 6-9.

## REFERENCES

1.  J. G. Torboux, *Alternating-Current Machinery*, International Book Company, Scranton, Pa., 1947.
2.  M. B. Stout, *Basic Electrical Measurements*, 2nd ed., Prentice-Hall, Inc., Englewood Cliffs, N.J., 1960, Chap. 15.
3.  F. K. Harris, *Electrical Measurements*, John Wiley & Sons, Inc., New York, 1952, Chap. 13.
4.  I. F. Kinnard, *Applied Electrical Measurements*, John Wiley & Sons, Inc., New York, 1956, Chap. 10.

Chapter 7

# RECORDERS, AND

Research and industrial processes demand that quantities such as flow, force, pressure, temperature, electrical power, current, and voltage be recorded as functions of time. Chapter 9 will describe methods of converting the magnitudes of physical quantities into corresponding magnitudes of electrical emf or current. Chapter 14 will describe methods of recording the magnitude of emf in discrete digital numbers. The present chapter will give methods of recording currents and voltages as a continuous analog function of time.

## 7-2. THE GALVANOMETER-TYPE OSCILLOGRAPH[1]

The galvanometer-type oscillograph is shown schematically in Fig. 7-1, and the construction of the galvanometer element used in these oscillographs is shown in Fig. 7-2. The galvanometer element has a single loop of fine silver-alloy wire suspended in the field of a permanent magnet. This loop carries the current supplied to the galvanometer. A small mirror is mounted

# OSCILLOGRAPHS, TAPE

# CATHODE-RAY OSCILLOSCOPES

on the loop. A beam of light from the light source is reflected from this mirror onto a moving sheet of light-sensitive paper which records the deflection of the element as a function of time.

The oscillograph is schematically shown in Fig. 7-1, and the complete unit is shown in Fig. 7-3. It usually has several galvanometer elements, each recording its deflection on the sensitive paper. Often, a second beam is supplied from a fixed mirror which is reflected from the galvanometer mirror onto a rotating mirror. The rotating mirror reflects this beam of light onto a fixed screen. When the rotating mirror has six sides, as shown in Fig. 7-1, it will produce a stationary picture of one cycle of the input signal on the screen when its revolutions per second are one sixth of the cycles per second of the input signal. This system permits the viewing of a repeating function while it is being recorded.

The galvanometer units can be constructed with a diameter of 0.2 in. or less, and 2 to 3 in. long. These units comprise the moving element of the galvanometer, and they are set in a fixed frame of the permanent magnets. Five or more units per inch can be constructed, and 50 or more galvanometers are included in a single oscillograph. The sensitive paper is usually 12 in. wide and records the deflection of all the active galvanometers. Two galvanometers are generally used with timing signals to identify the magnitude of the time coordinate. Other galvanometers may be used for special pulse-signal markers. Timing lines at every 0.1 or 0.01 sec can be recorded together with reference lines running the length of the paper. These instruments have a

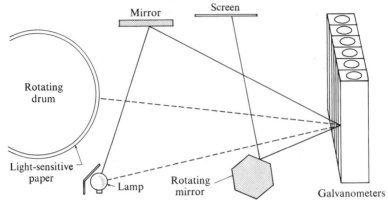

**Fig. 7-1.** *Schematic drawing of a galvanometer-type oscillograph*

high sensitivity, and the frequency response depends on the construction of the galvanometer element.

The major disadvantage of this type of oscillograph is the time required for developing the light-sensitive paper. Attempts to overcome this difficulty include the use of a waxed paper. The light beam melts the wax, which collects powdered iron filings that leave a black line on the light trace. Another method uses a paper which is developed in approximately 1 min, when exposed to ultraviolet light, or 10 to 15 min when exposed to fluorescent light. There are several dry- and wet-type tank developers that can be connected directly to the oscillograph which will develop the paper within a few minutes after it is exposed.

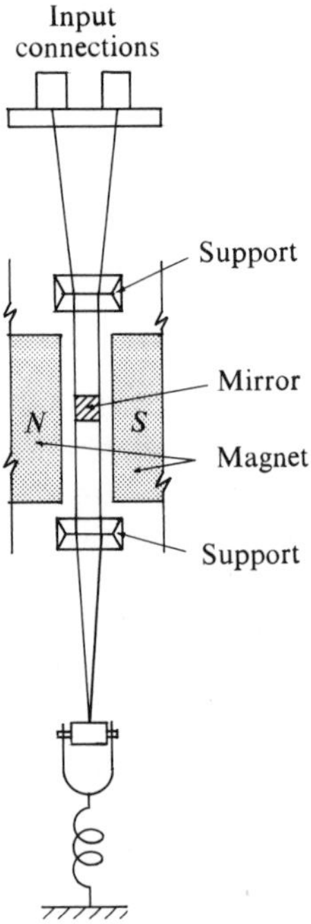

### The Response of an Oscillograph Galvanometer[1,2]

The equation of the motion of a galvanometer, when a sinusoidal voltage

$$e = E_m \sin (\omega t + \beta) \qquad (7\text{-}1)$$

is applied to the movement, is obtained by substituting the value of $e$ for $E$ in Eq. (3-16). Then

**Fig. 7-2.** *Oscillograph galvanometer*

$$\frac{d^2\theta}{dt^2} + \frac{D}{J}\frac{d\theta}{dt} + \frac{S\theta}{J} = \frac{GE_m}{JR}(\sin \omega t + \beta) \qquad (7\text{-}2)$$

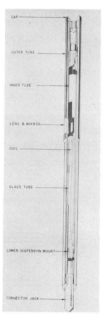
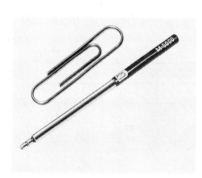

**Fig. 7-3.** *Galvanometer-type recording oscillograph* (*courtesy of the Minneapolis-Honeywell Company*)

A complete solution of this equation is

$$\theta = \theta_m \left\{ \sin\left(\omega t + \beta - \psi\right) \right.$$

$$- \frac{\epsilon^{-\omega_o t}}{\sqrt{1 - \gamma^2}} \left[ \gamma \sin\left(\omega_o \sqrt{1 - \gamma^2}\, t + \sin^{-1}\sqrt{1 - \gamma^2}\right) \sin\left(\beta - \psi\right) \right.$$

$$\left. + \left(\omega / \omega_o\right) \sin\left(\omega_o \sqrt{1 - \gamma^2}\, t\right) \cos\left(\beta - \psi\right) \right] \right\} \qquad (7\text{-}3)$$

and the steady-state solution is

$$\theta = \frac{\theta_{dc}}{\sqrt{1 + (4\gamma^2 - 2)(\omega/\omega_o)^2 + (\omega/\omega_o)^4}} \sin(\omega t + \beta - \psi) \qquad (7\text{-}4)$$

where

$$\theta_{dc} = \frac{GE_m}{RS} \qquad (7\text{-}5)$$

which is the steady-state value of $\theta$ when a constant voltage $E_m$ is applied to the movement. The maximum value of the steady-state value of $\theta$ is $\theta_m$. The angle $\psi$ is the angle between the applied voltage and the galvanometer movement. It is obtained by the equation

$$\psi = \tan^{-1} \frac{2\gamma(\omega/\omega_o)}{1 - (\omega/\omega_o)^2} \qquad (7\text{-}6)$$

and $\gamma$ is the relative damping $(D/D_c)$. The angle the deflection $\theta$ lags behind the angle of the applied voltage.

The maximum deflection of the galvanometer under steady-state operation is

$$\theta_m = \frac{\theta_{dc}}{\sqrt{1 + (4\gamma^2 - 2)(\omega/\omega_o)^2 + (\omega/\omega_o)^4}} \qquad (7\text{-}7)$$

The ratio of $\theta_m/\theta_{dc}$ is an index to the amplitude distortion of the galvanometer. This ratio is sometimes defined as the *relative amplitude* of the element. It will be noted that the angle of lag $\psi$ and the relative amplitude ($\theta_m/\theta_{dc}$) are

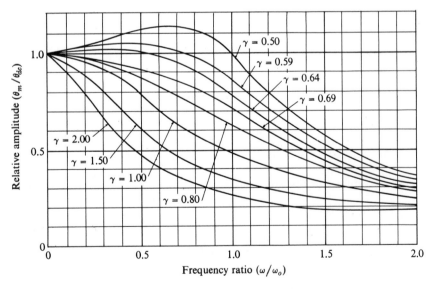

**Fig. 7-4.** *Galvanometer frequency response*

both functions of the frequency and the damping. When $\gamma$ and $\omega/\omega_o$ are known, $\psi$ and $\theta_m/\theta_{dc}$ can be determined. Figure 7-4 gives the relative amplitude as a function of the ratio $\omega/\omega_o$. The angle of lag of the galvanometer is given as a function of $\omega/\omega_o$ in Fig. 7-5. These curves give the steady-state response to a sinusoidal input. It is very difficult to analyze the transient response. Some manufacturers define the ratio $\theta/\theta_{dc}$ as the relative displacement and give the relative displacement as a function of time for a step-function input. This response is given in Fig. 7-6. The values of the relative damping $\gamma$ are marked on the curves in Figs. 7-4, 7-5, and 7-6.

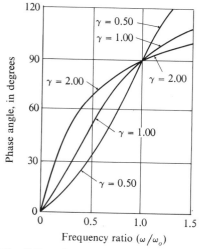

Fig. 7-5. *Phase angle*

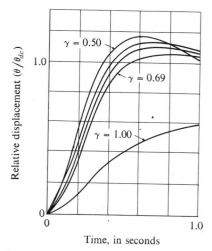

Fig. 7-6. *Step-function response*

The galvanometer elements have natural frequencies from 40 to more than 7,000 cycles per second or have a flat frequency response of $\pm 5$ percent up to 5,000 cycles per second or higher. Their nominal coil resistance ranges from 20 to 120 ohms and requires an external damping resistance of 120 to 350 ohms, depending on the construction of the galvanometer. Galvanometers with high-frequency response have fluid damping. Although they have a nominal resistance of 20 to 50 ohms, the damping changes only slightly with variations in source resistance through the range from 3 to 100 ohms. The current sensitivity varies from 0.01 in./$\mu$a to 0.3 in./ma, with a corresponding voltage sensitivity of 0.1 in./mv to 9.6 in./v.

The linearity of the galvanometer is within $\pm 2$ percent for deflections of $\pm 10$ cm, but it is decreased as the deflection is increased, because the surface of the paper is flat and thus the distance the light travels from the galvanometer element to the paper is increased.

These galvanometer oscillographs are very useful in industrial and research work. They have a much higher frequency response than do pen recorders, and they can record several instantaneous values on the same chart. They are seldom more accurate than ± 5 percent. For more accurate records they should be calibrated prior to each test.

## 7-3. MAGNETIC TAPE RECORDERS[3]

Magnetic tapes are used extensively for recording instrument measurements as a function of time. They have a *wide frequency range* from direct current to megacycles. They have a *wide dynamic range* which exceeds 50 db. This permits the linear recording from full-scale signal level to 1/3 of 1 percent of full scale. They have *low distortion*. The magnitude of the electrical signal input is stored in magnetic memory and this electrical signal can be reproduced when desired. This, in turn, can be analyzed by automatic data-reduction methods, to be described in a later chapter. The recorded signal is immediately available, with no time lost in processing. The recorded signal can be played back, or reproduced, as many times as desired without loss of the signal. When all the information has been processed, the signal is erased, and the tape may be used to record a new set of data.

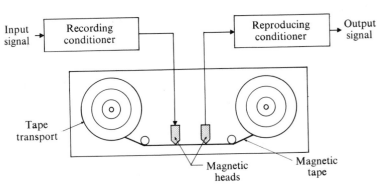

**Fig. 7-7.** *Basic magnetic tape recorder*

Magnetic tape permits multichannel recording. Finally, this tape provides a method of changing the time base. Data may be recorded at very high speeds and played back at speeds slow enough to be recorded with a galvanometer oscillograph or other data-reduction equipment.

### Basic Components of a Magnetic Tape Recorder

A magnetic tape recorder has three basic components. The first consists of the *conditioning devices*, which amplify, filter, and otherwise modify the input signal to a magnitude, a form, or a code that can be properly recorded on the tape. Other conditioning devices modify the signal read from the tape to a form, a magnitude, or a code that can be properly read by the output data-reduction equipment.

The second component is the *magnetic head* which, during the recording process, converts the electrical signal into varying states of magnetization of the magnetic material on the tape. During the reading or playback process, it converts these variations into an electrical signal.

The third component is the *tape transport*. It moves the tape smoothly and at a constant speed across the head of the recorder. A sketch of the arrangement of these components is shown in Fig. 7-7. A more detailed sketch of the recording or receiving head and the magnetic tape is shown in Fig. 7-8.

### Direct-Recording Process

The recording head in Fig. 7-8 consists of a winding on a magnetic ring, with two air gaps. One gap is bridged by the magnetic tape. The magnetic pattern impressed on the tape is directly proportional to the flux density

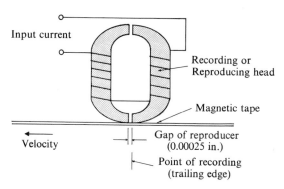

**Fig. 7-8.** *Recording or reproducing head and magnetic tape*

produced at the gap. The relationship between the current in the winding and the flux density is shown in Fig. 7-9(*a*). The nonlinearity between the current in the coil and the flux density produces distortion in the signal applied to the magnetic tape, as is clearly shown in this figure. To avoid this distortion, a high-frequency bias of constant amplitude is applied in series with the signal input to the recorder. The input signal, the bias signal, and the combined input and bias signal are shown in Fig. 7-9(*b*). When the magnitude of the signal is limited so that the peak values of the combined input and bias signal lie on the straight portion of the magnetization, the signal recorded on the tape will have the form shown in Fig. 7-9(*c*). This wave form will be reproduced by the reproducing head. This signal is conditioned by filtering

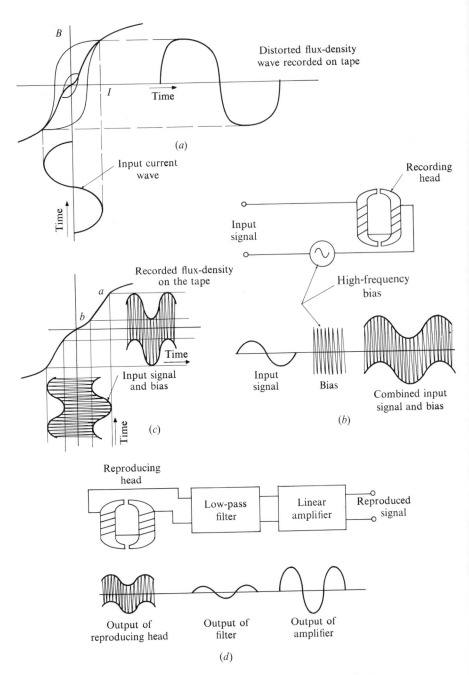

**Fig. 7-9.** *High-frequency bias magnetic tape recording and reproducing*

out the high-frequency component, thus reproducing, with very little distortion, the wave form of the input signal. This signal is amplified to a magnitude compatible to the input of the data-reduction equipment, as shown in Fig. 7-9($d$).

There is another factor that must be considered in conditioning the direct-recorded signal. This is illustrated in the following example. The signal in Fig. 7-9($b$) is sinusoidal and

$$I_1 = I_m \sin 2\pi f t \qquad (7\text{-}8)$$

The component of the flux produced by the signal current $I_1$ is

$$\begin{aligned} \phi_1 &= k_1 I_1 \\ &= k_1 I_m \sin 2\pi f t \\ &= \phi_m \sin 2\pi f t \end{aligned} \qquad (7\text{-}9)$$

where

$k_1 =$ constant

$I_m =$ maximum value of the signal current

$f =$ frequency of the current

$\phi_m =$ maximum value of the component of flux produced by the current

The signal recorded on the tape will be proportional to $\phi$. The flux through the reproducing head, when this tape is being read, is proportional to $\phi_1$ or

$$\phi_2 = k_2 \phi_1$$

where

$\phi_2 =$ flux produced in the reading head

$k_2 =$ constant of proportionality

Then

$$\phi_2 = k_2 \phi_m \sin 2\pi f t$$

The emf induced in the coil on the reading head is

$$\begin{aligned} e &= -N_2 \frac{d\phi_2}{dt} \\ &= -2\pi f k_2 N_2 \phi_m \cos 2\pi f t \\ &= k_3 f \phi_m \cos 2\pi f t \end{aligned} \qquad (7\text{-}10)$$

where

$N_2 =$ number of turns on the reading head

$k_3 =$ a constant equal to $-2\pi k_2{}^2 N_2$

From Eqs. (7-8) and (7-9),

$$k_1 I_1 = \phi_m \sin 2\pi f t \qquad (7\text{-}11)$$

Equations (7-10) and (7-11) have the same form, except that the magnitude of the induced emf is directly proportional to the frequency. Then the rms value of the output voltage is

$$E = KI_1 f \qquad (7\text{-}12)$$

where $K$ is a constant. It can be shown that the rise in the output with an increase in frequency is 6 db/octave. The output amplifier must have an attenuation of 6 db/octave, as shown in Fig. 7-10, to correct for the gain with frequency of the reproducing head.

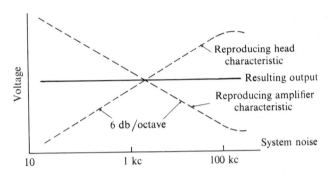

**Fig. 7-10.** *Reproducing head and amplifier characteristics*

The flux $\phi$ between the two poles of the reproducing head is the average of the flux upon the tape under the air gap. This flux is proportional to the input current when the wavelength on the tape is large compared with the gap of the reproducing head, as shown in Fig. 7-11(a). When the wavelength on

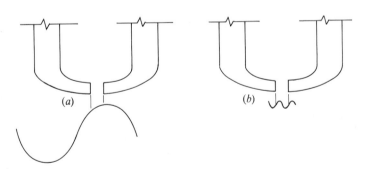

**Fig. 7-11.** *Gap effects*

the tape is equal to the air gap, the output of the reproducing head is zero, as shown in Fig. 7-11(b). The wavelength is

$$\lambda = \frac{v}{f} \qquad (7\text{-}13)$$

where

$\lambda$ = wavelength on the tape, in inches
$v$ = tape speed, in inches per second
$f$ = frequency, in cycles per second.

When the frequency is large, the velocity of the tape must be increased in order to keep the wavelength large compared to the length of the gap of the recorder. The increase in tape speed increases the amount of tape required to record the signal and shortens the life of the reproducing head.

A common width of the air gap is 0.00025 in. and a common tape speed is 60 in./sec. At 100,000 cycles per second

$$\lambda = \frac{60}{100,000} = 0.0006 \text{ in.}$$

and the wavelength of the pattern on the tape is 2.4 times the width of the air gap of the recorder. In this reproducer the output drops off rapidly when the frequency exceeds this value.

Another factor that limits the frequency range is the inherent noise of the system. When the frequency is less than 50 cycles per second, the noise exceeds the input signal. This determines the lower limit of the frequency range. The relative signal output as a function of frequency is shown in Fig. 7-12 for tape speeds of 15, 30, and 60 in./sec.

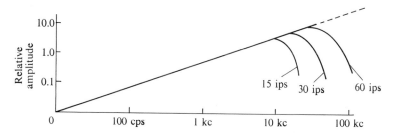

**Fig. 7-12.** *Reproducing-head output*

The condition of the magnetic tape is an important factor in determining the quality of the magnetic tape recorder. Slightly protruding spots on the surface, due to nodules or clusters of oxide on the tape, will produce *dropouts* at these points.

In summing the characteristics of direct recording, its frequency response is from 50 cycles per second to more than 300,000 cycles per second. It has good dynamic response and can take overloads without sudden increase in distortion. It is used to record signals where the information is contained in the relation between frequency and amplitude, such as spectrum analysis of noise. It is used for recording voice and in multiplexing a number of simultaneous channels of information into one channel of tape recording.

### Frequency-Modulation Recording

Frequency modulation (FM), as the name implies, uses the variation of frequency to carry the desired information, instead of varying the amplitude. This process is shown in Fig. 7-13. The modulator contains an oscillator with a center frequency $f_o$ when the input is zero. The variation of this frequency

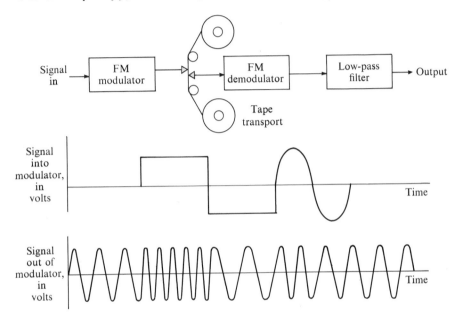

**Fig. 7-13.** *Frequency-modulation recording system*

will be directly proportional to the input signal. To illustrate, let the center frequency be 50,000 cycles per second. Let an input signal of 1 volt produce a 40 percent change from the center frequency or a variation of $0.4 \times 50,000$ or a 20,000-cycles-per-second variation from the center frequency. Then a $+1$-volt input to the modulator will produce an output frequency of 70,000 cycles per second, and a zero-volt input will produce an output frequency of 50,000 cycles per second. The operation of an FM modulator can easily be checked by applying a known input voltage and measuring the frequency output with an electronic counter. This signal is applied to the tape with no further conditioning, as the signal is independent of amplitude. The FM demodulator converts the difference between the center frequency and the frequency on the tape to a voltage proportional to this difference. This system will record from d-c voltages to several thousand cycles per second. It is used extensively for recording the voltages from the force and pressure transducers and accelerometers. These transducers are described in Chap. 11.

FREQUENCY-DIVISION MULTIPLEXING. Multiplexing is the process of placing several channels of information on one recording channel. Many devices are used to perform this operation. Only a few will be discussed here. Multiplexing is introduced here because the principle of frequency modulation is easily applied to multiplexing. The system known as frequency-division multiplexing is shown in Fig. 7-14. The direct-recording system has

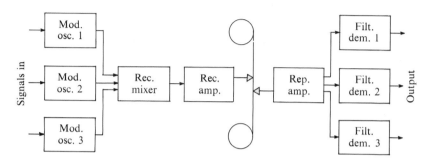

**Fig. 7-14.** *Frequency-division multiplexing FM system*

a wide frequency range. To illustrate, when the tape speed is 60 in./sec the recorder has a flat response from 50 cycles per second to 100 kc. Several signals can be recorded in this range. For 10 signals, frequencies of 5, 15, 25, 35, 45, 55, 65, 75, 85, and 95 kc are used as center frequencies of 10 FM modulators. By limiting the maximum deviation from the center frequency in each FM modulator to ± 1 kc, each modulator will have a total band width of 2 kc. The outputs of the 10 FM modulators are recorded on the magnetic tape. To reproduce these signals, the output of the reproducing system is passed through a set of band-pass filters in parallel. Each filter is constructed so that only one of the input signals will pass through it. For example, the lowest center frequency is 5 kc. The output of this modulator has a frequency range from 4 to 6 kc. This component of the playback signal is separated from the other signal frequencies with a band-pass filter which will allow frequencies from 4 to 6 kc to pass through it with no attenuation but will offer high attenuation to all other frequencies. Each of the other signals is separated from another by a filter capable of passing only signals in the correct band-pass range. The outputs of these filters are demodulated with the discriminator design for the given center frequency.

    Any variation of the tape speed will cause unwanted modulation of the carrier frequency and will result in noise. This limitation is called *flutter* and *wow*. It is particularly acute for frequency-division multiplex systems. For example, when the 5-kc signal is modulated to 40 percent of the center frequency, 1 percent variation in speed will produce a 1 percent change in the center frequency, but the signal noise produced by this change in speed will be

$$\text{Percent noise} = \frac{100 \times \% \text{ variation in speed}}{\% \text{ modulation}} = \frac{100}{40} = 2.5\%$$

The 95-kc signal will also be varied by 1 percent, but it will be modulated to only 2 percent of its center frequency, and the noise produced by a 1 percent variation in speed will be

$$\text{Percent noise} = \frac{100}{2} = 50\%$$

This indicates that a better choice of center frequencies and band widths could be made. The choice will require that each center frequency be so spaced from the other center frequencies that it can have the same percent modulation.

This proportional frequency spacing is illustrated in Table 7-1. The

**Table 7-1**

| Channel | Lower frequency limit | Center frequency | Upper frequency limit |
|---|---|---|---|
| 1 | 66,666 | 83,333 | 100,000 |
| 2 | 22,222 | 27,777 | 33,333 |
| 3 | 7,407 | 9,259 | 11,111 |
| 4 | 2,469 | 3,086 | 3,704 |
| 5 | 823 | 1,029 | 1,234 |
| 6 | 274 | 343 | 411 |

maximum frequency is 100 kc. Each frequency band has a $\pm 20$ percent modulation of its center frequency and 1 octave spacing between the limits of each band. To obtain six channels of FM recording, a lower limit of the frequency must be reduced to 272 cycles per second. Now consider the limits of the speed variation required to reduce the noise in these two systems to 2 percent. The uniformly spaced system requires less than 0.04 percent, or 4 parts in 10,000, speed variation, while the proportionally spaced system requires only 0.4 percent, or 4 parts in 1,000, speed variation. Yet four channels of recording have been lost, and the minimum frequency has dropped from 400 to 272 cycles per second.

Usually, the percent modulation of the center frequency is reduced to about 7.5 percent, and the spacing between channels is decreased to a fraction of an octave. This system requires good speed control and sharp cutoff filters. See Prob. 7-4 for an example of this system.

The advantages of the FM recording process are that it (1) will record direct current, (2) is free from dropout effects, and (3) is independent of amplitude variations and accurately reproduces the wave form of the input signal. The disadvantages of FM recording are that it requires (1) a high tape speed, (2) additional circuits in the modulators and demodulators, and (3) a high quality of tape transport and speed control. In brief, it is expensive.

### Digital Tape Recorders

Instrumentation systems and computers use codes made up of a combination of two symbols—0 and 1. These two symbols are expressed in many ways. The 1 may be a hole in a paper tape or in a card, and the 0 may be the absence of the hole in a paper tape or in a card. A positive magnetized space at a given place on a magnetic tape with a negative magnetization on the tape

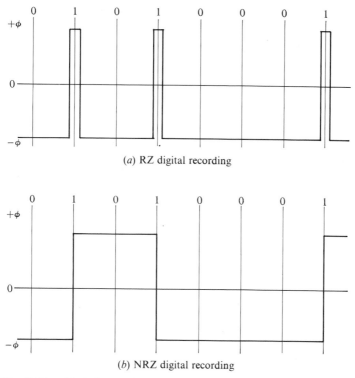

(a) RZ digital recording

(b) NRZ digital recording

**Fig. 7-15.**   *Digital-recording systems*

before or after this place on a magnetic tape may express a 1, and no change in the negative magnetization at a given place on the magnetic tape may express a 0. This system of expressing 1's and 0's is defined as the *return-to-zero* (*RZ*) *method*. This method is illustrated by the graph in Fig. 7-15(a). Another method uses the change from either a positive to a negative or from a negative to a positive state to express a 1 at a given place on the tape, and no change of state at a given place on the tape to express a 0. This is defined as the *non-return-to-zero* (*NRZ*) *method* of expressing 1's and 0's. This method is illustrated by the graph in Fig. 7-15(*b*). Some of the codes for expressing numbers in combinations of 1's and 0's are given in Chaps. 13 and 14.

The code for a given number may be expressed as a series of pulses on a single channel representing the desired combination of 1's and 0's by either the RZ or the NRZ method. This is a serial system of writing numbers. A faster and more common system uses a multichannel tape and inscribes the complete number at a given place on the tape. This requires a recording channel for each of the digits, 1 or 0, required to express the number. This is a *parallel* system of writing numbers.

The process of recording numbers in a digital-coded form is very simple. It requires only an amplifier in the recorder and another amplifier in the reproducer to condition the signal. The on and off conditions are functions neither of frequency nor of amplitude, yet there are a few problems in this type of recording. The major one is in tape dropout errors or loss of pulses and spurious pulses. The loss of pulses becomes more critical as the period of the pulse decreases. This is expressed in pulses per inch of tape. Many recorders use 200 pulses/in. and 60 in./sec tape speed, but some tape recorders use 500 pulses/in. and a tape speed of 120 in./sec. Packing densities greater than 1,000 pulses/in. have been obtained.

As a check on the tape dropout errors, some systems record the information twice. This is called the use of *redundancy* (because the second recording would be redundant if the system were perfect). A second method uses the logic of the number code to indicate, on a separate channel of the tape, if one of the 1's is missing. If an even number of 1's is missing, no error will be recorded. This is known as the *parity check*. Systems of parity checking have been developed which will check not only the parity of the words written across the tape but also that of the numbers recorded in each tape channel. In some equipment the parity checks have been used to insert the missing information due to dropouts on the magnetic tape, as well as to indicate the errors that have been made. This system is very effective in detecting and reducing tape dropouts errors.

In parallel recording of digital information, the recording head and the reproducing head must remain at right angles to the tape at all times. If the tape becomes skewed, the signals on the different channels will not be read at the same instant of time, and errors will result. Very accurate alignment of the tape is necessary to avoid this error.

The advantages of digital tape recording are (1) high accuracy, (2) insensitivity to tape speed, (3) simple conditioning equipment, and (4) the fact that recorded information can be fed directly into computers and tabulators. The disadvantages are (1) poor tape economy, and the facts that (2) most information from transducers requires analog-to-digital converters to prepare the digital information for the tape recorder, and (3) a high quality of tape and transport is required.

A multichannel recording head is shown in Fig. 7-16, and a tape transport, with its amplifiers and accessory racks to condition the signal for recording and for reproducing several channels of information, is shown in Fig. 7-17.

**Fig. 7-16.** *Fourteen-channel recording heads (courtesy of Ampex Corporation)*

## 7-4. THE CATHODE-RAY OSCILLOSCOPE

The cathode-ray oscilloscope is built around the cathode-ray tube. A schematic drawing of this tube is shown in Fig. 7-18(*b*). An electron gun is located at the base of the tube. It consists of a heated cathode, accelerating and focusing electrodes, a pair of horizontal deflection plates, and a pair of vertical deflection plates. The electron gun emits a stream of electrons which are sharply focused upon a fluorescent screen in the other end of the tube. The location of the spot where the stream of electrons strikes the screen is a function of the relative voltages on the deflection plates. The intensity of the fluorescent spot on the screen is controlled by varying the potential on the accelerating electrodes in the electron gun, and the sharpness of the spot is controlled by varying the potential on the focusing electrodes.

To reproduce a picture of a signal with a repetitive wave form, a sawtooth or repetitive ramp voltage is applied to the horizontal deflection plates. This voltage produces a uniform horizontal motion of the spot appearing on the fluorescent screen. This spot is returned to its original position at the end of each cycle of the saw-tooth wave. The blanking circuit shuts off the electron stream while the trace returns to its original position so that the return path will not appear on the screen. The signal voltage is applied to the vertical

**Fig. 7-17.** *Recorder-reproducer with accessory racks (courtesy of Ampex Corporation)*

deflection plates through attenuator and amplifier circuits which are adjusted to give the desired amplitude to the trace. Horizontal and vertical position controls apply bias voltages to the horizontal and vertical deflection plates, respectively, which bring the trace to the desired position on the screen. An elementary block diagram of the circuits of a cathode-ray oscilloscope is shown in Fig. 7-18(*a*), and a cathode-ray oscilloscope is shown in Fig. 7-19.

The cathode-ray oscilloscope has a very-high-frequency response, extending into several hundred megacycles per second. Permanent records of the information obtained with a cathode-ray oscilloscope require photographic equipment. Nonrepetitive or transient voltages are recorded with

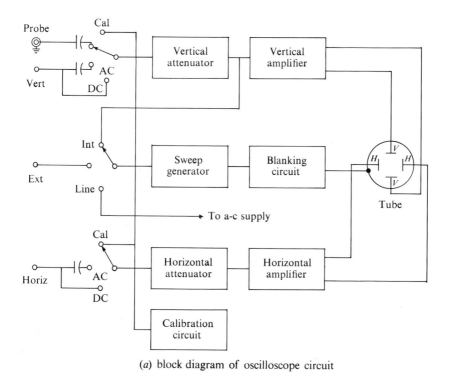

(*a*) block diagram of oscilloscope circuit

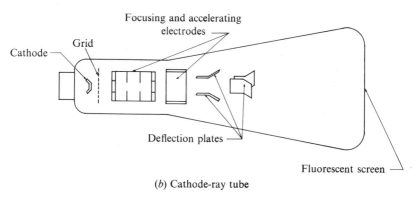

(*b*) Cathode-ray tube

**Fig. 7-18.** *Elementary diagram of a cathode-ray oscilloscope and tube*

high-speed cameras. The time coordinate is obtained by moving the photographic film with the camera shutter open.

Calibrating voltages produced within the oscilloscope are used to calibrate the scales on the screen. Usually, the calibrating voltage has a square wave form, and its voltage is given from peak to peak.

## Phase-Angle Measurement with a Cathode-Ray Oscilloscope[4]

The cathode-ray oscilloscope is used to measure phase angle in addition to recording voltage wave shapes and transients. The phase angle $\theta$ of a voltage $V_2$ with respect to a voltage $V_1$ is obtained by applying $V_2$ to the

**Fig. 7-19.** *The cathode-ray oscillograph (courtesy of Tektronix, Inc.)*

vertical input and $V_1$ to the horizontal input of the oscilloscope. The relation-ship of the two waves is illustrated in Fig. 7-20(a), and the resultant pattern on the oscilloscope is given in Fig. 7-20(b). The pattern on the oscilloscope is made symmetrical about the vertical and the horizontal axes by adjusting the input attenuators and the position controls. In Fig. 7-20(b) the spot is moving in a clockwise direction. The value of $V_2$ when $V_1$ first passes through zero, in Fig. 7-20(a), is $A$, and this value is marked on the pattern on the oscillo-scope in Fig. 7-20(b). The maximum value of the vertical trace on the scope is defined as $B$. Then the voltage $V_2$ leads the voltage $V_1$ by the angle

$$\theta = \sin^{-1} \frac{A}{B} \tag{7-14}$$

This angle lies between zero and 90 deg when the slope of the major axis of the elliptical figure on the scope is positive and the spot generating the figure on the oscilloscope is moving in a clockwise direction, as shown in Fig. 7-20($b$). When the spot in Fig. 7-20($b$) is moving in a counterclockwise direction, the phase angle is

$$\theta = -\sin^{-1}\frac{A}{B} \tag{7-15}$$

and the voltage $V_2$ lags the voltage $V_1$ by the angle $\theta$. When the major axis of the elliptical figure on the oscilloscope has a negative slope and the spot generating the figure is moving in a clockwise direction, the phase angle is

$$\theta = 180° - \sin^{-1}\frac{A}{B} \tag{7-16}$$

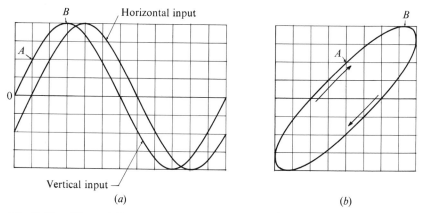

**Fig. 7-20.** *Phase-difference measurements with a cathode-ray oscilloscope*

and when the spot generating the figure is moving in a counterclockwise direction, the phase angle is

$$\theta = 180° + \sin^{-1}\frac{A}{B} \tag{7-17}$$

It is difficult to determine the direction of the spot generating the figure on the oscilloscope. Usually, there are some criteria in the circuit that will assist in determining the equation to be used.

**Comparison of Frequencies with a Cathode-Ray Oscilloscope[4]**

The figure formed by applying one frequency to the vertical input and another to the horizontal input of an oscilloscope is defined as a Lissajous figure. When the ratio of the two frequencies is an exact integer, the figures are stationary. The ratio of the frequency of the horizontal input to that of the vertical input is the ratio of the number of times the figure is tangent to the horizontal axis to the number of times the figure is tangent to the vertical axis. These are illustrated in Fig. 7-21. There are many other applications of a cathode-ray oscilloscope to electrical measurements. These can be found in the references at the end of this chapter.

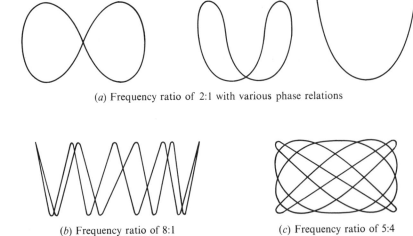

(a) Frequency ratio of 2:1 with various phase relations

(b) Frequency ratio of 8:1          (c) Frequency ratio of 5:4

**Fig. 7-21.**   *Comparing frequency ratios using Lissajous figures*

### PROBLEMS

**7-1.**   The relative damping $\gamma$ of a galvanometer is 0.6. (a) Plot a graph of the relative amplitude $\theta_m/\theta_{dc}$ and the angle of lag $\psi$ as a function of $f$ when the natural frequency of the galvanometer is 2,400 cycles per second. (b) What is the frequency range of this galvanometer that will have an amplitude distortion of less than $\pm 2$ percent?

**7-2.**   (a) Choose the values of $\gamma$ and $f_o$ of a galvanometer which must have a relative amplitude between 0.95 and 1.05 below 1,000 cycles per second. (b) What would the phase angle of this galvanometer be at 1,000 cycles per second?

**7-3.**   The gap of a tape reproducer is 0.00025 in. Determine the speed of the tape so as to have a satisfactory response at 50,000 cycles per second. Assume that $\lambda$ must be greater than 2.5 times the gap of the reproducer.

**7-4.**   A frequency-division multiplexer has a limit of $\pm 7.5$ percent modulation of each center frequency. The highest center frequency is 75,000 cycles per second. The spacing between the lowest frequency of one channel and the highest frequency of the next channel below it is 0.75 octave. The lowest frequency limit of the center frequencies is 400 cycles per second. Determine: (a) the number of channels possible; (b) the center frequency of each channel; (c) the upper frequency limit of each channel and the lower frequency limit of each channel (rounding off the frequencies to two significant figures and tabulating the answers); (d) the signal noise due to 0.1 percent variation in the speed of the tape.

**7-5.** List the advantages and disadvantages of a digital tape recorder.

**7-6.** A tape receives 12,000 numbers/sec, and the tape speed is 60 in./sec. Determine the number density of the tape.

**7-7.** Voltage $V_1$ is applied to the horizontal input and voltage $V_2$ is applied to the vertical input of a cathode-ray oscilloscope. $V_1$ and $V_2$ have the same frequency. The slope of the major axis of the figure on the oscilloscope is positive. The maximum vertical value is 2.5 divisions, and the point where the figure crosses the vertical axis is 1.2 divisions. The figure is symmetrical about the horizontal and vertical axes. Determine the possible phase angles of $V_2$ with respect to $V_1$.

**7-8.** A Lissajous figure on an oscilloscope is stationary and has six vertical maximum values and five horizontal maximum values. The frequency of the horizontal input is 1,500 cycles per second. Determine the frequency of the vertical input.

**7-9.** The frequency bandwidth of an AM signal is equal to the frequency of the carrier plus and minus the highest frequency of the AM signal. It is desired to record as many channels as possible of AM signals on a direct-recording magnetic tape. The frequency response of each AM signal is 5,000 cps, or a total bandwidth of the carrier frequency is 10,000 cps. Each bandwidth is separated from the next by one octave. Determine (*a*) the maximum number of AM signals that can be recorded on a direct-recording magnetic tape with a maximum frequency response of 200,000 cps and (*b*) the carrier frequency of each AM signal.

**7-10.** Improved methods of recording on magnetic tape have increased the frequency response of direct-recording magnetic tapes to 300 kc. How many more channels of information can be recorded on this tape than could be recorded on the tape in Prob. 7-9?

**7-11.** The Inter-Range Instrumentation Group (IRIG) of telemetry users has set a maximum center of 70 kc for FM frequency-division multiplex systems. The average ratio of center frequencies is 1.35:1. The nominal channel width is 15 percent. The lowest center frequency is 400 cps. Construct a table showing (*a*) the center frequencies, (*b*) the bandwidth of each channel, and (*c*) the bandwidth between each channel using these criteria.

**7-12.** Define (*a*) RZ, (*b*) NRZ, (*c*) parallel system, (*d*) redundancy, and (*e*) parity check.

**7-13.** What is the accuracy of an FM tape recorder?

**7-14.** What determines the accuracy of a digital tape?

## REFERENCES

1. F. K. Harris, *Electrical Measurements*, John Wiley & Sons, Inc., New York, 1952.

2. I. F. Kinnard, *Applied Electrical Measurements*, John Wiley & Sons, Inc., New York, 1956.

3. P. J. Weber, *The Tape Recorder as an Instrumentation Device*, 2nd ed., Ampex Corporation, Redwood City, Cal., 1958.

4. F. E. Terman and J. M. Pettit, *Measurements in Radio Engineering*, 2nd ed., McGraw-Hill Book Company, Inc., New York, 1952.

# Chapter 8

# DIRECT-CURRENT

The basic bridge circuit is shown in Fig. 8-1. When the bridge is balanced points $c$ and $d$ are at the same potential, and no current flows through the detector. The current through $R_1$ equals the current through $R_3$, and the current through $R_2$ equals the current through $R_4$. Then

$$I_1 = I_3 \tag{8-1}$$

and

$$I_2 = I_4 \tag{8-2}$$

Also, the voltage drop from $a$ to $c$ must equal the voltage drop from $a$ to $d$, and the voltage drop $c$ to $b$ equals the voltage drop from $d$ to $b$, as $c$ and $d$ are at the same potential. Then

$$R_1 I_1 = R_2 I_2 \tag{8-3}$$

and

$$R_3 I_3 = R_4 I_4 \tag{8-4}$$

Dividing Eq. (8-3) by Eq. (8-4) gives

$$\frac{R_1 I_1}{R_3 I_3} = \frac{R_2 I_2}{R_4 I_4}$$

# BRIDGES

From Eqs. (8-1) and (8-2),

$$\frac{R_1}{R_3} = \frac{R_2}{R_4}$$

or

$$R_1 R_4 = R_2 R_3 \tag{8-5}$$

Usually, $R_4$ is the unknown impedance. Then

$$R_4 = \frac{R_2}{R_1} R_3 \tag{8-6}$$

$R_2$ and $R_1$ are referred to as the ratio arms of the bridge, and $R_3$ is the standard arm. This basic circuit is used for both d-c and a-c bridges.

## 8-2. WHEATSTONE BRIDGE

A d-c bridge using resistances for $R_1$, $R_2$, $R_3$, and $R_4$, a current galvanometer for the detector, and a battery for the emf was developed by Sir Charles Wheatstone. This bridge still bears his name and is used extensively for measuring resistances from a fraction of an ohm to several thousand ohms.

The most important criterion in a bridge circuit is the accuracy of the bridge. This depends upon the accuracy of the components of the bridge. The limiting error of the measured impedance using a bridge circuit can be determined by the limiting errors of the components of the bridge circuit, as outlined in Chap. 2. Next in importance is the sensitivity of the bridge. The sensitivity of a bridge circuit is the ratio of the change in the detector indication to the change in the measured resistance. Thus, in the case of a Wheatstone bridge, the sensitivity is the ratio of the deflection of the galvanometer to the deviation of the measured resistance from the resistance required for balanced conditions.

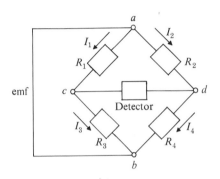

**Fig. 8-1.** *Basic bridge circuit*

### Calculation of the Sensitivity of a Bridge

The sensitivity of the bridge circuit shown in Fig. 8-1 is computed by converting the bridge circuit, looking into the circuit from the detector terminals $c$ and $d$, to a Thévenin generator. The impedance of the Thévenin generator is the impedance looking into the bridge circuit from terminals $c$ and $d$ with the source of emf replaced by its internal impedance. This circuit is shown in Fig. 8-2($a$), where $R_E$ is the impedance of the source of emf. For convenience, the delta-circuit $R_1$, $R_E$, and $R_3$ is converted to its equivalent wye-circuit $R_a$, $R_b$, and $R_c$, where

$$R_a = \frac{R_1 R_E}{R_1 + R_E + R_3}$$

$$R_b = \frac{R_E R_3}{R_1 + R_E + R_3} \tag{8-7}$$

$$R_c = \frac{R_1 R_3}{R_1 + R_E + R_3}$$

Then the impedance of the Thévenin generator is

$$R_o = R_c + \frac{(R_a + R_2)(R_b + R_4)}{R_a + R_b + R_2 + R_4} \tag{8-8}$$

The emf of the Thévenin generator is the emf across the terminals $c$ and

$d$ with the director removed from the circuit. The total current supplied to the bridge in Fig. 8-3($a$) is

$$I = \frac{E}{\dfrac{(R_1 + R_3)(R_2 + R_4)}{R_1 + R_2 + R_3 + R_4}} \qquad (8\text{-}9)$$

The voltage drop from $a$ to $c$ is

$$I_1 R_1 = I \frac{R_1(R_2 + R_4)}{R_1 + R_2 + R_3 + R_4} \qquad (8\text{-}10)$$

The voltage drop from $a$ to $d$ is

$$I_2 R_2 = I \frac{R_2(R_1 + R_3)}{R_1 + R_2 + R_3 + R_4} \qquad (8\text{-}11)$$

The voltage drop from $c$ to $d$ is

$$E_o = I_2 R_2 - I_1 R_1$$

$$= I \frac{R_2 R_3 - R_1 R_4}{R_1 + R_2 + R_3 + R_4}$$

Substituting Eq. (8-9) for $I$ gives

$$E_o = \frac{E(R_2 R_3 - R_1 R_4)}{(R_1 + R_3)(R_2 + R_4)} \qquad (8\text{-}12)$$

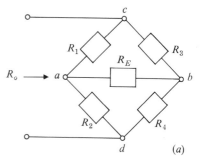

The equivalent Thévenin generator connected to the detector circuit will produce a current $I_g$ in the detector circuit equal to

$$I_g = \frac{E_o}{R_o + R_d}$$

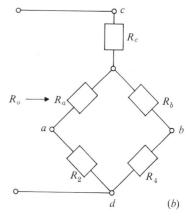

where $R_d$ is the impedance of the detector. Then, for a given deviation $\Delta R$ from the value of $R_4$ for a balanced condition, the sensitivity of the bridge is

$$S_B = \frac{d}{\Delta R} = \frac{S_i I_g}{\Delta R} \qquad (8\text{-}13)$$

where

$S_i$ = current sensitivity of the detector
$d$ = deflection

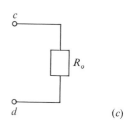

**Fig. 8-2.** *Thévenin equivalent impedance of a bridge circuit*

To illustrate, let $R_1 = 100$ ohms resistance, $R_2 = 1,000$ ohms resistance, $R_3 = 150$ ohms resistance, $R_4 = 1,505$ ohms resistance, $R_E = 1$ ohm resistance, $E = 3.00$ volts d-c, and the current sensitivity of the galvanometer be

0.5 mm/$\mu$a. The resistance of the detector $R_d$ is 150 ohms. Then, from Fig. 8-2($a$), the resistance of $R_a$ in Fig. 8-2($b$) is

$$R_a = \frac{R_1 R_E}{R_1 + R_E + R_3}$$

$$= \frac{(100)(1)}{100 + 1 + 150} = \frac{100}{251} = 0.398 \text{ ohms}$$

Similarly

$$R_b = \frac{R_E R_3}{R_1 + R_E + R_3}$$

$$= \frac{(1)(150)}{251} = 0.598 \text{ ohms}$$

$$R_c = \frac{R_1 R_3}{R_1 + R_E + R_3}$$

$$= \frac{(100)(150)}{251} = 59.8 \text{ ohms}$$

$$R_o = R_c + \frac{(R_a + R_2)(R_b + R_4)}{R_a + R_b + R_2 + R_4}$$

$$= 59.8 + \frac{(0.398 + 1,000)(0.598 + 1,505)}{0.398 + 0.598 + 1,000 + 1,505}$$

$$= 659.8 \text{ ohms}$$

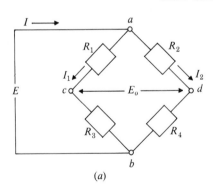

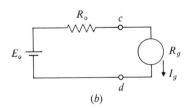

(a)

(b)

**Fig. 8-3.** *Thévenin equivalent circuit*

If the resistance of the battery $R_E$ were taken as zero, the resistance of the Thévenin generator would be

$$R_o = \frac{R_1 R_3}{R_1 + R_3} + \frac{R_2 R_4}{R_2 + R_4}$$

$$= \frac{(100)(150)}{100 + 150} + \frac{(1,000)(1,505)}{1,000 + 1,505}$$

$$= 660 \text{ ohms}$$

For slide rule accuracy, the resistance of the battery could be assumed to be zero in this problem.

The emf of the Thévenin generator is

$$E_o = \frac{E(R_2 R_3 - R_1 R_4)}{(R_1 + R_3)(R_2 + R_4)}$$

$$= \frac{(3)(1,000)(150) - (100)(1,505)}{(100 + 150)(1,000 + 1,505)}$$

$$= 0.546 \text{ volt}$$

The current through the galvanometer under this underbalanced condition is

$$I_d = \frac{E_o}{R_o + R_d} = \frac{0.546}{660 + 150}$$
$$= 0.000674 \text{ amp or } 674 \ \mu a$$

For the bridge to be balanced, the resistance $R_4$ should be

$$R_4 = \frac{R_2 R_3}{R_1} = \frac{(1,000)(150)}{100}$$
$$= 1,500$$

Then the deviation from the balanced value of $R_4$ is

$$\Delta R = 1,505 - 1,500$$
$$= 5 \text{ ohms}$$

and the bridge sensitivity is

$$S_B = \frac{S_i I_g}{\Delta R}$$
$$= \frac{(0.5)(674)}{5}$$
$$= 67.4 \text{ mm/ohm}$$

## 8-3. KELVIN BRIDGE

The Kelvin bridge is used for measuring resistances between one millionth of an ohm (or less) to 1 ohm. A Kelvin bridge circuit is given in Fig. 8-4. The resistance to be measured is $R_x$, the resistance between points 4 and 6. The standard resistance $R_s$ is the calibrated resistance between the adjustable contacts 3 and 5. There are two sets of ratio arms $R_A$ and $R_B$ forming one pair of ratio arms, and $R_a$ and $R_b$ forming the other pair of ratio arms. The settings of these ratios are the same. Then

$$\frac{R_A}{R_B} = \frac{R_a}{R_b} \tag{8-14}$$

At balance, $I_g = 0$, and the voltage drop from point 3 to point 1 is the same as from 3 through point 5 to point 2. Then

$$V_{3\text{-}1} = V_{3\text{-}5\text{-}2}$$

where the subscripts indicate the points in the part of the circuit included by the symbol.

Also

$$V_{3\text{-}1} = \frac{R_B}{R_A + R_B} V_{3\text{-}1\text{-}4}$$

$$= \frac{R_B}{R_A + R_B} I_s \left[ R_s + R_x + \frac{R_{5\text{-}7\text{-}6}(R_a + R_b)}{R_{5\text{-}7\text{-}6} + R_a + R_b} \right] \tag{8-15}$$

and

$$V_{3\text{-}5\text{-}2} = I_s R_s + I_s \left[ \frac{R_{5\text{-}7\text{-}6}(R_a + R_b)}{R_{5\text{-}7\text{-}6} + R_a + R_b} \right] \left[ \frac{R_b}{R_a + R_b} \right]$$

$$= I_s \left\{ R_s + \left[ \frac{R_{5\text{-}7\text{-}6}(R_a + R_b)}{R_{5\text{-}7\text{-}6} + R_a + R_b} \right] \left[ \frac{R_b}{R_a + R_b} \right] \right\} \tag{8-16}$$

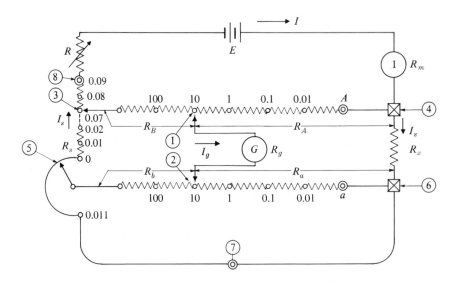

**Fig. 8-4.** *Kelvin bridge circuit*

Equating these expressions for $V_{3\text{-}1}$ and $V_{3\text{-}5\text{-}2}$ and solving for $R_x$ gives

$$R_x = \frac{R_A + R_B}{R_B} R_s - R_s + \frac{R_{5\ 7\text{-}6}(R_a + R_b)}{R_{5\text{-}7\text{-}6} + R_a + R_b} \left[ \left( \frac{R_A + R_B}{R_B} \right) \left( \frac{R_b}{R_a + R_b} \right) - 1 \right]$$

$$= R_s \frac{R_A}{R_B} + \frac{R_{5\text{-}7\text{-}6}}{R_{5\text{-}7\text{-}6} + R_a + R_b} \left[ \left( \frac{R_A}{R_B} + 1 \right) R_b - (R_a + R_b) \right]$$

$$= R_s \frac{R_A}{R_B} + \frac{R_{5\text{-}7\text{-}6} R_b}{R_{5\text{-}7\text{-}6} + R_a + R_b} \left[ \frac{R_A}{R_B} - \frac{R_a}{R_b} \right]$$

But, from Eq. (8-14), $R_A/R_B$ is equal to $R_a/R_b$ and

$$R_x = R_s \frac{R_A}{R_B} \qquad (8\text{-}17)$$

The total resistance of $R_A + R_B$ is equal to $R_a + R_b$, and each of these resistances is usually about 1,000 ohms. The numbers on the step terminals in these resistors give the ratio of $R_A/R_B$ or $R_a/R_b$ when these terminals are connected to the galvanometer. The resistance $R_s$ is the sum of the resistance of the fixed resistors and the resistance of the slide-wire between points 3 and 5. In most Kelvin bridges the maximum allowable current in $R_s$ is approximately 10 amp. The resistance in series with the emf source is to prevent the current from exceeding this value. With the values given in Fig. 8-4, this Kelvin bridge will measure resistance from 10 ohms to a fraction of 0.00001 ohm, depending on the resolution of the slide-wire calibration.

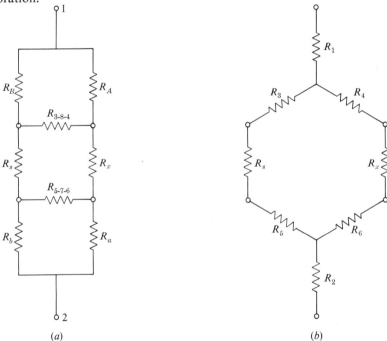

(a)  (b)

**Fig. 8-5.** *Thévenin equivalent generator resistance of a Kelvin bridge*

The current through the galvanometer in a Kelvin bridge circuit can be determined by converting the bridge circuit to the galvanometer terminals 1 and 2 to an equivalent Thévenin generator circuit. The circuit for determining the resistance $R$ of the Thévenin generator with the battery replaced by its internal resistance is shown in Fig. 8-5(a). The delta-circuit $R_A$,

$R_B$, $R_{3-8-4}$ is converted to the equivalent wye-circuit $R_1$, $R_3$, $R_4$, and the delta-circuit $R_a$, $R_b$, $R_{5-7-6}$ is converted to the equivalent wye-circuit $R_2$, $R_5$, $R_6$, as shown in Fig. 8-5(b). Solving for the total resistance gives

$$R_o = R_1 + R_2 + \frac{(R_3 + R_5 + R_s)(R_4 + R_6 + R_x)}{R_3 + R_4 + R_5 + R_6 + R_s + R_x} \qquad (8\text{-}18)$$

The emf of the Thévenin generator is the difference $V_{3-5-2}$ and $V_{3-1}$, as given by Eqs. (8-15) and (8-16) where the current $I_s$ is

$$I_s = I \frac{R_A + R_B}{R_s + R_x + \dfrac{R_{5-7-6}(R_a + R_b)}{R_{5-7-6} + R_a + R_b} + R_A + R_B} \qquad (8\text{-}19)$$

and

$$I = \frac{E}{R_{3-8} + R + R_m + \dfrac{(R_A + R_B)\left[R_s + R_x + \dfrac{R_{5-7-6}(R_a + R_b)}{R_{5-7-6} + R_a + R_b}\right]}{R_A + R_B + R_s + R_x + \dfrac{R_{5-7-6}(R_a + R_b)}{R_{5-7-6} + R_a + R_b}}} \qquad (8\text{-}20)$$

Then

$$E_o = V_{3-5-2} - V_{3-1} \qquad (8\text{-}21)$$

and the current through the galvanometer is

$$I_g = \frac{E_o}{R_o + R_g} \qquad (8\text{-}22)$$

The sensitivity of the bridge circuit can be determined by Eq. (8-13).

The advantage of this circuit is that the resistances $R_{3-8}$, $R_g$, $R_{5-7-6}$, and $R_m$ do not enter into the solution of $R_x$, and the leads from $a$ to 6, $A$ to 4, 3 to $R_B$, and 5 to $R_b$ are negligible compared with the resistance of the ratio arms.

#### 8-4. APPLICATION OF BRIDGE CIRCUITS

The bridge circuits are used in circuits to measure nonelectrical quantities such as strain or temperature. The resistance strain gage and the resistance thermometer are transducers in which the quantity being measured produces a change in the resistance of the sensing element. In some circuits a servo-motor is used to balance the bridge circuit, as shown in Fig. 8-6. Fixed resistors are used for the ratio arms, and the standard resistance includes a fixed resistance $R_s$ and a multiturn slide-wire resistance which has a magnitude corresponding to the change in the resistance of the sensing element. The position of the shaft of the potentiometer to obtain a balance of the bridge is calibrated to read the magnitude of the quantity being measured.

The sensing elements are sometimes affected by unwanted temperature change. It is possible to insert a small resistance in series with the sensing element which has a temperature coefficient equal to the negative of the temperature coefficient of the sensing element. This will balance the unwanted temperature change in the circuit. Usually, this compensation is

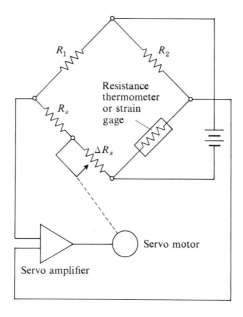

**Fig. 8-6.** *Self-balancing bridge*

made by trial-and-error methods using a controlled oven temperature for testing the circuit. Electrothermal effects are also troublesome when the sensing element is at one temperature and the bridge is at another. Instrumentation systems using strain gages should be calibrated frequently to be sure that there is no drift and that the calibration is correct. These sensing units will be discussed further in Chap. 11.

Other d-c bridges are used in measuring resistances. These bridges and their applications are discussed in the references at the end of this chapter.

## PROBLEMS

**8-1.** The ratio arms of a Wheatstone bridge are $R_1 = 1,000$ ohms and $R_2 = 100$ ohms. The standard-resistance branch $R_3$ is 500 ohms, and the unknown resistance $R_4$ is 50.3 ohms. A 3-volt battery with negligible reactance is connected to the bridge. The galvanometer has a current sensitivity of 0.5 mm/$\mu$a and a resistance of 75 ohms. Determine: (*a*) the deflection of the galvanometer under the unbalanced condition; (b) the sensitivity of the bridge.

**8-2.** The components of a Wheatstone bridge have a limiting error of $\pm 0.1$ percent. Determine the limiting error of the resistance measured with this bridge.

**8-3.** The bridge in Prob. 8-1 has steps of 0.1 ohm in its standard-resistance branch. Determine the resolution in ohms and in percent of the resistance being measured when the unknown resistance is 50 ohms. Assume that the galvanometer can be read to 0.1 mm and $S_i$ is 1.5 mm/$\mu$a.

**8-4.** (a) Determine the effect of changing the resistance arms $R_1$ and $R_2$ in Prob. 8-1 to 100 and 10 ohms respectively, upon the sensitivity of the bridge. (b) If the maximum allowable current in the bridge resistance is 25 ma, is it safe to make this change?

**8-5.** In the Kelvin bridge shown in Fig. 8-4, points 1 and 2 are set at the ratio of 10, point 3 is set at the terminal marked 0.07 ohm, and point 5 is set at 0.0063 ohm. The resistance of the galvanometer is 100 ohms, and its sensitivity is 0.05 mm/$\mu$a. The resistances $R_A + R_B = R_a + R_b = 1,100$ ohms. The resistance from point 6 to point 7 is negligible, and the resistance of the battery circuit from point 8 to point 4 is 4.4 ohms. The current $I$ is 10 amp. Determine: (a) the unknown resistance; (b) the current in the galvanometer if the bridge setting remained the same and the unknown resistances were increased by 0.005 ohm (the resistance from point 6 through 7 to the slide-wire being negligible); (c) the sensitivity of the Kelvin bridge; (d) the resolution of the Kelvin bridge when one division of the slide-wire resistor is 0.0001 ohm and it is assumed that the scale on the slide-wire resistor and the galvanometer can be read to 0.2 of a division.

**8-6.** In Fig. 8-1 $R_1 = 250$ ohms, $R_2 = 750$ ohms, $R_3$ is a decade resistance box with the steps of the largest decade 100 ohms and the steps of the smallest decade 0.1 ohm. Assume the galvanometer will detect any change in $R_3$. Determine the resolution of the Wheatstone bridge.

**8-7.** In Prob. 8-6 the unknown resistance is $R_4$. The resistance $R_3$ is a decade box, and each resistor of the box has an accuracy of $\pm 0.05$ percent. $R_1$ and $R_2$ are accurate to 0.02 percent. $R_3$ is 153.7 ohms when a balance is obtained. Determine (a) the resistance of the unknown and (b) the percent limiting error.

**8-8.** In Fig. 8-1 $R_1 = 500$ ohms, $R_2 = 1,000$ ohms, and $R_3 = 415.7$ ohms. The battery emf is 1.53, and the battery resistance is 0.1 ohm. The unknown resistance $R_4$ is 831.5 ohms. The resistance of the galvanometer is 123 ohms. (a) Determine the current in the galvanometer. (b) The galvanometer reads 4.2 mm. Determine the sensitivity of the galvanometer. (c) Determine the sensitivity of the bridge.

**8-9.** In Prob. 8-8 $R_3$ is switched to 15.7 ohms. The current rating of $R_1$ and $R_2$ is 5 ma each, and of $R_3$ is 50 ma. The galvanometer will be damaged if the current exceeds six times its full-scale (50-$\mu$m) current. Determine whether any of the components will be damaged.

**8-10.** In Fig. 8-4 $R_B = R_b = 500$ ohms, $R_A = R_a = 5,000$ ohms, $R_s = 0.0571$ ohm under balanced conditions. Determine the resistance of $R_x$.

**8-11.** In Prob. 8-10 $R_m = 0.12$ ohm, $R_{67} = 0.0065$ ohm, $R_{57} = 0.0088$ ohm, $R_{38} = 0.040$ ohm, the current in the ammeter is 10.1 amp, and the battery voltage is 6.31 v. Determine (*a*) the resistance of $R_x$; (*b*) the current in the galvanometer when $R_s = 0.056$ ohm, the resistance of the galvanometer is 87 ohms, and the resistance of the battery is negligible; (*c*) the sensitivity of the Kelvin bridge.

## REFERENCES

1. M. B. Stout, *Basic Electrical Measurements*, 2nd ed., Prentice-Hall, Inc., Englewood Cliffs, N.J., 1960.

2. F. K. Harris, *Electrical Measurements*, John Wiley & Sons, Inc., New York, 1952.

3. I. F. Kinnard, *Applied Electrical Measurements*, John Wiley & Sons, Inc., New York, 1956.

4. W. C. Michels, *Electrical Measurements and Their Applications*, D. Van Nostrand Company, Inc., Princeton, N.J., 1957.

5. Ernest Frank, *Electrical Measurement Analysis*, McGraw-Hill Book Company, Inc., New York, 1959.

# Chapter 9

# ALTERNATING-CURRENT

## 9-1. INTRODUCTION

The discussion of basic circuits in Chap. 8, applies equally as well to a-c bridges as it does to d-c bridges. The only difference is that the voltage, the current, and the impedance are expressed in the conventional phasor form. Then Eq. (8-6) becomes

$$r_4 + jx_4 = \frac{r_2 + jx_2}{r_1 + jx_1}(r_3 + jx_3)$$

$$= \frac{r_1 r_2 r_3 + x_1 x_2 r_3 - r_1 x_2 x_3 + r_2 x_1 x_3}{r_1{}^2 + x_1{}^2}$$

$$+ j\frac{r_1 r_2 x_3 + x_1 x_2 x_3 + r_1 r_3 x_2 - r_2 r_3 x_1}{r_1{}^2 + x_1{}^2}$$

or

$$r_4 = \frac{r_1 r_2 r_3 + x_1 x_2 r_3 - r_1 x_2 x_3 + r_2 x_1 x_3}{r_1{}^2 + x_1{}^2} \tag{9-1}$$

and

$$x_4 = \frac{r_1 r_2 x_3 + x_1 x_2 x_3 + r_1 r_3 x_2 - r_2 r_3 x_1}{r_1{}^2 + x_1{}^2} \tag{9-2}$$

184

Then, if $x_4$ is inductive,

$$L_4 = \frac{x_4}{2\pi f} \qquad (9\text{-}3)$$

or, if $x_4$ is capacitive,

$$C_4 = \frac{1}{2\pi f x_4} \qquad (9\text{-}4)$$

The bridge equations can be expressed using admittance instead of impedance, or a combination of impedances and admittances. Thus

$$Z_4 = Z_2 Z_3 Y_1 \qquad (9\text{-}5)$$

or

$$Y_4 = \frac{Y_2 Y_3}{Y_1} = Y_2 Y_3 Z_4 \qquad (9\text{-}6)$$

These forms may be more convenient for the solution of some bridge circuits. The solution of a few typical bridge circuits will be discussed here; broader and more complete discussions of a-c bridge circuits are given in the references listed at the end of this chapter.

It will be noted that Eqs. (9-1) and (9-2) must both be satisfied before balanced conditions can be obtained. It will also be observed that the solutions for $r_4$ and for $x_4$ include the components of the other three impedance

185

branches. Therefore, to balance an a-c bridge, it is necessary to adjust alternatively at least two components of the bridge until both Eqs. (9-1) and (9-2) are satisfied.

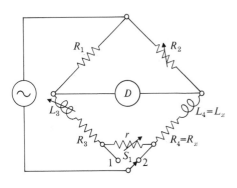

**Fig. 9-1.** *Inductance-comparison bridge*

The a-c bridge cannot use the sensitive d'Arsonval measurement or the suspended-type galvanometer with a permanent magnet for a field as a null detector, as these instruments respond only to direct current. An earphone has been used effectively as a null detector. A cathode-ray oscilloscope is a very effective null-indicating device. There are several models of null detectors which have high-gain amplifiers with a flat frequency response from 50 cycles per second to a megacycle and a d-c output which is measured with a d'Arsonval movement.

Other factors that affect a-c bridges are stray capacitances and unwanted residual quantities in the components. Shielding and residuals will be discussed briefly later in this chapter.

## 9-2. THE INDUCTANCE-COMPARISON BRIDGE[1,2]

The circuit of an inductance-comparison bridge is shown in Fig. 9-1 where $Z_1$ is the resistance $R_1$, $Z_2$ is the resistance $R_2$, $Z_3$ is a standard Brooks inductometer having a variable inductance $L_3$ and a fixed resistance $R_3$ similar to the inductometer in Fig. 9-2, and $Z_4$ is the unknown impedance having a resistance $R_x$ and an inductance $L_x$. The variable resistance $r$ is in series with $R_3$ when switch $S_1$ is in position 2, and it is in series with $R_x$ when switch $S_1$ is in position 1. The resistances $R_3$ and $R_x$ are fixed, and, by trial and error $r$ and $C_3$ are adjusted until a balance is obtained. When switch $S_1$ is in position 1, the solutions for $R_x$ and $L_x$ by Eqs. (9-1) and (9-2) are

$$R_x + r = \frac{R_1 R_2 R_3}{R_1{}^2} = \frac{R_2}{R_1} R_3 \qquad [9\text{-}7(a)]$$

and

$$\omega L_x = \frac{R_1 R_2 \omega L_3}{R_1{}^2} = \frac{R_2}{R_1} \omega L_3 \qquad [9\text{-}7(b)]$$

or

$$L_x = \frac{R_2}{R_1} L_3 \qquad (9\text{-}8)$$

When switch $S_1$ is in position 2

$$R_x = \frac{R_2}{R_1}(R_3 + r)$$

This is a very simple bridge and is unusually easy to balance, as $L_x$ is the product of $L_3$ and the constant $R_2/R_1$. Equation (9-6) can be satisfied by adjusting $L_3$. Similarly, Eqs. (9-5) and (9-7) can be satisfied by adjusting $r$.

**Fig. 9-2.** *A Brooks inductometer (courtesy of Leeds and Northrup Co.)*

The Brooks inductometer used in this bridge is shown in Fig. 9-2. It consists of one set of coils arranged in a fixed pattern on the stator and another set of coils on the rotating center portion of the inductometer. The coils are connected in series, and the inductance is varied by rotating the rotor which varies the mutual impedance of the coils. The instrument is calibrated to read directly in millihenries.

## 9-3. THE CAPACITANCE BRIDGE WITH A WAGNER GROUND[1]

A capacitance bridge is shown in Fig. 9-3. $R_1$ and $R_3$ are adjusted until the detector indicates that the bridge is balanced with the switch in the 2 position. Then the switch is moved to the 1 position, and $R_G$ is adjusted until a balance is obtained. The switch is then returned to the 2 position, and $R_1$ and $R_3$ are again adjusted until balance is obtained. This process is repeated until the bridge is balanced when the switch is in either the 1 or the 2 position.

Then points $a$ and $b$ are at ground potential, and the bridge is balanced. This eliminates the effect of stray capacitance from points $a$ and $b$ to ground, which would produce an error in the bridge circuit. This system of obtaining ground potential at points $a$ and $b$ is called the *Wagner ground connection*.

The values of the unknown $R_x$ and $C_x$ are obtained by substituting the values of the bridge components into Eq. (9-5), giving

$$R_x + \frac{1}{j\omega C_x} = \frac{R_2}{R_1}\left(R_3 + \frac{1}{j\omega C_3}\right)$$

Then

$$R_x = \frac{R_2}{R_1} R_3 \qquad (9\text{-}9)$$

and

$$C_x = \frac{R_1}{R_2} C_3 \qquad (9\text{-}10)$$

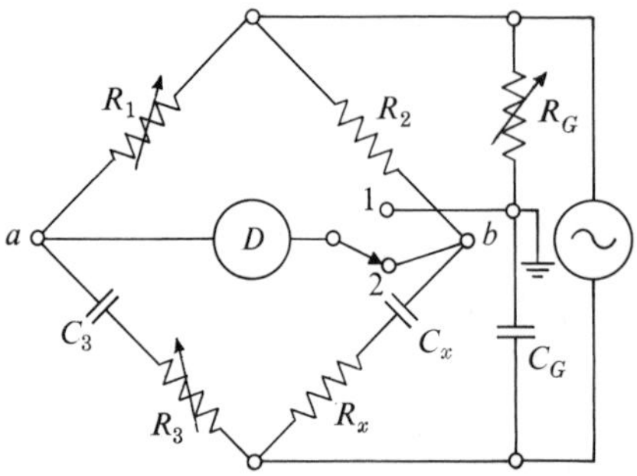

**Fig. 9-3.** *Capacitance bridge with a Wagner ground connection*

## 9-4. THE BRIDGE-T NETWORK[1,3]

There are other networks that are effective for impedance measurements. One of these circuits is the bridge-T network shown in Fig. 9-4($a$). A null reading of the detector is obtained when the admittance from point 1 to point 3 is zero. Using a wye-delta transformation on the circuit in Fig. 9-4($a$) gives the circuit shown in Fig. 9-4($b$) where

$$Y_{1\text{-}3} = \frac{Y_{1\text{-}2} Y_{3\text{-}2}}{Y_{1\text{-}2} + Y_{3\text{-}2} + Y_{4\text{-}2}} = \frac{-\omega^2 R_x C^2}{1 + j\omega R_x\left(2C - \dfrac{1}{\omega^2 L_x}\right)} \qquad (9\text{-}11)$$

Then the total admittance from point 1 to point 3 is

$$Y = \frac{1}{R} + Y_{1\text{-}3}$$

$$= \frac{1}{R} - \frac{\omega^2 R_x C^2}{1 + j\omega R_x\left(2C - \dfrac{1}{\omega^2 L_x}\right)}$$

$$= \frac{1 + j\omega R_x\left(2C - \dfrac{1}{\omega^2 L_x}\right) - \omega^2 R R_x C^2}{R + j\omega R R_x\left(2C - \dfrac{1}{\omega^2 L_x}\right)} = 0$$

Then

$$\omega^2 R R_x C^2 = 1$$

or

$$R_x = \frac{1}{\omega^2 R C^2} \qquad (9\text{-}12)$$

and

$$2C = \frac{1}{\omega^2 L_x}$$

or

$$L_x = \frac{1}{2\omega^2 C} \qquad (9\text{-}13)$$

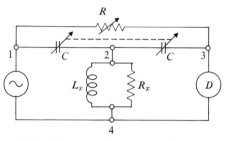

(*a*) Bridge-T network for measuring inductance

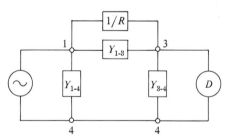

(*b*) The circuit obtained from a wye-delta transformation of a bridge-T network

**Fig. 9-4.** *The bridge-T network*

Thus, when $R$ and $C$ are adjusted until a null is obtained, the values of $R_x$ and $X_x$ are determined, using the values of $R$, $C$, and $\omega$ in Eqs. (9-12) and (9-13).

## 9-5.  THE PARALLEL-T CIRCUIT [1]

A parallel-T circuit is another network that is effectively used as a null-type measuring circuit. Its basic circuit is shown in Fig. 9-5(*a*). A null in

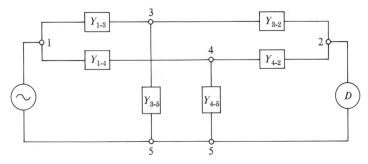

(a) A parallel-T circuit

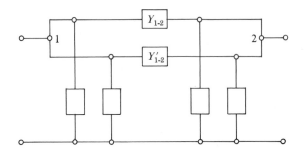

(b) The circuit obtained from a wye delta transformation of a parallel-T circuit

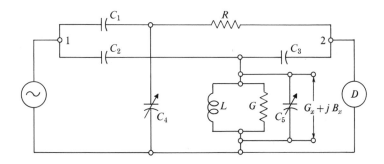

(c) A parallel-T measuring circuit

**Fig. 9-5.** *The parallel-T circuit*

the detector is obtained when the admittance between point 1 and point 2 is zero. This admittance is determined by converting the two wye circuits in Fig. 9-5(a) to the two delta circuits shown in Fig. 9-5(b). Then the total conductance between point 1 and point 2 is

$$Y = Y_{1\text{-}2} + Y'_{1\text{-}2}$$

Applying this analysis to the measuring circuit in Fig. 9-5(c) gives

$$G_x = \frac{\omega^2 C_1 C_3 R}{C_2} \Delta C_4 \qquad (9\text{-}14)$$

and

$$B_x = \omega \Delta C_5 \qquad (9\text{-}15)$$

where $\Delta C_4$ is the difference between $C_4$ when a null is obtained without the unknown admittance in the circuit and $C_4$ when a null is obtained with the unknown admittance in the circuit. Similarly, $\Delta C_5$ is the difference between $C_5$ when a null is obtained without the unknown admittance in the circuit and $C_5$ when a null is obtained with the unknown admittance in the circuit. When the unknown admittance is a capacitance $C_x$, it is read directly as

$$C_x = \Delta C_5 \qquad (9\text{-}16)$$

## 9-6. THE STORAGE-FACTOR AND THE DISSIPATION-FACTOR MEASUREMENTS [1,3,4]

It is sometimes more convenient to know the inductance and the storage factor $Q$ of a coil than to know the resistance. The storage factor is defined by the equation

$$Q = \tan \theta = \frac{X}{R} = \frac{B}{G} \qquad (9\text{-}17)$$

The $Q_x$ of an unknown impedance can be measured using a comparison impedance bridge. From Eqs. (9-7) and (9-8),

$$Q_x = \frac{\dfrac{R_2}{R_1} \omega L_3}{\dfrac{R_2}{R_1} \cdot R_3 - r}$$

$$= \frac{\omega L_3}{R_3 - \dfrac{R_1}{R_2} r} \qquad (9\text{-}18)$$

Similarly, the $Q_x$ of an impedance using a bridge-T network, from Eqs. (9-12) and (9-13), is

$$Q_x = \frac{\dfrac{1}{2\omega C}}{\dfrac{1}{\omega^2 R C^2}} = (1/2)\omega R C \qquad (9\text{-}19)$$

A resonant circuit, supplied by a constant-voltage source, is shown in Fig. 9-6. This is an effective circuit for measuring the $Q_x$ of a coil. The capacitor is adjusted until the voltage across the capacitor $V_c$ is at maximum. The constant voltage of the generator is $V_g$. Then

$$Q_x = \frac{X_L}{R_x} = \frac{IX_L}{IR_x} = \frac{V_C}{V_g} \tag{9-20}$$

and the voltage $V_C$ can be calibrated in $Q_x$.

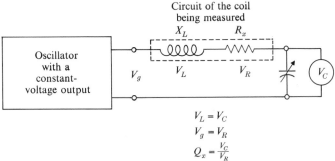

$V_L = V_C$

$V_g = V_R$

$Q_x = \dfrac{V_C}{V_R}$

**Fig. 9-6.** *A Q-meter circuit*

The impedance of a capacitance is frequently given in capacitance and the *dissipation factor D* of the capacitance. The dissipation factor is defined by the equation

$$D = \cot \theta = \frac{R}{X} = \frac{G}{B} \tag{9-21}$$

The dissipation factor of the unknown capacitor circuit in Fig. 9-3 is

$$D_x = \omega R_x C_x$$

Then, from Eqs. (9-9) and (9-10),

$$D_x = \omega R_3 C_3 \tag{9-22}$$

Thus the dissipation factor is determined from the known components of the balanced a-c bridge.

### 9-7. RESIDUALS OF A-C BRIDGE COMPONENTS[1,5]

The unwanted quantities unavoidably present in an impedance are called the residuals. The presence of resistance in an inductance has been recognized, but it is not always evident that an inductance also includes a complicated network of capacitances that are usually lumped into either an equivalent series or a shunt capacitance. Thus the equivalent circuit of an inductance may be constructed as the parallel circuit in Fig. 9-7(*a*) or the series circuit in Fig. 9-7(*b*). Therefore, an inductor becomes a resonant circuit at a given frequency. The equivalent series impedance of the parallel circuit in Fig. 9-7(*a*) is

$$Z_s = \frac{(R + j\omega L)\left(\dfrac{1}{j\omega C}\right)}{R + j\left(\omega L - \dfrac{1}{\omega C}\right)}$$

$$= \frac{\omega L - jR}{\omega CR - j(1 - \omega^2 LC)}$$

$$= \frac{R + j\omega[L(1 - \omega^2 LC) - CR^2]}{(\omega CR)^2 + (\omega^2 LC)^2 - 2\omega^2 LC + 1}$$

Then

$$R_s = \frac{R}{(\omega CR)^2 + (\omega^2 LC)^2 - 2\omega^2 LC + 1} \qquad (9\text{-}23)$$

and

$$X_s = \frac{\omega[L(1 - \omega^2 LC) - CR^2]}{(\omega CR)^2 + (\omega^2 LC)^2 - 2\omega^2 LC + 1} \qquad (9\text{-}24)$$

(*a*) Equivalent circuit of an inductor or resistor

(*b*) Series equivalent circuit of an inductor or resistor circuit

**Fig. 9-7.** *The equivalent circuit of an inductor or a resistor*

In the inductance, $R$ and $C$ are small compared with $L$. Even $\omega^2 LC$ is small compared with $L$. Then $(\omega^2 LC)^2$ and $CR^2$ terms can be neglected. This gives

$$R_s = \frac{R}{1 - 2\omega^2 LC} \qquad (9\text{-}25)$$

and

$$X_s = \frac{\omega L(1 - \omega^2 LC)}{1 - 2\omega^2 LC} \qquad (9\text{-}26)$$

where $R_s$ and $X_s$ are the equivalent series resistance and series reactance of the circuit, respectively, and the equivalent series inductance is

$$L_s = \frac{L(1 - \omega^2 LC)}{1 - 2\omega^2 LC} \qquad (9\text{-}27)$$

As $\omega$ increases, the approximations in Eqs. (9-25), (9-26), and (9-27) are not valid. At $\omega^2 LC = 1$, the equivalent series resistance of the inductance becomes

$$R_s = \frac{1}{\omega^2 C^2 R} \qquad (9\text{-}28)$$

and the equivalent series reactance becomes

$$X_s = -\frac{\omega C R^2}{(\omega C R)^2}$$

$$= -\frac{1}{\omega C} \text{ (capacitive)} \tag{9-29}$$

Slightly below this value of $\omega$, the circuit will be in series resonance, and the impedance of the coil will be pure resistance. Above this frequency the coil will have capacitive reactance.

The storage factor $Q$ of a coil is

$$Q = \frac{\omega L_s}{R_s} = \frac{\omega[L(1 - \omega^2 LC) - CR^2]}{R} \approx \frac{\omega L(1 - \omega^2 LC)}{R} \tag{9-30}$$

The equivalent circuit for a resistor is the same as for a coil. The difference between the resistor and the coil consists of the relative values of the components in the circuit. In the resistor, $R$ is large and $L$ and $C$ are small. When $\omega^2 LC$ in Eqs. (9-23) and (9-24) is very much less than 1, the equivalent series resistance of the resistor is

$$R_s = \frac{R}{1 + \omega^2 C(CR^2 - 2L)} \tag{9-31}$$

and the equivalent series reactance of the resistor is

$$X_s = \frac{\omega(L - CR^2)}{1 + \omega^2 C(CR^2 - 2L)} \tag{9-32}$$

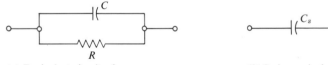

(a) Equivalent circuit of a capacitor

(b) Series equivalent circuit of a capacitor

**Fig. 9-8.** *The equivalent circuit of a capacitor*

The equivalent circuit of a capacitor is given in Fig. 9-8. It is the capacitance $C$ shunted with a high resistance $R$ such that the conductance $G = 1/R$ is very small. Then the equivalent series impedance is

$$Z_s = R_s + jX_s = \frac{\dfrac{R}{j\omega C}}{R + \dfrac{1}{j\omega C}}$$

$$= \frac{R}{\omega^2 R^2 C^2 + 1} - j\frac{\omega R^2 C}{\omega^2 R^2 C^2 + 1}$$

Then

$$R_s = \frac{R}{\omega^2 R^2 C^2 + 1} \qquad (9\text{-}33)$$

and

$$X_s = \frac{\omega R^2 C}{\omega^2 R^2 C^2 + 1} \qquad (9\text{-}34)$$

The equivalent series capacitance of the circuit is

$$C_s = \frac{\omega^2 R^2 C^2 + 1}{\omega^2 R^2 C} \qquad (9\text{-}35)$$

It will be observed that

$$X_s = \frac{1}{\omega C}$$

and

$$R_s = \frac{1}{\omega^2 R C^2}$$

when $\omega^2 R^2 C^2 \gg 1$. Then $C_s = C$, and $R_s$ approaches zero.

The dissipation factor $D$ of the equivalent circuit of a capacitance is

$$D = \frac{R_s}{X_s} = \frac{1}{\omega R C} = \frac{1/R}{\omega C} \qquad (9\text{-}36)$$

## 9-8. SHIELDING [1,5]

The effect of shielding two resistors in series is shown in Fig. 9-9. Figure 9-9(a) shows the two resistors with their stray capacitance to ground and between the two resistors. Figure 9-9(b) shows the shields around the two resistors with the shields and the common terminal connected to ground. Figure 9-9(c) shows the equivalent circuit of the shielded resistors. The stray capacitances shown in Fig. 9-9(a) will vary with the configuration of the surrounding objects, while the capacitors in Fig. 9-9(c) are fixed and are unaffected by the capacitance between the shield and the surrounding objects. The circuit in Fig. 9-9(c) would remain the same if the resistors were replaced by inductances or capacitors. Figure 9-9(d) shows a capacitor with its stray capacitance to ground. Figure 9-9(e) shows a grounded shield around the capacitor, and Fig. 9-9(f) is the equivalent circuit of this shielded capacitor. Note that the capacitances from point $A$ to ground and from point $B$ to ground are fixed in Fig. 9-9(f), while the stray capacitances in Fig. 9-9(d) depend on the configuration of the surrounding objects. Similarly, Fig. 9-9(g) shows a shielded capacitor with the shield connected to terminal $B$, and Fig. 9-9(h) is the equivalent circuit of this shielded capacitor. The circuit in Fig. 9-9(h) may still have stray capacitance from the shield and terminal $B$ to ground, but the capacitance between terminals $A$ and $B$ is fixed and free from external effects.

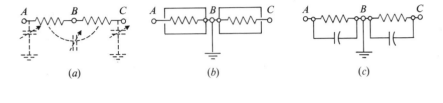

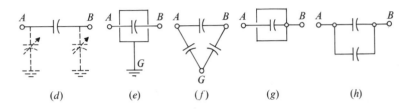

**Fig. 9-9.** *Equivalent circuits of shielded and unshielded components of an a-c circuit*

Figure 9-10 shows the stray capacitance of a bridge circuit. The capacitance $C_1$ is connected from point 2 to ground through the primary winding of the output transformer of the oscillator, and capacitor $C_2$ is also connected from point 2 to ground. These two capacitors shunt the bridge input but have no effect on the balance of the bridge. The stray capacitance $C_4$ shunts the

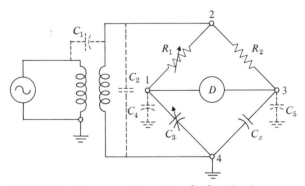

**Fig. 9-10.** *Stray capacitance in a bridge circuit*

bridge capacitance $C_3$, and the stray capacitance $C_5$ shunts the capacitance $C_x$. These capacitances affect the balance of the bridge. Figure 9-11($a$) shows capacitor $C_3$ shielded and connected to terminal 4 and ground. This fixes the total capacitance between points 1 and 4. If the capacitor $C_3$ is calibrated with this shield, the calibration will give the total capacitance between points

1 and 4. The unknown capacitance $C_x$ is enclosed in a shield which is connected to point 0 of a shunting circuit $R_s$ and $C_s$. This circuit is the same as the shunting circuit of the Wagner ground in Fig. 9-3, except that point 0 is not connected to ground. The bridge is balanced by trial and error until there

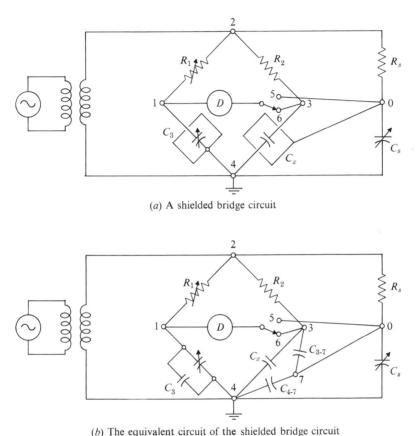

(*a*) A shielded bridge circuit

(*b*) The equivalent circuit of the shielded bridge circuit

**Fig. 9-11.** *Shielding in a bridge circuit*

is no deflection of the detector when the switch is in either position 5 or position 6. Then point 3 and point 0 are at the same potential. Then points 3 and 7 are at the same potential, and capacitor $C_{3-7}$ has no effect on the circuit. Capacitor $C_{4-7}$ shunts capacitor $C_s$ and has no effect on the bridge balance. The capacitance $C_x$ is the only component between points 3 and 4 that has any effect on the bridge balance. Therefore, the capacitance $C_x$ can be measured without the effects of stray capacitance.

Very extensive shielding is used in radio-frequency bridges. These methods are described in the references listed at the end of this chapter. Often, these bridges are balanced without the unknown impedance in the circuit. Then the unknown is connected to the bridge, and the bridge is again balanced. The unknown impedance is computed from the changes in the components of the bridge.

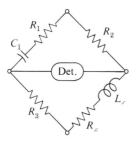

(*a*) Hay inductance bridge

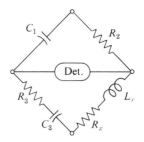

(*b*) Owen inductance bridge

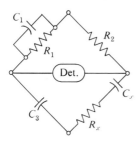

(*c*) Schering capacitance bridge

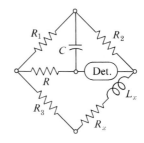

(*d*) Anderson inductance bridge

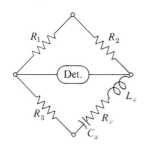

(*e*) Resonance bridge

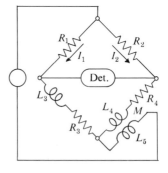

(*f*) Heaviside mutual inductance bridge

**Fig. 9-12.** *Alternating-current bridge circuits*

Not only is shielding effective in preserving the magnitude of the components of a bridge; it is even more important in keeping noise out of measuring systems. Both magnetic and electrostatic shielding are necessary to keep stray electromagnetic and electrostatic fields from generating unwanted emf's in the measuring circuits. Care should be taken to shield the leads from an oscillator to a bridge and from the bridge to the detector. There should be only one ground in a measuring system; otherwise ground-loop currents may produce serious noise in the system.

## PROBLEMS

**9-1.** A Maxwell bridge has the following impedances:

$$Z_1 = \frac{1}{\dfrac{1}{R_1} + j\omega C_1}$$

$$Z_2 = R_2$$
$$Z_3 = R_3$$
$$Z_4 = R_x + j\omega L_x \text{ (unknown)}$$

$R_1$ and $R_2$ are variable. (*a*) Determine the values of $R_x$ and $X_x$ in terms of $R_1$, $R_2$, $R_3$, and $C_1$. (*b*) What is the main advantage of this circuit? (*c*) What is its disadvantage?

**9-2.** An Owen bridge has the following impedances:

$$Z_1 = \frac{1}{j\omega C_1}$$

$$Z_2 = R_2$$

$$Z_3 = R_3 + \frac{1}{j\omega C_3}$$

$$Z_4 = R_x + j\omega L_x \text{ (unknown)}$$

$R_3$ and $C_3$ are variable. Determine the values of $R_x$, $X_x$, and the $Q$ of the unknown in terms of $C_1$, $R_2$, $R_3$, $C_3$, and $\omega$.

**9-3.** A Schering bridge has the following impedances:

$$Z_1 = \frac{1}{\dfrac{1}{R_1} + j\omega C_1}$$

$$Z_2 = R_2$$

$$Z_3 = \frac{1}{j\omega C_3}$$

$$Z_4 = R_x + \frac{1}{j\omega C_x}$$

$C_1$ and $R_2$ are variable.
Determine the values of $R_x$, $C_x$, and the dissipation factor $D$ of the unknown in terms of $R_1$, $C_1$, $R_2$, $C_3$, and $\omega$.

**9-4.** In Fig. 9-4(a) $R$ is 1 megohm, $C$ is 1 $\mu$f, and $L_x$ is 0.01 henry. (a) Find the frequency at which the bridge-T network will indicate balance. (b) Find the required resistance of $R_x$.

**9-5.** The parallel-T circuit in Fig. 9-5(a) has the following components: $Y_{1-3}$ = $Y_{3-2}$ = $\omega C$, $Y_{1-4}$ = $Y_{4\,2}$ = $1/R$, $Y_{4-5}$ = $2\omega C$, and $Y_{3-5}$ = $2/R$. Determine the value of $\omega$ to obtain a null detection.

**9-6.** In Fig. 9-3, $R_1$ is 521 ohms, $R_2$ is 1,200 ohms, $C_3$ is 0.045 $\mu$f, and $R_3$ is 12.1 ohms. The frequency is 10,000 cycles per second. (a) Determine the values of $R_x$ and $C_x$. (b) It is found that $R_1$ has 2 $\mu$h series inductance and 550 $\mu\mu$f shunt capacitance, $R_2$ has 5 $\mu$h series inductance and 1,050 $\mu\mu$f shunt capacitance, $C_3$ has 1.5 meghoms shunt resistance, and $R_3$ is unchanged. Determine the error in measuring $R_x$ and $C_x$ in part (a).

**9-7.** In Fig. 9-10, $R_1$ = 728 ohms, $R_2$ = 120 ohms, and $C_3$ = 0.093 $\mu$f. (a) Neglecting the shunting capacitances, determine the value of $C_x$. (b) Now let the shunt capacitances have the values $C_1$ = 227 $\mu\mu$f, $C_2$ = 434 $\mu\mu$f, $C_4$ = 293 $\mu\mu$f, and $C_5$ = 172 $\mu\mu$f. Determine the error in solving for $C_x$ in part (a).

**9-8.** An Anderson inductance-bridge circuit is shown in Fig. 9-12(d). Prove that

$$L_x = CR_2 \left( R_3R_5 \frac{R_3R_5}{R_1} \right)$$

and

$$R_x = \frac{R_2R_3}{R_1}$$

in this circuit. Which components would you choose as the variables? Why?

**9-9.** A resonance-bridge circuit is shown in Fig. 9-12(e). Prove that

$$C = \frac{1}{\omega^2 L}$$

$$L = \frac{1}{\omega^2 C}$$

and

$$f = \frac{1}{2\pi \sqrt{LC}}$$

when the bridge is balanced.

**9-10.** A Heaviside mutual-inductance-bridge circuit is shown in Fig. 9-12(f). The emf in $L_4$ due to the current in $L_5$ is

$$E_M = (I_1 + I_2)M$$

Prove that

$$M = \frac{R_2L_3 - R_1L_4}{R_1 + R_2}$$

and

$$R_1R_4 = R_2R_3$$

when the bridge is balanced.

## REFERENCES

1. M. B. Stout, *Basic Electrical Measurements*, 2nd ed., Prentice-Hall, Inc., Englewood Cliffs, N.J., 1960.

2. F. K. Harris, *Electrical Measurements*, John Wiley & Sons, Inc., New York, 1952.

3. F. Kinnard, *Applied Electrical Measurements*, John Wiley & Sons, Inc., New York, 1956.

4. W. C. Michels, *Electrical Measurements and Their Applications*, D. Van Nostrand Company, Inc., Princeton, N.J., 1957.

5. Ernest Frank, *Electrical Measurement Analysis*, McGraw-Hill Book Company, Inc., New York, 1959.

# Chapter 10

**10-1. THE POTENTIOMETER AND ITS OPERATION** [1]

The potentiometer is a network designed to measure an unknown emf by balancing it against a known voltage drop. It is very accurate and consumes no power from the circuit containing the unknown emf when the circuit is balanced.

A simple potentiometer circuit is shown in Fig. 10-1. It contains three loops. The loop defined as the *working circuit* includes the working battery, the working resistance, the calibrating resistance, and the measuring resistance. The calibrating resistance includes the calibration slide-wire and the fixed resistance $R_s$. The measuring resistance includes the measuring slide-wire and 16 equal fixed resistances. When switch $S_1$ is closed to the right, a loop is formed containing the emf to be measured, the galvanometer with its protective resistance, and the portion of the measuring resistance which lies between the contact $E$ and the slide-wire contact $G$. When switch $S_1$ is closed to the left, a loop is formed containing the galvanometer with its protective resistance, the standard cell, and the position of the calibrating resistance between the junction $D$ and the sliding contact $B$. The total resistance of the measuring slide-wire is the same as the resistance of each of the 16 fixed resistances in the measuring resistance. When the correct current flows

202

# POTENTIOMETERS

through these resistances, all the fixed resistances and the measuring slide-wire have a voltage drop of 0.1000 volt each. The measuring slide-wire is divided into a scale with 200 equal divisions. Then each division of the slide-wire has a 0.0005 volt drop. This scale will be zero at junction $F$ and 0.1000 volt at junction $H$, and the voltage drop from junction $F$ to the sliding contact $G$ is read to 0.0005 volt and estimated to 0.0001 volt. Similarly, with the correct current flowing through the working circuit, the voltage drop across the resistance $R_s$ is 1.0160 volt, and the voltage drop across the calibrating slide-wire is 0.0400 volt. The calibrating slide-wire has 80 scale divisions with 0.00005 volt drop between each division. The scale is 1.01600 at junction $C$ and 1.02000 at $A$ junction. Then the scale on the calibrating slide-wire reads the voltage drop from junction $D$ to the sliding contact $B$.

To obtain the correct current in the working circuit, the sliding contact $B$ is set at a voltage drop equal to the emf of the standard cell. Switch $S_1$ is closed to the left, and switch $S_2$ is left open. Then the working resistance is adjusted until the galvanometer indicates zero current. Next, switch $S_2$ is closed, increasing the sensitivity of the circuit, and a finer adjustment of the working resistance is made. Under these conditions the correct current will flow through the working circuit. This adjustment must be made often, as the emf of the working battery drifts slightly.

To determine the magnitude of the emf to be measured, switch $S_1$ is closed to the right, and switch $S_2$ is opened. Then contacts $E$ and $G$ are adjusted until the galvanometer indicates zero current. Switch $S_2$ is then closed, and contact $G$ is again adjusted to obtain a finer adjustment of the voltage balance. The emf to be measured is the sum of the voltage drop from junction $F$ to contact $E$ and the voltage drop from junction $F$ to the sliding

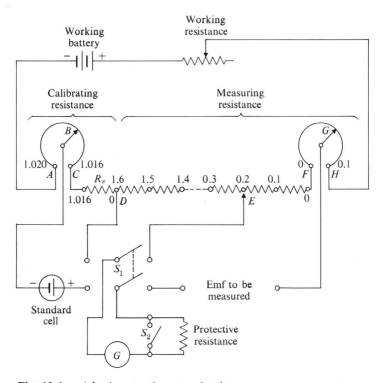

**Fig. 10-1.** *A basic potentiometer circuit*

contact $G$, which is the sum of the number at $E$ and the number read on the slide-wire scale at $G$. The range of this potentiometer is zero to 1.7000 volts, and the resolution is 0.0001 volt.

If the current in the working circuit were 0.05 amp, the resistance of each of the fixed resistors in the measuring circuit would be 2 ohms. The resistance of the slide-wire in the measuring circuit would be 2 ohms, the resistance of $R_s$ would be 20.32 ohms, and the resistance of the calibrating slide-wire would be 0.8 ohm.

## 10-2. DUO-RANGE POTENTIOMETER[1,2]

A modified circuit of a student potentiometer is given in Fig. 10-2. To calibrate this circuit the double-pole switch is closed to calibration position, and the potentiometer is set to the emf of the standard cell. The working resistance is then varied until the balance is obtained. In order to protect this circuit during the preliminary adjustment, a two-position key is placed in

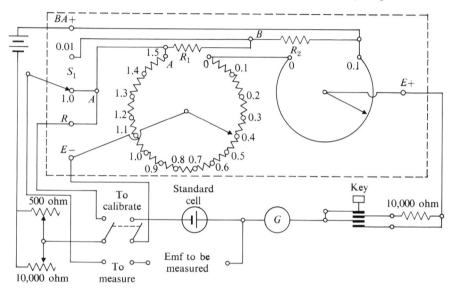

**Fig. 10-2.** *A duo-range potentiometer*

series with the galvanometer. In the first position of the key, a 10,000-ohm resistance is inserted in series with the galvanometer. After the preliminary adjustment is made, the key is pushed to the second position which shorts out the 10,000-ohm resistance, giving the galvanometer greater sensitivity for final adjustments.

The unknown emf is measured by closing the double-pole switch to the TO MEASURE position. In this position the battery circuit to the potentiometer may be connected through switch $S_1$ to the 0.01 position, or the 1.0 position. In the 1.0 position the potentiometer reads the voltage marked on its resistance adjustments. In the 0.01 position it reads the voltage marked on the potentiometer multiplied by 0.01.

The operation of this duo-range circuit can be better studied using the simplified circuit in Fig. 10-3. Figure 10-3(a) shows a simplified circuit of this potentiometer with the calibrating circuit omitted. When the switch is closed to the 1.0 position and the circuit is balanced so that no power is received from the unknown emf, the working circuit is essentially that shown in Fig. 10-3($b$). The total resistance of the measuring resistance $R_M$ is 160 ohms. The current $I_M$ flowing through $R_M$ is 10 ma, giving a total voltage drop across $R_M$ of 1.6 volts. When the battery circuit is connected to $C$ instead of $B$, the

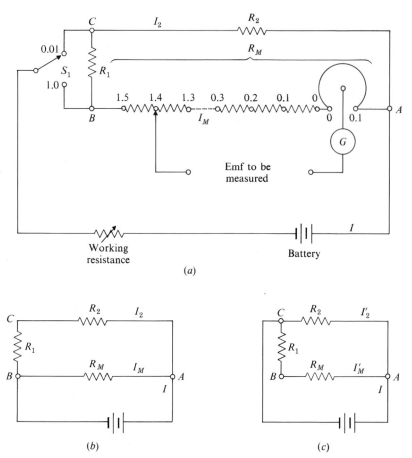

Fig. 10-3. *Elementary circuits of a duo-range potentiometer*

working circuit is essentially that shown in Fig. 10-3($c$), and the current $I'_M$ through $R_M$ is reduced to one hundredth of its former value $I_M$, in Fig. 10-3($b$) or 0.1 ma. This gives a voltage drop across $R_M$ of 0.016 volt. Referring to Fig. 10-3($a$), it will be observed that the potentiometer circuit is calibrated with the battery connected to the 1.0 position. When the switch is closed to the 0.01 position, the current in the working circuit $I$ must remain constant. This requires that the resistance from $A$ to $B$ in the circuit of Fig.

10-3(b) must equal the resistance from A to C in the circuit of Fig. 10-3(c). Equating the resistance from A to B in Fig. 10-3(b) in terms of $R_1$ and $R_2$, and $R_M$ to the resistance between A and C in Fig. 10-3(c), also expressed in terms of $R_1$, $R_2$, and $R_M$, gives

$$\frac{R_2(R_1 + R_M)}{R_1 + R_2 + R_M} = \frac{R_M(R_1 + R_2)}{R_1 + R_2 + R_M}$$

or

$$R_1R_2 + R_2R_M = R_1R_M + R_2R_M$$

Solving for $R_2$ gives

$$R_2 = R_M \qquad (10\text{-}1)$$

For the working current to remain the same when switch $S_1$, Fig. 10-3(a), is changed from position 1.0 to 0.01, the voltage drop from A to B in Fig. 10-3(b) must equal the voltage drop from A to C in Fig. 10-3(c). Then

$$I_M R_M = I_2' R_2 = I_2' R_M$$

or

$$I_M = I_2' \qquad (10\text{-}2)$$

To make the solution for $R_1$ in this circuit general, let M be the factor by which the voltage drop in $R_M$ is multiplied when switch $S_1$ is connected to B to obtain the voltage drops in $R_M$ when $S_1$ is connected to C. Then

$$MI_M R_M = I_M' R_M$$

or

$$I_M' = MI_M \qquad (10\text{-}3)$$

Then, in Fig. 10-3(c),

$$I_M'(R_1 + R_M) = I_2' R_2$$

Substituting the values of $I_M'$, $I_2'$, and $R_2$ in Eqs. (10-3), (10-2), and (10-1) in this equation gives

$$MI_M(R_1 + R_M) = I_M R_M$$

or

$$R_1 = \frac{R_M}{M} - R_M = R_M\left(\frac{1}{M} - 1\right) = R_M\left(\frac{1 - M}{M}\right) \qquad (10\text{-}4)$$

In the circuit in Fig. 10-3, M is 0.01 and $R_M$ is 160 ohms. Then

$$R_1 = 160\,\frac{1 - 0.01}{0.01} = (99)(160) = 15{,}840 \text{ ohms}$$

and, using Eq. (10-1),

$$R_2 = R_M = 160 \text{ ohms}$$

## 10-3.  MULTIPLE-RANGE POTENTIOMETERS

A multiple-range potentiometer consists of a basic measuring resistor $R_M$ and an associated circuit which will multiply the values read on the basic scale of the potentiometer by fixed multiplying factors. It is also desirable to have a circuit in which the components of the circuit can be determined in terms of the measuring resistance $R_M$ and the multiplying factors.

A circuit meeting these requirements is shown in Fig. 10-4. The multiplying factors $M1$, $M2$, etc., to a total of $MN$ ranges are the factors by which

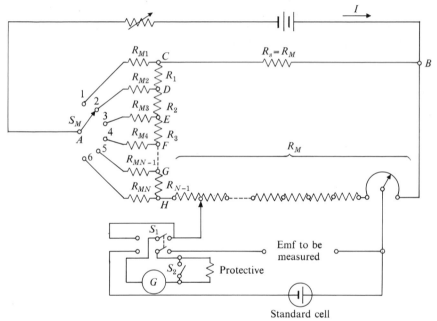

**Fig. 10-4.** *Multiple-range potentiometer*

the voltage-drop scale on resistance $R_M$ is multiplied to obtain the voltage drops in $R_M$ when switch $S_M$ is connected to 1, 2, 3, etc. The relation of these multiplying factors is as follows:

$$M1 < M2 < M3 < \ldots < M(N-1) < MN$$

The ratios of the multiplying factors are proportional to the current flowing through $R_M$ when these multiplying factors are used. Then

$$\frac{M1}{M2} = \frac{I \dfrac{R_M}{R_1 + R_2 + R_3 + \ldots + R_{N-1} + R_M}}{I \dfrac{R_1 + R_M}{R_1 + R_2 + R_3 + \ldots + R_{N-1} + R_M}}$$

or

$$M1\,(R_1 + R_M) = M2\,R_M \qquad (10\text{-}5)$$

where $I$ is the current in the battery circuit. Similarly,

$$M2\,(R_1 + R_2 + R_M) = M3\,(R_1 + R_M) \qquad (10\text{-}6)$$

$$M3\,(R_1 + R_2 + R_3 + R_M) = M4\,(R_1 + R_2 + R_M) \qquad (10\text{-}7)$$

and

$$M(N-1)(R_1 + R_2 + R_3 + \ldots + R_{N-1} + R_M)$$
$$= MN\,(R_1 + R_2 + R_3 + \ldots + R_{N-2} + R_M) \qquad (10\text{-}8)$$

Solving for $R_1$ in Eq. (10-5)

$$R_1 = \frac{M2\,R_M - M1\,R_M}{M1}$$
$$= R_M\left(\frac{M2}{M1} - 1\right) = R_M\frac{M1}{M1}\left(\frac{M2}{M1} - 1\right) \qquad (10\text{-}9)$$

From Eq. (10-5),

$$R_1 + R_M = \left(\frac{M2}{M1}\,R_M\right) \qquad (10\text{-}10)$$

Substituting Eq. (10-10) in Eq. (10-6) and solving for $R_2$,

$$R_2 = R_M\left(\frac{M3}{M1} - \frac{M2}{M1}\right)$$
$$= R_M\frac{M2}{M1}\left(\frac{M3}{M2} - 1\right) \qquad (10\text{-}11)$$

Similarly, the resistance $R_i$, where $i$ may be any integer from $I$ to $N - 1$, is

$$R_i = R_M\frac{M_i}{M_1}\left(\frac{M_{i+1}}{M_i} - 1\right) \qquad (10\text{-}12)$$

In this analysis the current supplied by the battery is assumed to be constant. To satisfy this condition, the resistance from $A$ to $B$ must remain constant, regardless of the position of switch $S_M$. With the value of $R_M$, which is determined by the base range of the voltage to be measured, that is, for the multiplier $M1$, and the current to be used in the measuring resistance, the resistance $R_{BC}$ from $B$ to $C$, $R_{BD}$ from $B$ to $D$, $R_{BE}$ from $B$ to $E$, etc., can be obtained. A resistance $R$ greater than $R_{BC}$, $R_{BD}$, or $R_{BE}$, etc., is chosen as the resistance from $A$ to $B$.

Then

$$R_{M1} = R - R_{BC}$$
$$R_{M2} = R - R_{BD}$$
$$R_{M3} = R - R_{BE} \qquad (10\text{-}13)$$

etc.

Thus the components of the range-changing circuit can be determined by Eqs. (10-12) and (10-13).

There are many types of circuits used for this purpose, but this circuit gives the general idea of the problems involved and the criterion that must be met in designing a good multirange potentiometer circuit. Circuits of this type are used in standard potentiometers and in self-balancing potentiometers where a wide range of emfs is to be measured.

### 10-4. ZERO-SUPPRESSION POTENTIOMETERS

Many potentiometers, especially self-balancing potentiometers, use a single slide-wire as their measuring circuit. The accuracy obtainable with such a potentiometer depends on the percent linearity of the slide-wire. If a slide-wire potentiometer measured a total voltage of 1 mv and the linearity was $\pm 0.1$ percent, the error would be $\pm 0.1$ percent of 1 mv or $\pm 0.001$ mv. If this same circuit were used in a multirange potentiometer to measure 1 mv, 10 mv, and 100 mv, the error of the 1 mv scale would be $\pm 0.001$ mv; on the

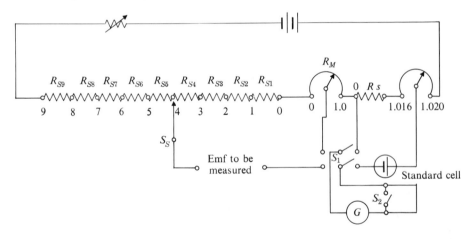

**Fig. 10-5.** *Zero-suppression potentiometer*

10-mv scale, the error would be $\pm 0.01$ mv; on the 100-mv scale, the error would be $\pm 0.1$ mv. It is possible to arrange this 1-mv potentiometer in a manner that would limit the error to $\pm 0.001$ mv and yet extend the range of the potentiometer. This could be done by suppression of the zero voltage point, as shown in Fig. 10-5. Note that this circuit is essentially the same as Fig. 10-1. The slide-wire would still have a measuring range of 1 mv. If the voltage to be measured were in excess of 1 mv but less than 2 mv, the switch $S_S$ would be shifted from zero position to position 1. This would add the voltage drop across $R_{S1}$, or 1 mv, to the measuring circuit. $R_{S1}$ would have the same value of resistance as $R_M$. In other words, the total voltage drop across $R_{S1}$ and $R_M$ would now be 2 mv, and the slide-wire would measure from 1 mv to 2 mv. If this potentiometer were to be used to measure the voltage between 2 and 3 mv, the switch $S_S$ would be shifted to position 2, and the slide-wire would read from 2 mv to 3 mv. In this manner $R_M$ reads the fractional part of a millivolt while the position of $S_S$ indicates the number of millivolts to which the fraction is to be added.

Some self-balancing potentiometers using this circuit have an automatic switching arrangement for $S_S$. Thus, when the sliding contact on $R_M$ reaches the zero position, it automatically shifts $S_S$ one step to the right. When it reaches the 1.0 position of $R_M$, it automatically shifts $S_S$ one step to the left. Thus the potentiometer ultimately reaches a balanced position. As $S_S$ is shifted, an indicator shows the amount of zero suppression. When this instrument is used with the digital readout system, the position of $S_S$ will determine the digits to the left of the decimal point, while the position of the sliding contact on $R_M$ will determine the digits to the right of the decimal point. Potentiometers of this type have been used with 50 steps or more of zero suppression. The accuracy of these instruments is greater than that of multi-range instruments.

## 10-5. LEEDS AND NORTHRUP TYPE K-2 POTENTIOMETER[4]

The Leeds and Northrup Type K-2 potentiometer is a precision instrument found in many laboratories. It has a triple range and is used for standardizing and calibrating voltmeters and ammeters. It is also used in physical and chemical laboratories for the measurement of $p$H, oxidation, reduction, polarization, and contact potential. This potentiometer is shown in Fig. 10-6. Its three ranges are 0–1.61 volts, 0–0.161 volt, and 0–0.0161 volt. The measuring circuit consists of 15 resistors of about 5 ohms each with a dial switch having brushes and studs, and a continuously adjusted slide-wire of about 5.5 ohms. The slide-wire consists of 11 turns. This slide-wire is enclosed in the cylindrical portion of the potentiometer, with a knob and a handle on the top. One scale division on the slide-wire is equal to 50 $\mu$v on the high range, 5 $\mu$v per division on the medium range, and 0.5 $\mu$v per division on the low range. The standard-cell dial is graduated from 1.0176 to 1.0204 volts. The circuit diagram of this potentiometer is shown in Fig. 10-7. It has three galvanometer sensitivity pushbuttons—high, medium, and low—and fine, medium, and coarse adjustments of the working-circuit current. It is a high-precision instrument and is ample for most laboratory work.

Fig. 10-6. Leeds and Northrup Type K-2 potentiometer (courtesy Leeds and Northrup Co.)

## 10-6. LEEDS AND NORTHRUP TYPE K-3 UNIVERSAL POTENTIOMETER[4]

The Leeds and Northrup Type K-3 universal potentiometer is specifically designed to meet the needs of precision laboratory work. It includes rapid reading with minimum interpolation error. Measurements are unaffected by thermals, and it operates under difficult ambient conditions without static or leakage disturbance. Its function is similar to the K-2 potentiometer, but

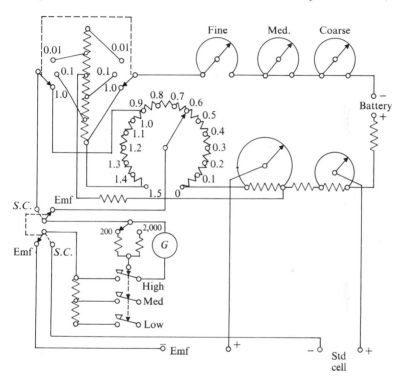

**Fig. 10-7.** *The circuit of a Leeds and Northrup Type K-2 potentiometer*

it has a distinct advantage in the ease of reading the measured emf. Its streamlined effect is shown in Fig. 10-8. The balance between the potentiometer voltage and the unknown voltage is obtained by operating a 15-step switch in 0.1-volt steps, a 10-step switch in 0.01-volt steps, and a one-turn slide-wire continuously adjusted from −0.001 to +0.010 volt. The 1.611, 0.1611, and 0.01611-volt ranges are provided by means of a range-selector switch. The range of the standard-cell dial is from 1.0174 to 1.0205 volts.

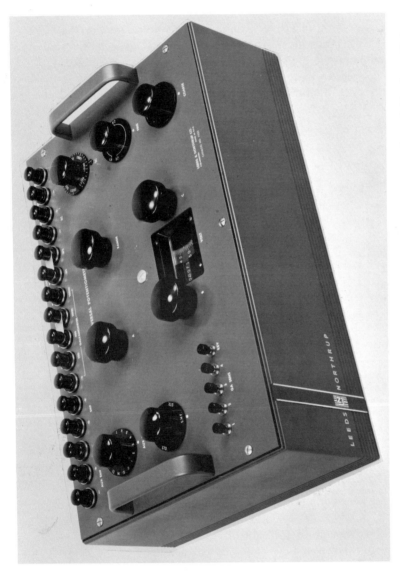

**Fig. 10-8.** Leeds and Northrup Type K-3 potentiometer (courtesy Leeds and Northrup Co.)

It has a built-in galvanometer damping resistance circuit with binding-post connections for a CDRX of 100, 400, 2,000, or 10,000 ohms. The four galvanometer sensitivity keys provide sensitivities of approximately 1, 1/20, 1/400, and 1/10,000. An additional key is provided to reverse the connections to the emf being measured.

The ranges of the Type K-3 universal potentiometer are provided by a conventional potentiometer decade arrangement plus two Wenner elements. The operation of the Wenner element is shown in Fig. 10-9. The resistors $A$ and $B$ are equal and linear. Thus currents $I$, $I_1$, and $I_2$ remain constant when

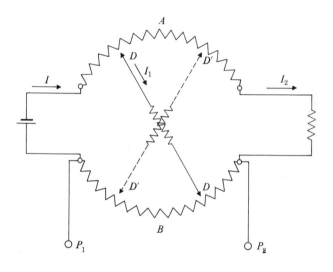

**Fig. 10-9.** *The circuit of a Wenner element*

the sliding contact $D$ is moved from $D$ to $D'$. As the pointer is moved from $D$ to $D'$, the voltage across $P_1$–$P_2$ will vary owing to the change in a portion of the resistance $P_1$–$P_2$ in which the current $I_1$ and $I_2$ flows. Thus an even change in potential can be obtained between $P_1$ and $P_2$ without varying the load on the battery. In the K-3 potentiometer, one Wenner element is made up of a 10-step resistance on each side of the element. Therefore, a 10-step voltage change between $P_1$ and $P_2$ is obtained. This is employed in the 10-step control unit. The range switch, the balance stepping switches, and the slide-wire control knobs are all connected to a direct-reading dial so that the output voltage of this instrument can be read directly from the numbers on the dial. This increases the speed of operation and the accuracy of reading the measured emf.

## 10-7.  MULTIRANGE PORTABLE POTENTIOMETERS

The student potentiometer and the Leeds and Northrup K-2 and K-3 potentiometers all require auxiliary equipment, including a battery, standard cell, and galvanometer, together with switches and a key. It is often desirable to have a portable self-contained instrument. The Leeds and Northrup 7655 portable potentiometer has the standard cell and battery included within the case of the instrument. This is a single-range unit. Leeds and Northrup also make double- and triple-range portable potentiometers and a portable model of the K-3 potentiometer. The ranges and accuracy of some of the portable potentiometers are as follows: Range 0 to 1.110 volts, $\pm 0.001$ volt; 0 to 0.111

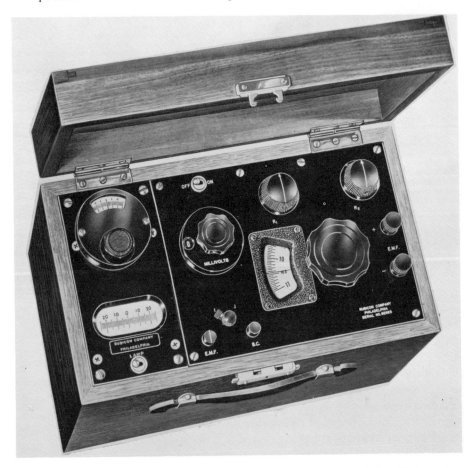

**Fig. 10-10.** *A portable precision potentiometer (courtesy of the Minneapolis-Honeywell Regulator Company)*

volt, $\pm 0.0001$ volt; 0 to 0.011 volt, $\pm 0.00003$ volt. The Rubicon Company also makes a duo-range portable potentiometer. It is shown in Fig. 10-10, and the circuit of this potentiometer is given in Fig. 10-11. A No. 6 dry cell is used to supply the current for the working circuit. The range of the stepping

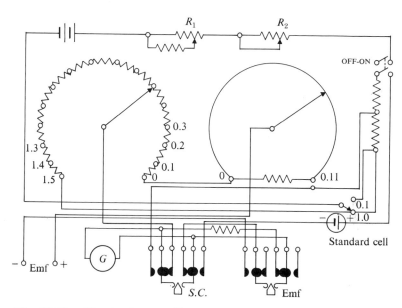

**Fig. 10-11.** *Circuit of a portable precision potentiometer*

switch is from 0 to 15 mv. The range switch can be shifted from a multiplying factor of 1 to a multiplying factor of 0.1. The galvanometer in this potentiometer is of a suspension-mirror type. It has a light source utilizing a 1.5-volt lamp with mirrors and a frosted, etched-glass screen. This potentiometer is very sensitive, easy to operate, and has high precision. It is very convenient for high-precision work where a portable instrument is desired.

**10-8. VOLT BOX**

Most general-purpose potentiometers have a maximum range in the neighborhood of 1.6 volts. A voltage-dividing resistance, called a volt box, is often used to measure higher voltages. The circuit of the Leeds and Northrup volt box is shown in Fig. 10-12. It is a multirange unit with taps for 3, 7.5, 15, 30, 75, 150, and 300 volts maximum, with 200 ohms per volt and a limiting error of $\pm 0.04$ percent. When the potentiometer is properly adjusted, no current is drawn from the voltage-dividing resistance; therefore, the voltage supplied to the potentiometer is the exact ratio of the tapped resistance to the total resistance across the emf source. It is no longer true that there is no current drawn from source of emf. In this particular case the current drawn from the voltage source is a maximum of 5 ma. Less current would be drawn if the unit were a higher ohms-per-volt instrument.

### 10-9.  CURRENT MEASUREMENT WITH A POTENTIOMETER

The current in a circuit can be measured accurately with a potentiometer if a standard shunt of specified resistance is used. For example, if the resistance of a shunt were 0.01 ohm, a current of 100 amp would produce a

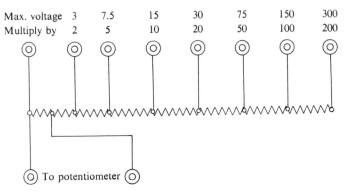

| Max. voltage | 3 | 7.5 | 15 | 30 | 75 | 150 | 300 |
|---|---|---|---|---|---|---|---|
| Multiply by | 2 | 5 | 10 | 20 | 50 | 100 | 200 |

To potentiometer

**Fig. 10-12.** *Circuit of a volt box*

voltage drop across the shunt of 1 volt, which could easily be measured on a standard potentiometer. Likewise, the shunt having a resistance of 0.1 ohm would have a 1-volt drop across the shunt if a current of 10 amp were flowing through the circuit. Standard shunts are designed for use in calibrating ammeter circuits. Multiple shunts can be obtained; for example, the Leeds and Northrup multiple-range shunt has ranges of 0.075, 0.15, 0.3, 0.75, 1.5, 3, and 7.5 amp. Thus shunt is used to calibrate low-range ammeters using a potentiometer. The shunt is calibrated to produce a voltage drop of 1.5 volts at the value of current specified.

### 10-10.  AMMETER AND VOLTMETER CALIBRATION

The circuit shown in Fig. 10-13 is used to calibrate d-c ammeters and voltmeters. When the voltmeter is to be calibrated, the power to the voltmeter circuit is supplied through a variable voltage-dividing resistance. This enables the voltmeter to be set at the desired value. This voltage-dividing resistance should have sufficient resistance to limit the current flowing through it to a safe value, yet have sufficient capacity to supply the necessary current to the voltage box. The voltage is adjusted until the voltmeter reads the desired value, and the potentiometer is used to determine the true value of this voltage. Similarly, when an ammeter is to be calibrated, the circuit should

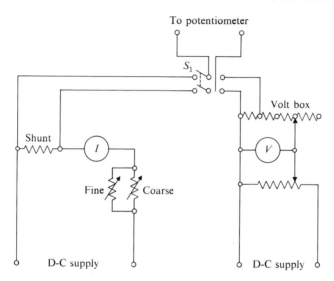

**Fig. 10-13.** *Circuit for calibrating ammeters and voltmeters*

have sufficient current-carrying capacity to supply the required current to the ammeter circuit and an adjustable load resistance to give the desired ammeter reading. Then the true current is measured with the potentiometer. Either an error curve or a calibration curve can be obtained for the instruments being calibrated.

## 10-11. POTENTIOMETER SENSITIVITY [2]

The sensitivity of a potentiometer circuit is defined as the ratio of the deflection of the galvanometer to the unbalanced emf in the loop containing the emf to be measured. To analyze the unbalanced conditions in a potentiometer circuit, refer to the circuit given in Fig. 10-1. Let the sum of the internal resistance of the battery and the working resistance be $R_W$, the resistance of the calibrating circuit from $A$ to $D$ be $R_C$, the resistance from $B$ to $D$ be $R_2$, the resistance of the measuring circuit from $D$ to $H$ be $R_M$, the resistance from $E$ to $G$ be $R_1$, the internal resistance of the standard cell be $R_{sc}$, the resistance of the galvanometer and its protective resistance be $R_G$, and the internal resistance of the emf to be measured be $R_x$. A simplified circuit showing these resistances is given in Fig. 10-14(a). In this circuit the voltage drop across $R_1$ is $E_1$ when the measuring circuit is balanced, the voltage drop across $R_2$ is $E_2$ when the circuit calibrating is balanced, the emf to be measured is $E_x$,

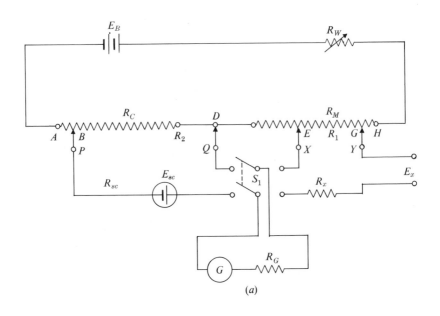

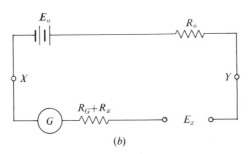

**Fig. 10-14.** *The equivalent circuit of a potentiometer*

and the emf of the standard cell is $E_{sc}$. When the switch $S_1$ is closed to the right, the circuit above the points $X$-$Y$ can be reduced to a Thévenin generator having a generated emf of $E_O$ and an internal resistance of $R_O$, where $E_O$ is the voltage from $E$ to $G$, with the circuit open at $X$; $R_O$ is the resistance between $E$ and $G$, with the circuit open at $X$ and $Y$; and $E_B$ is replaced by the internal resistance of the battery. Then

$$R_O = \frac{R_1(R_W + R_C + R_M - R_1)}{R_W + R_C + R_M} \qquad (10\text{-}14)$$

It is sometimes more convenient to express $R_1$ in terms of $E_1$. This is done by replacing $R_1$ by its equivalent.

$$R_1 = \frac{R_M}{E_M} E_1$$

Then

$$R_O = \frac{\dfrac{R_M}{E_M} E_1 \left[ R_W + R_C + R_M \left( 1 - \dfrac{E_1}{E_M} \right) \right]}{R_W + R_C + R_M} \qquad (10\text{-}15)$$

The generated emf of the Thévenin generator $E_O$ is equal to the emf under balanced conditions when no current is flowing in the galvanometer circuit. The current flowing through the galvanometer is

$$I_G = \frac{E_O - E_x}{R_O + R_G + R_x} = \frac{E_1 - E_x}{R_O + R_G + R_x} \qquad (10\text{-}16)$$

When $E_x$ is equal to $E_1$ the circuit is balanced, and the galvanometer current is zero.

The potentiometer sensitivity, as defined above, is

$$S_p = \frac{d}{E_1 - E_x}$$

But

$$d = S_i I_g = S_i \frac{E_1 - E_x}{R_O + R_G + R_x}$$

where $S_i$ is the current sensitivity of the galvanometer. Then

$$S_p = \frac{S_i}{R_O + R_G + R_x} \qquad (10\text{-}17)$$

As an example, let

$$
\begin{array}{ll}
R_M = 170 \text{ ohms} & E_M = 1.70 \text{ volts} \\
R_C = 102 \text{ ohms} & E_C = 1.020 \text{ volts} \\
R_W = \phantom{0}29 \text{ ohms} & E_B = 3.00 \text{ volts} \\
R_G = 150 \text{ ohms} & E_1 = E_O = 1.0831 \text{ volts} \\
R_x = 0.25 \text{ ohm} & E_x = 1.0834 \text{ volts} \\
S_i = 200 \text{ mm}/\mu a &
\end{array}
$$

Then substituting Eq. (10-15) gives

$$R_O = 69.206 \text{ ohms}$$

and the sensitivity of the potentiometer is

$$S_p = \frac{200}{69.2 + 150 + 0.25}$$

$$= 0.911 \ \text{mm}/\mu\text{v}$$

In this measurement a difference of 1 $\mu$v between the voltage measured and the voltage drop of the potentiometer circuit would give a deflection of 0.911 mm on the galvanometer. Thus the potentiometer has a resolution of better than 1 mm per $\mu$v.

**10-12. PROTECTION OF THE STANDARD CELL AND GALVANOMETER IN A POTENTIOMETER CIRCUIT**

When the potentiometer shown in Figs. 10-1 and 10-14 is being calibrated and switch $S_1$ is closed to the left, the circuit can be reduced to the circuit shown in Fig. 10-15, where the portion of the circuit above the points $P$–$Q$ is reduced to the Thévenin generator. The internal resistance of the Thévenin generator $R'_O$, referring to Fig. 10-14, is

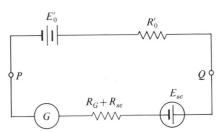

$$R'_O = \frac{R_2(R_W + R_M + R_C - R_2)}{R_W + R_M + R_C} \quad (10\text{-}18)$$

and the generated emf $E'_O$ is

$$E'_O = E_2$$

**Fig. 10-15.** *Equivalent circuit of the calibrating circuit of a potentiometer*

where $E_2$ is the voltage drop read on the calibrating slide-wire between $B$ and $D$. The current $I'_g$ through the galvanometer is

$$I'_g = \frac{E_{sc} - E_2}{R_G + R_{sc} + R_O} \quad (10\text{-}19)$$

The galvanometer may be damaged by excessive current in this circuit; an equally critical component to overcurrent in this circuit is the standard cell, in which the current should be limited to less than 0.1 ma. The usual procedure of using a shunt resistance across the galvanometer for protection not only fails to protect the standard cell but increases the current through it. Therefore, a series resistance is used to limit the current in both the standard cell and the galvanometer. This series resistance should be sufficiently large to protect the circuit if the polarity of the standard cell should accidentally be reversed. Then the current in the galvanometer circuit becomes

$$I'_g = \frac{E_{sc} + E_2}{R_G + R_{sc} + R_O} \tag{10-20}$$

Limiting $I_g$ to 0.1 ma, and assuming 1.0200 volts for the emf of the standard cell, the total resistance of the calibrating circuit in Fig. 10-14 will be

$$R_G + R_{sc} + R_O = \frac{1.02 + 1.02}{0.0001} = 20{,}400 \text{ ohms}$$

Thus a series resistance of 20,000 ohms should be sufficient to protect the galvanometer and standard cell.

## 10-13. SELF-BALANCING POTENTIOMETERS[4]

A self-balancing potentiometer applies the unbalanced emf that normally produces the current through the galvanometer to the input of an amplifier. The output of the amplifier drives a motor that balances the potentiometer. The input to the amplifier is a d-c emf, and d-c amplifiers are difficult to keep stable, as they have a tendency to drift. To avoid this difficulty, a converter is inserted between the potentiometer and the amplifier. This converter consists of a vibrating reed which is excited with alternating current. The reed operates a single-pole, double-throw switch which reverses the flow of current through the primary winding of a transformer twice for each vibration cycle of the reed. The secondary voltage of the transformer is the input voltage of the amplifier. This converts the unbalanced d-c emf from the potentiometer circuit to alternating current, which is easily amplified. When the polarity of the d-c emf supplied to the converter is reversed, the phase of the output of the amplifier is shifted 180 deg. The output of the amplifier is applied to one phase of a two-phase induction motor. The other phase of the induction motor is supplied from a line supplying a constant a-c emf which is 90 deg out of phase with the emf supplied to the converter. The output of the amplifier on one phase of the induction motor will either lead or lag, by 90 deg, the line emf applied to the other phase of the motor. The rotation of the motor is determined by the phase of the output of the amplifier which, in turn, is dependent upon the polarity of the d-c emf supplied to the converter. Thus, if the emf being measured is greater than the balancing voltage drop, the motor will turn in one direction; if the balancing voltage drop is greater than the emf being measured, the motor will rotate in the reverse direction. The motor shaft is connected to the sliding contact on the measuring resistance in such a way that the rotation of the motor will always decrease the unbalance in the potentiometer circuit. This will keep the circuit balanced under steady conditions and approaching balance under changing conditions. The error under changing conditions will depend upon the rate of change of the emf being measured and the response of the instrument.

The circuit diagram of a Leeds and Northrup Speed-O-Max self-balancing potentiometer is shown in Fig. 10-16. This circuit has a thermocouple input, and the potentiometer is used to record the temperature at the thermocouple. The emf produced by the thermocouple is a function of not only the

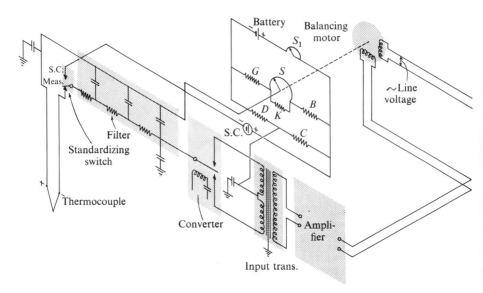

**Fig. 10-16.** *Circuit of a self-balancing potentiometer* (*courtesy of the Leeds and Northrup Company*)

temperature of the "hot" junction of the thermocouple but also the temperature of the junction of the thermocouple connection to the instrument circuit or reference junction. In many thermocouple instruments the reference-junction temperature is held at 150° or 200°F. This is not practical in this instrument. Therefore, the variation of the temperature of the reference junction is compensated for by an electrical temperature-compensating circuit. The voltage drop across the resistance $D$, which is made of a nickel-copper alloy, compensates for the change in temperature of the reference junction. The resistance $G$ balances the voltage drop across the resistance $D$ at the base temperature. Zero suppression may also be included in resistance $G$. The resistance $K$ and the slide-wire $S$ comprise the measuring circuit. The resistance $B$ produces the correct voltage drop for calibrating the circuit with the standard cell. The working resistance is $S_1$. The signal supplied to the potentiometer is filtered with a low-pass filter. The filter capacitors across the input circuit have no effect upon the d-c emf supplied to the potentiometer, but variations in the input signal and any stray a-c signals that may be impressed upon the input signal are smoothed out by the filter. The indicator on the self-balancing potentiometer usually includes an ink pen that records the output of the potentiometer on a strip chart. The chart is driven by a clock motor. The gear train between the clock motor and the chart roller can be varied to obtain the desired chart speed.

A view of the mechanism of the Leeds and Northrup Speed-O-Max recorder, with its chart, balancing motor, chart-drive motor, amplifier, and standard cell, is shown in Fig. 10-17. The newer types of self-balancing

**Fig. 10-17.** *A self-balancing potentiometer* (*courtesy of the Leeds and Northrup Company*)

potentiometer circuits use zener diode circuits for the reference voltage instead of a standard cell.

The recording pen on these instruments may be replaced by a recording head which will print a distinct point on the recording chart at the instant the reading is desired, together with a number identifying this reading. Thus several readings of different quantities may be recorded in sequence, and a printed number by each point identifies the quantity being measured. This is known as a multipoint recorder. Using this method, many different quantities may be recorded on the same chart. A Brown multipoint recorder is shown in Fig. 10-18. Other recording instruments use two complete self-balancing potentiometers, each operating a recording pen. Thus a *dual-trace potentiometer recorder* is produced.

These self-balancing potentiometers plot the desired emf as a function of time. It is often desired to plot one emf as the function of another emf. This is done by having one self-balancing potentiometer control the position of the rolls while another self-balancing potentiometer controls the position of the recording pen. This type of instrument is shown in Fig. 10-19. They are

**Fig. 10-18.** *A multipoint potentiometer (courtesy of the Minneapolis-Honeywell Regulator Company)*

**Fig. 10-19.** *A moving-chart X-Y recorder (courtesy of the Leeds and Northrup Company)*

called *X–Y Recorders*. In some *X–Y* recorders, one self-balancing potentiometer circuit moves a recording pen in the *X*-direction while another self-balancing potentiometer circuit moves the recording pen in the *Y*-direction at right angles to the *X*-direction, while the paper remains stationary. The Moseley Autograf, shown in Fig. 10-20, is this type of *X–Y* recorder.

There are many variations of *X–Y* recorders; the present discussion covers only the general operation of these instruments. The emf used in *X–Y* recorders may not necessarily measure only voltages. The measured emf may be the output of a transducer that may measure light intensity, pressures, strains, displacements, or other physical quantities. Thus, with the use of *X–Y* recorders and the appropriate transducer, one physical quantity may be plotted against another physical quantity. Self-balancing potentiometers are used in a variety of operations. They are even used in dividing and multiplying networks in analog computers and in special-function generators. The latter applications will be discussed in more detail in Chap. 12.

The response time of a self-balancing potentiometer depends upon the gain of the amplifier and the speed of the self-balancing motor. The minimum time required for the pointer to move from minimum position to maximum

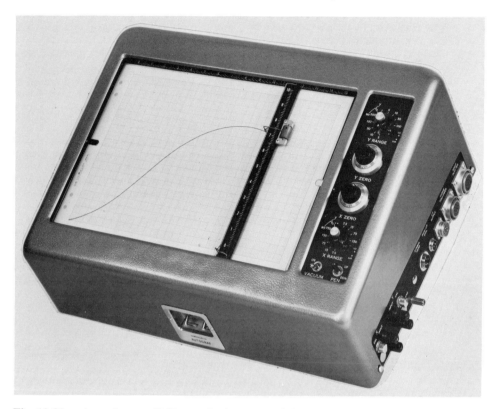

**Fig. 10-20.** *A moving-pen X-Y recorder (courtesy of the F. L. Moseley Company)*

position on a 10-in. strip chart is about one fourth of a minute. Compared with many other types of recording instruments, this is a very slow response; where these speeds can be used, however, the self-balancing potentiometer is a very reliable and practical instrument.

## PROBLEMS

**10-1.** In Fig. 10-1 the emf of the working battery is 3.03 volts. The current in the working circuit is 2.0 ma. Determine: (*a*) the resistance of the working resistor; (*b*) the resistance of the slide-wire in the measuring circuit; (*c*) the resistance of each of the resistors in the measuring circuit; (*d*) the resistance of $R_s$; (*e*) the resistance of the slide-wire in the calibrating circuit.

**10-2.** In Fig. 10-1 the resistance of the measuring resistance is 170 ohms. The resistance of the standard cell is 173 ohms. The resistance of the galvanometer is 53 ohms. The emf of the working battery is 3.03 volts, and the emf of the standard cell is 1.0184 volts. The working battery has neglible resistance, and the standard cell has a resistance of 63 ohms. The current sensitivity of the galvanometer is 6 mm/$\mu$a. Find: (*a*) the sensitivity of the potentiometer when $R_x = 0$ and $E_x = 0.8$ volts; (*b*) the resistance of the protective resistance to protect the standard cell if the polarity of the standard cell were reversed.

**10-3.** In Fig. 10-3 the current in the battery circuit is 75 ma under calibrated conditions. Determine the resistance of $R_1$ and $R_2$.

**10-4.** The resistance of the measuring slide-wire in Fig. 10-2 is 10 ohms. Determine the resistance of $R_1$ and $R_2$ to obtain ranges of 1.0 and 0.1 of the calibrated scale.

**10-5.** In Fig. 10-4 the measuring resistance $R_M$ consists of an 11-ohm slide-wire and 15 equal 10-ohm resistances. The ranges of the potentiometers are 1.61, 0.161, 0.0161, and 0.00161. Determine the resistance of $R_1$, $R_2$, $R_3$, $R_{M1}$, $R_{M2}$, $R_{M3}$, $R_{M4}$, and $R$. Use the smallest possible resistance in the design.

**10-6.** Design a potentiometer with a range of 0 to 5 mv with four steps of zero suppression, using an 11-ohm slide-wire in the measuring circuit. Use a 6.3-volt battery.

**10-7.** Design a Wenner-difference potentiometer, as shown in Fig. 10-9, using a 3-volt battery which will vary the voltage drop from $P_1$ to $P_2$ from 0.25 volt to 0.50 volt. The resistance of each slide-wire is 10 ohms.

**10-8.** Design a volt-box circuit to measure 3-, 7.5-, 15-, 30-, 75-, and 150-volt ranges, and having 10,000 ohms per volt, to be used with a 0–1.6-volt-range potentiometer.

**10-9.** Design a shunt to be used with a 0–1.6-volt-range potentiometer, to measure 0–1.5-, 0–3-, 0–6-, and 0–15-amp ranges.

**10-10.** A self-balancing slide-wire potentiometer has a 10-in. scale and a sensitivity of 10 in. per mv. The backlash and coulomb friction require a movement of the motor equivalent to a scale deflection of 0.055 in. An input of 56 $\mu$a to the servo amplifier is required to produce a sufficient output of the amplifier to operate the servomotor. (*a*) Determine the dead zone in percent of full scale. (*b*) The motor will drive the indicator from zero to full scale in 0.25 sec. Determine the dead time in seconds.

**REFERENCES**

1. F. K. Harris, *Electrical Measurements*, John Wiley & Sons, Inc., New York, 1952, Chap. 6.

2. M. B. Stout, *Basic Electrical Measurements*, 2nd ed., Prentice-Hall, Inc., Englewood Cliffs, N.J., 1960, Chap. 7.

3. Ernest Frank, *Electrical Measurement Analysis*, McGraw-Hill Book Company, Inc., New York, 1959, Chap. 9.

4. *Speedomax Type G Instruments*, *ND 46(1)*, Leeds & Northrup Co., Philadelphia, Pa., 1952.

# Chapter 11

# NONELECTRICAL QUANTITIES

## 11-1. INTRODUCTION

Many physical conditions, such as temperature, humidity, and pressure, and nonelectrical quantities, such as distance, force, torque, and radiation, are measured with sensing elements which convert the magnitude of the physical quantity or condition into an electrical quantity. In turn, the electrical quantity is measured by standard methods, giving the magnitude of the quantity or condition being measured. Elements which convert physical quantities or conditions into electrical quantities are called *transducers*.

## 11-2. BONDED-RESISTANCE STRAIN GAGES[1,2,3]

The bonded-resistance strain-gage is a grill of resistance wire, usually 1 mil in diameter or less, bonded with adhesive material to a structure. When the structure is strained, the resistance of the wire changes owing to changes in the length and the diameter of the wire. The change in the resistance of the bonded-resistance strain gage is measured with a Wheatstone bridge. The change in the standard resistance of the bridge is calibrated in terms of the strain of the gage.

# MEASUREMENT OF

# AND CONDITIONS

The change in the cross-sectional area of the wire in a resistance strain gage produced by a strain $e$ is

$$\Delta A = \frac{\pi d^2}{4} - \frac{\pi (d - \mu e d)^2}{4} = \frac{\pi d^2}{4}(2\mu e - \mu^2 e^2)$$

where

$\mu$ = Poisson's ratio
$d$ = diameter of the wire

Then the change in resistance $\Delta R_1$ produced by this change in area is

$$\Delta R_I = R_S \frac{\Delta A}{A} = R_S(2\mu e - \mu^2 e^2) = R_S e(2\mu - \mu^2 e)$$

where $R_S$ is the unstrained resistance of the gage. The change in the resistance produced by the change in the length is

$$\Delta R_2 = R_S \frac{\Delta L}{L} = R_S e$$

Then the change in the resistance of the wire produced by the strain is

$$\Delta R_S = \Delta R_1 + \Delta R_2 = R_S e(1 + 2\mu - \mu^2 e)$$

231

The strain is very small, so the $e^2$ term can be neglected. Then

$$\Delta R_S = R_S e(1 + 2\mu) \tag{11-1}$$

The ratio of the unit change of resistance to the unit change of length is defined as the *gage factor*. Then the gage factor $G_f$ is

$$G_f = \frac{\Delta R_S/R_S}{\Delta L/L} = \frac{\Delta R_S/R_S}{e}$$
$$= 1 + 2\mu \tag{11-2}$$

For wire of large diameter, Poisson's ratio is about 0.3. Using this value in Eq. (11-2) gives a gage factor of 1.6. This result is not verified by experience, as the gage factors vary from $-12$ for some nickel alloys to $+5$ for iridium-platinum gages. The nominal values of the gage factor of some common materials are listed in Table 11-1.

### Table 11-1

| Material | Composition | Gage factor |
|---|---|---|
| Nickel | | $-12.1$ |
| Manganin | Ni, 0.04; Mn, 0.12; Cu, 0.84 | $+0.47$ |
| Nichrome | Ni, 0.80; Cr, 0.20 | $+2.0$ |
| Advance | | $+2.1$ |
| Constantan | | $+2.1$ |
| Capel | | $+2.4$ |
| Chromel | Ni, 0.64; Fe, 0.25; Cr, 0.11 | $+2.5$ |
| Iso-elastic | Ni, 0.36; Cr, 0.08 Fe, 0.52; Mo, 0.005 | $+3.5$ |
| Soft iron | | $+4.2$ |
| Platinum | | $+4.8$ |
| Carbon | | $+20.0$ |
| Doped crystals | | 100 to 5,000 |

Commercial solid-state strain gages using doped crystal structures, however, have gage factors from 100 to 5,000. These gages are becoming very popular in modern instrumentation systems.

The resistance strain gage is usually made in the form of a grill of fine wire. The wire is approximately 1 mil in diameter. A grill of this wire is shown in Fig. 11-1. This wire grill is cemented to a thin paper sheet or to a very thin Bakelite sheet and covered with a protective covering of paper, felt, or thin Bakelite. This is the usual form of a commercial bonded-resistance strain gage. The size of the grill varies with the application. They can be as small as 1/8 by 1/8 in. square. Usually, they are larger, but seldom more than 1 in. long and 1/2 in. wide.

The most difficult problem in the use of bonded strain gages is the process of bonding the gage to the structure to be strained. The adhesive material must hold the gage firmly to the structure, yet it must have sufficient elasticity to give under strain without losing its adhesive properties. It should also be resistant to environmental conditions such as temperature and humidity.

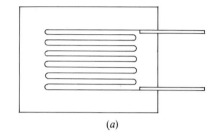

(a)

Figure 11-2(a) shows a single strain gage mounted on a cantilever beam. When a force $F$ is applied to the beam, the gage will be in tension, and the resistance of the gage will increase. The increase in resistance is measured with a Wheatstone bridge, as shown in Fig. 11-2(b). The change in the resistance of the gage is

$$\Delta R_{S4} = \frac{R_2 \, \Delta R_3}{R_1} \qquad (11\text{-}3)$$

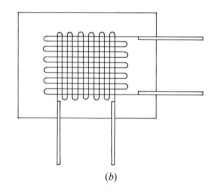

(b)

where $\Delta R_3$ is the change in $R_3$ to rebalance the bridge after the strain is applied to the gage and $R_2/R_1$ is the scale factor for the reading $\Delta R_3$. The magnitude of $\Delta R_3$ for a given $\Delta R_{S4}$ is

$$\Delta R_3 = \frac{R_1}{R_2} \Delta R_{S4} \qquad (11\text{-}4)$$

The gage sensitivity of the circuit shown in Fig. 11-2(b) is the ratio of the output $k \, \Delta R_3$ to the strain $e$, where $k$ is the scale factor of the $\Delta R_3$ readout or indicator. Then, for this circuit the gage sensitivity is

$$S_g = \frac{k \, \Delta R_3}{e} \qquad (11\text{-}5)$$

But, from Eq. (11-2), the strain is

$$e = \frac{\Delta R_S}{R_S G_f} = \frac{\Delta R_{S4}}{R_{S4} G_f}$$

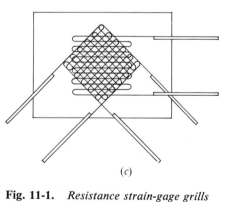

(c)

**Fig. 11-1.** *Resistance strain-gage grills*

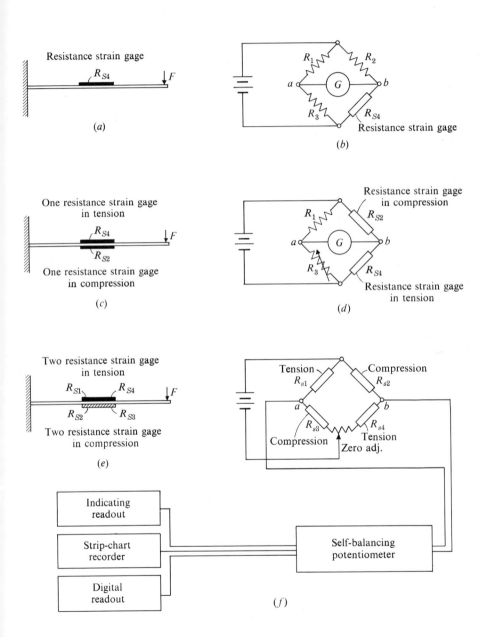

**Fig. 11-2.** *Strain-gage mountings and bridge circuits*

Then the gage sensitivity becomes

$$S_g = \frac{k \, \Delta R_3 \, R_{S4} G_f}{\Delta R_{S4}}$$

Substituting the value of $\Delta R_3$, given in Eq. (11-4), in this equation gives

$$S_g = \frac{k R_1 \, \Delta R_{S4} \, R_{S4} G_f}{R_2 \, \Delta R_{S4}}$$

$$= \frac{R_1}{R_2} k R_{S4} G_f \tag{11-6}$$

When $R_1 = R_2$,

$$S_g = k R_{S4} G_f \tag{11-7}$$

This gives the gage sensitivity of this circuit in terms of the resistances of the unstrained strain gage, the gage factor of the strain gage, and the scale factor of the readout system.

There are two gages mounted on the cantilever beam in Fig. 11-2(c). The gage $R_{S4}$ on the upper surface is in tension and the gage $R_{S2}$ on the lower surface is in compression. These gages are connected in a bridge circuit, as shown in Fig. 11-2(d). The change in $R_3$ to rebalance the bridge after a strain has been produced by the application of a force $F$ is

$$\Delta R_3 = \frac{R_1}{R_{S2}} \left( \frac{R_{S2} \, \Delta R_{S4} + R_{S4} \, \Delta R_{S2}}{R_{S2} - \Delta R_{S2}} \right)$$

Usually, the resistances of the strain gages are nearly equal, and it will be assumed that

$$R_{S2} = R_{S4} = R_S$$

Also $R_{S2}$ is very much larger than $\Delta R_{S2}$, and it will also be assumed that

$$R_{S2} \cong R_{S2} - \Delta R_{S2} = R_S$$

and that

$$\Delta R_{S2} = \Delta R_{S4} = \Delta R_S$$

Then

$$\Delta R_3 \cong \frac{R_1}{R_{S2}} (\Delta R_{S4} + \Delta R_{S2}) = 2\Delta R_S \frac{R_1}{R_2} \tag{11-8}$$

The gage sensitivity of the circuit in Fig. 11-2(d) is also given by Eq. (11-5) where

$$e = \frac{\Delta R_S}{R_S G_f}$$

Then

$$S_g = \frac{k\,\Delta R_3}{e}$$

$$= \frac{k\left(2\,\Delta R_S \dfrac{R_1}{R_2}\right)}{\dfrac{\Delta R_S}{R_S G_f}} = \frac{R_1}{R_2}\,kR_2 G_f$$

When $R_1 = R_2$,

$$= 2kR_S G_f \qquad\qquad (11\text{-}9)$$

Thus the circuit in Fig. 11-2($d$) has twice the sensitivity of the circuit in Fig. 11-2($b$).

Four strain gages are mounted on the cantilever shown in Fig. 11-2($e$). Two gages are in tension and two are in compression. These gages are connected in a bridge circuit, as shown in Fig. 11-2($f$), where gages $R_{S2}$ and $R_{S3}$ are in compression, and $R_{S1}$ and $R_{S4}$ are in tension. It can be shown that the sensitivity of this circuit is four times greater than the bridge circuit in Fig. 11-2($b$). The galvanometer of the usual bridge has been replaced with a self-balancing potentiometer, and a low-resistance slide-wire has been connected between $R_{S3}$ and $R_{S4}$ to adjust the bridge so that the self-balancing potentiometer reads zero when no force is applied to the beam. The change in the resistance of the gages owing to the force $F$ on the beam unbalances the bridge and produces an emf between terminals $a$ and $b$. This emf is read with the self-balancing potentiometer which is calibrated to read the force $F$. The output of the self-balancing potentiometer could be either an indicator, a digital readout, a strip-chart recorder, or any desired combination of these readout systems, as shown in Fig. 11-2($f$).

Bonded resistances have many applications and adaptations. They are used in load cells which measure force by the strain of the structure to which the gage is applied. They are used in wind-tunnel measurements. The model under test is attached to a beam which enters the model from its aft position, extends through the model, and is attached internally to the forepart of the model. The portion of the beam inside the model has several flexures which permit deflections in the desired direction and are reinforced to prevent deflections in other directions. Gages are mounted on these flexures in such a way that the *drag force, side force, lift force, yaw torque, pitch torque*, and *roll torque*, with reference to a given point in the model, can be measured. These forces and moments are shown in Fig. 11-3 with reference to three mutually perpendicular axes through the model. This strain-gage system and support is called a *sting balance*.

Bonded-resistance strain gages are used extensively for analyzing the dynamic strains in complex structures, such as the stress and the strain in bridges, automobiles, and farm equipment, where the output of the bridge can be recorded with an oscillograph calibrated to read the instantaneous strain or stress as a function of time.

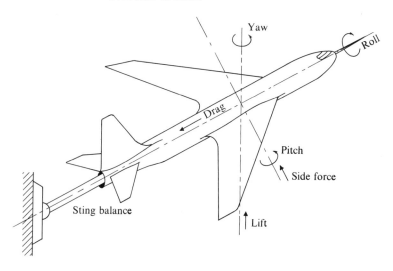

**Fig. 11-3.** *A sting balance and aerodynamic model*

## 11-3.  UNBONDED-RESISTANCE STRAIN GAGES[2,4]

The unbonded-resistance strain gages are also used extensively in instrument work to measure displacement. They can also measure force, acceleration, or pressure. The arrangement of one form of unbonded-resistance gage is shown in Fig. 11-4(*a*). The loops of resistance wire $R_1$, $R_2$, $R_3$, and $R_4$ are wound so that the wires are in tension, even in the position of maximum deflection of the moving member. The loops are connected in a bridge circuit as shown in Fig. 11-4(*b*), and the current flowing in the indicator is calibrated to read the magnitude of the quantity being measured. The resistance of each loop is usually 350 ohms, as recording galvanometers require about 350 ohms of shunt resistance for optimum response. Bridge resistances from 50 ohms to 20,000 ohms are available for matching other indicating equipment such as magnetic tape recorders, cathode-ray oscilloscopes, telemetering systems, and automation equipment.

When these gages measure the strain in a structure, they can be calibrated to read the force applied to the structure, and the unit then is a force dynamometer. If the armature of the displacement transducer is attached to a bellows or a diaphragm, the unit becomes a pressure pickup. When the armature is attached to a spring-suspended mass, it measures acceleration. An unbonded strain-gage accelerometer is shown in Fig. 11-15.

The *sensitivity of the transducer circuit* in Fig. 11-4 is defined by some manufacturers as the open-circuit voltage in microvolts due to a unit input of the quantity to be measured with 1 volt applied to the input terminals. Under these conditions it is equal to the emf of an equivalent Thévenin generator looking into the bridge circuit from the output terminals. This factor is usually given by the manufacturer. When the sensitivity of the transducer is

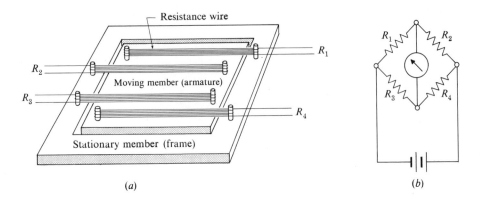

(a)
(b)

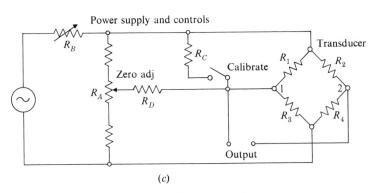

(c)

**Fig. 11-4.** *Unbonded strain gage and calibrating circuit*

$S$, the input voltage to the bridge is $E$, and number of units of the measured quantity is $Q$, the equivalent emf of a Thévenin generator is $SQE$. The resistances of $R_1$, $R_2$, $R_3$, and $R_4$ in Fig. 11-4 are assumed to be equal. The equivalent resistance of the equivalent Thévenin generator of the bridge is

$$R = R_1 = R_2 = R_3 = R_4$$

The current in the output circuit of the transducer is

$$I_o = \frac{SQE}{R + R_o} \tag{11-10}$$

where $R_o$ is the resistance of the output circuit. The voltage $E_o$ across the output circuit is

$$E_o = I_o R_o = \frac{SQER_o}{R + R_o}$$

$$= \frac{SQE}{\dfrac{R}{R_o} + 1} \tag{11-11}$$

When $R_o \gg R$,

$$E_o = SQE \tag{11-12}$$

Equation (11-10) is used for low-resistance outputs such as microammeters, and Eqs. (11-11) and (11-12) are used for high-impedance instruments such as potentiometers and instruments using electronic amplifiers.

It is often desirable to calibrate a strain-gage circuit without applying a known strain to the gage. For example, in Fig. 11-4, if the input to the transducer were a given number of units $Q$, the circuit could be calibrated by closing the calibration switch in Fig. 11-4(c), thus shunting resistance $R_1$ with the calibrating resistance $R_C$. The value of the calibrating resistance can be determined by the use of the following equation:

$$R_C = \left(\frac{10^6}{4QS} - 0.5\right)R \tag{11-13}$$

where

$R_C =$ calibrating resistor value, in ohms

$R =$ resistance of each of the four bridge arms, in ohms

$S =$ calibration factor in microvolts open-circuit output per volt input per unit mechanical input

$Q =$ number of units of input (pressure, acceleration, etc.) simulated by the calibrating resistor

If it is convenient to use a stock resistor as the calibrating resistor, the number of scale units $Q$ produced by a given resistor $R_C$ will be given by

$$Q = \frac{10^6}{4S}\left(\frac{R}{R_C + 0.5R}\right) \tag{11-14}$$

If a calibrating resistor gives a deflection in the wrong direction, it should be shifted to an adjacent arm. The circuit shown in Fig. 11-4(c) is equally applicable to bonded strain gages. When alternating current is used on a resistance strain gage, the output of the gage is usually converted into a d-c voltage by the use of a discriminator, as shown in Fig. 11-5. The a-c supply is usually from an oscillator, and frequencies from 1,000 to 10,000 cycles are used in this circuit. The advantage of using alternating current on a resistance strain gage is that thermal emfs are avoided, but the use of alternating current produces a phase-shift problem and requires the addition of an oscillator and a discriminator circuit.

**Fig. 11-5.** *Block diagram of an a-c-operated strain gage, oscillator, and discriminator*

## 11-4. DIFFERENTIAL TRANSFORMER [4,5,6]

A differential transformer is a very effective instrument for measuring small displacements. A simple form is shown in Fig. 11-6(*a*). It has an input or primary winding wound on the center part of a tube, and an output or secondary winding with half its turns on each end of the tube. The two secondary windings are wound in opposite directions, so that the emfs induced in the two secondary windings oppose each other. A ferromagnetic

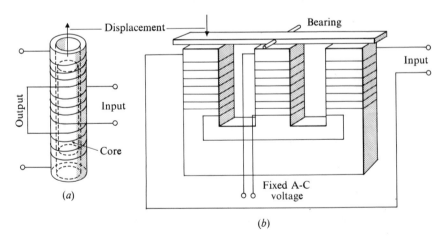

**Fig. 11-6.** *A differentiated transformer*

core is located in the center of the tube. Its position determines the flux linkage with each coil. When the core is in the upper position, more flux links with the upper coil than with the lower coil, and the emf output will be a function of the displacement of the core and will have the phase relation of the emf of the upper coil. Similarly, when the core is in the lower position, more flux links with the lower coil than with the upper coil, and the emf output will be 180 deg out of phase with the emf of the upper coil. When the output of this differential transformer is amplified and supplied to one phase of a two-phase motor, as shown in Fig. 11-7, the rotation of the motor will be

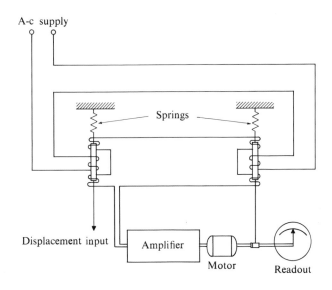

**Fig. 11-7.** *A servo system using differential transformers to measure displacement*

determined by the position of the core. The motor moves the core of a similar differential transformer. In this transducer the output of this balancing transformer opposes the output of the input transformer, and the motor will turn until the outputs of the two transformers are equal. The indicator on the motor shaft will read the displacement.

Another type of differential transformer is shown in Fig. 11-6(*b*). The transformer primary winding is wound on the center leg of an **E**-shaped magnetic core, and the output windings are wound on the other two legs of the core. The armature rotates about an axis in the center of the beam. When the armature is displaced, the reluctance of the magnetic circuit through one half of the secondary-winding circuit is decreased, and the reluctance of the magnetic circuit through the other half of the secondary winding is increased. Again, the induced emfs in the two halves of the secondary winding oppose each other, and the operation of this transformer is the same as that of the transformer in Fig. 11-6(*a*). Displacements in fractions of microinches can be measured with these instruments.

## 11-5. VARIABLE-CAPACITY DISPLACEMENT INSTRUMENTS [3,4]

The capacitance of a capacitor is a function of the area of the plates of the capacitor $A$, the distance between the plates $d$, and the dielectric constant of the material between the plates $k$. Then

$$C = k \frac{A}{d} \qquad (11\text{-}15)$$

The variation of the distance between the plates of a capacitor will thus produce a variation in its capacitance. Figure 11-8(a) shows a cantilever-type spring plate of a capacitor which is displaced toward the second plate of the capacitor, increasing its capacitance with increased displacement.

Two silvered-quartz diaphragms form a capacitor in Fig. 11-8(b). The displacement of these diaphragms varies the capacitance of this capacitor. This type of unit forms a very satisfactory pressure gage. If the pressure is reduced to a perfect vacuum between the plates, the unit will measure absolute pressure of the surrounding medium. Quartz is used because it has very low mechanical hysteresis. This unit has a high temperature coefficient; this must be taken into consideration when precise measurements are made.

Rotational displacement can be measured with an arrangement such as that shown in Fig. 11-8(c). As the rotor-plates of the capacitor are displaced in the counterclockwise direction, the capacitance increases. This can be effectively adapted to the measurement of torques in a shaft.

The change in capacitance can be measured with an a-c bridge circuit, but the usual system of measuring this change in capacitance employs an oscillator circuit, where the change in the capacitance of the transducer produces a change in the frequency of the oscillator. The frequency of a fixed-frequency oscillator, as shown in Fig. 11-8(d), is modulated with the frequency of the capacity-controlled oscillator. A frequency equal to the difference in frequencies is produced and fed to a readout circuit. To illustrate, if the frequency of the oscillator controlled by the capacitance element were varied 2,000 cycles per second from its zero-position frequency by a deflection $d$, and if the frequency of the standard fixed-frequency oscillator and the zero-displacement frequency of the transducer were the same, the difference frequency in the output of the modulator circuit would be 2,000 cycles per second. This frequency could be counted on an electronic counter, and the counter would read 2,000. This count would be a function of the input displacement. When the frequency of the two oscillators is fed to a discriminator circuit, the output of the discriminator is proportional to the frequency difference. This output can be measured by the proper readout system. Care

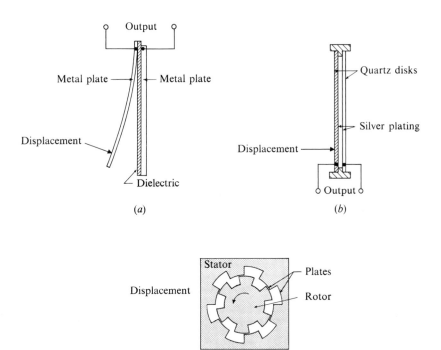

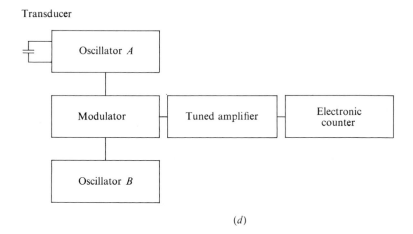

**Fig. 11-8.** *Variable-capacitance transducers, mixer, and counter circuit*

must be taken to shield properly the sensing element and the input circuit to these capacitance-sensing elements in order to avoid noise.

## 11-6. RELUCTANCE-TYPE DISPLACEMENT INSTRUMENTS [4,5]

The inductance of a coil varies with the variation of the reluctance of the magnetic circuit. One variable-reluctance instrument consists of a ferromagnetic armature which varies the air gap of a ferromagnetic yoke, as shown in Fig. 11-9(*a*). Another reluctance instrument varies the position of a ferromagnetic core in a coil, as shown in Fig. 11-9(*b*). The variation of the inductance of a coil by varying the reluctance of the path of the magnetic flux through the coil can be measured with an a-c bridge, or it can replace the capacitor transducer in Fig. 11-8, where it produces a variation in the frequency of the oscillator, and this change in frequency can be read as described above.

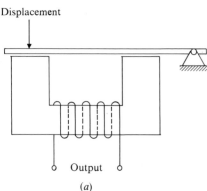

(*a*)

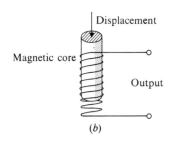

(*b*)

**Fig. 11-9.** *Reluctance-type displacement transducers*

## 11-7. DYNAMIC DISPLACEMENT MEASUREMENTS [5,6]

The measurement of displacement under continually changing conditions can be measured with the instruments described above. The readout system must be modified to respond to the sensing element and record the output in graphical form. Self-balancing potentiometer recorders are limited to only a few cycles per second. A recorder using a modified d'Arsonval movement can record outputs with frequencies of more than 100 cycles per second. The galvanometer-type recorder with a mirror and light beam can record frequencies up to several thousand cycles per second. Frequency-modulation tape recorders will respond to more than 20,000 cycles per second, and a direct-recording tape will respond to 200 kc or 300 kc. Beyond this range, a cathode-ray oscilloscope must be used.

## 11-8. LOAD CELLS AND LOAD RINGS

Load cells and load rings are examples of instruments that use the strain of the cell or ring for force measurements. The material used in load cells and load rings must have a constant coefficient of elasticity over the range of

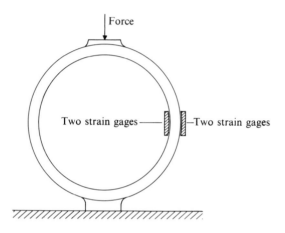

**Fig. 11-10.** *A load-ring force transducer*

the instrument. Steel is the most common material used for load cells and load rings. They are precisely made and calibrated. A sketch of a load ring is shown in Fig. 11-10. The strain in the cell produced by the load is measured with strain gages.

## 11-9. PIEZOELECTRIC DEVICES[7,8]

Piezoelectric crystals produce an emf when they are deformed. Conversely, a varying emf applied to the proper axis of the crystal will produce a deformation of the crystal. These deformations are shown in Fig. 11-11. Common piezoelectric materials include Rochelle salts, ammonium dihydrogen phosphate, lithium sulfate, dipotassium tartrate, potassium dihydrogen phosphate, quartz, and ceramics A and B. All but the quartz and ceramics A and B are man-made crystals grown from aqueous solutions under carefully controlled conditions. The ceramic materials were developed by Brush Electronic Company. They are polycrystalline in nature and are, basically,

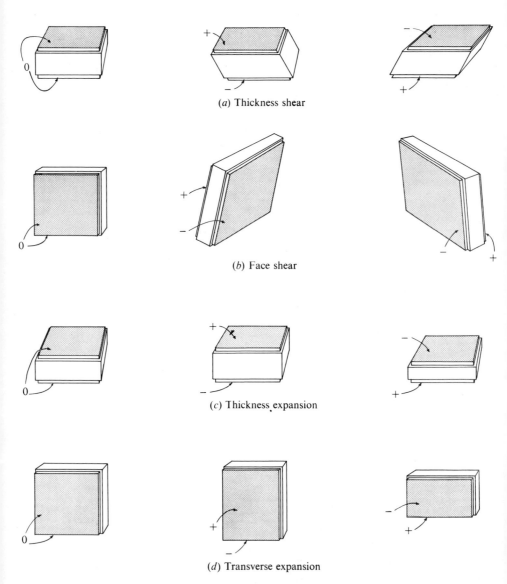

(a) Thickness shear

(b) Face shear

(c) Thickness expansion

(d) Transverse expansion

**Fig. 11-11.** *Basic deformations of piezoelectric plates (courtesy Brush Electronics Co.)*

## Table 11-2

### Properties of Piezoelectric Materials[7]

| Material | Cut | Basic plate action | Stress in $\frac{volts/meter}{newton/meter^2}$ | Maximum safe stress in $newton/meter^2$ | Maximum safe operating temperature | Minimum safe humidity | Maximum safe humidity | Typical applications |
|---|---|---|---|---|---|---|---|---|
| Multiply by | | | $10^{-3}$ | $10^6$ | 1 | 1 | 1 | |
| Rochelle Salt at 30°C | 0°X | FS | 180 | 14 | 45 | 40 | 70 | Twister bimorphs |
| | 45°X | LE | 90 | 14 | 45 | 40 | 70 | Underwater sound transducers |
| | 0°Y | FS | 664 | 14 | 45 | 40 | 70 | |
| | 45°Y | LE | 332 | 14 | 45 | 40 | 70 | Underwater sound transducers |
| | L | TE | 100 | 14 | 45 | 40 | 70 | |
| Ammonium dihydrogen phosphate (ADP) | 0°Z | FS | 354 | 20 | 125 | 0 | 94 | Twister bimorphs |
| | 45°Z | LE | 177 | 20 | 125 | 0 | 94 | Underwater sound transducers |
| | L | TE | 77.5 | 20 | 125 | 0 | 94 | |
| Lithium sulfate LH | 0°Y | TE | 175 | 15 | 75 | 0 | 95 | |
| | 0°Y | VE | 148 | 15 | 75 | 0 | 95 | Hydrophones |
| Dipotassium tartrate (DKT) | 45°Z | LE | 192 | 10 | 100 | 0 | 70 | Frequency-control filters |
| | 0°Z | TS | 192 | 10 | 100 | 0 | 70 | Frequency control |
| | 0°Z | FS | 384 | 10 | 100 | 0 | 70 | Frequency-control filters |
| Potassium dihydrogen phosphate (KDP) | 45°Z | LE | 55.8 | — | 150 | 0 | 95 | |
| | 0°Z | FS | 102 | — | 150 | 0 | 95 | Electro-optical properties |

### Table 11-2 *continued*

| Material | Cut | Basic plate action | Stress in $\dfrac{volts/meter}{newton/meter^2}$ | Maximum safe stress in $newton/meter^2$ | Maximum safe operating temperature | Minimum safe humidity | Maximum safe humidity | Typical applications |
|---|---|---|---|---|---|---|---|---|
| Quartz | 0°X | TE | 50 | 95 | 550 | 0 | 100 | Ultrasonic transducers; underwater sound transducers |
|  | 0°X | LE | 50 | 95 | 550 | 0 | 100 |  |
|  | AT | FS | 82.4 | 100 | 550 | 0 | 100 | Frequency-control filters |
| Tourmaline | 0°Z | TE | — | — | — | 0 | 100 |  |
|  | 0°Z | VE | — | — | — | 0 | 100 | Pressure gages |
| Ceramic A nominal values at 25°C | — | TE | 12.6 | 80 | 100 | 0 | 100 | Ultrasonic transducers; underwater sound transducers |
|  | — | LE | 5.2 | 80 | 100 | 0 | 100 | Underwater sound transducers |
|  | — | VE | 2.2 | 80 | 100 | 0 | 100 |  |
| Ceramic B nominal values at 25°C | — | TE | 13.0 | 80 | 100 | 0 | 100 | Ultrasonic transducers; underwater sound transducers |
|  | — | LE | 5.3 | 80 | 100 | 0 | 100 | Underwater sound transducers |
|  | — | VE | 2.4 | 80 | 100 | 0 | 100 |  |

FS: Face shear plate      TE: Thickness expander plate
LE: Length expander plate      VE: Volume expander plate

made of barium titanate. They do not have piezoelectric properties in their original state. These properties are produced by a special polarizing treatment. The properties of piezoelectric plates cut from these crystals depend upon the axis of the cut. The crystals are subject to temperature effects and should not be used above a given temperature. The properties of several piezoelectric materials are given in Table 11-2. Many piezoelectric materials are water-soluble and dissolve in a high-humidity environment The maximum humidity under which an unprotected crystal should operate is given in the next-to-the last column of Table 11-2. More material on the properties of these materials can be obtained from the Brush Electronics Company brochure, *Piezotronic Technical Data.*

A typical operation of a piezoelectric plate is shown in Fig. 11-12. The varying force applied to a thickness expander plate such as that in Fig.

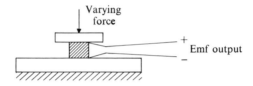

**Fig. 11-12.** *Basic operation of a piezoelectric transducer*

11-11(*c*) will produce a voltage at the surface of the plate. These transducers have a very good frequency response and are used extensively for dynamic measurements.

### 11-10. VELOCITY MEASUREMENTS[4,5]

Linear velocity is the linear displacement per unit time, such as feet per minute, miles per hour, etc. A few methods of measuring linear velocity will now be described. An electronic counter is used to count the revolutions per minute of a wheel that is rotating in contact with a flat surface. The wheel is at right angles to the surface so that the axis of the wheel moves parallel to the surface. The product of the circumference of the wheel in feet and the revolutions per minute is the linear velocity of the axis in feet per minute. A photoelectric-controlled timing circuit is used to measure the time taken to travel a given distance. This distance divided by the time gives the average speed while traveling a given distance. The latter method is used in ballistic tests to measure the velocity of rifle bullets using a given ammunition. When there is no earth reference, the acceleration is measured with a transducer which converts the acceleration to a proportional emf. This emf is integrated by the integrating circuit described in Chap. 12. The output voltage of the integrating circuit is proportional to the velocity. Its magnitude is the product of the scale factor of the transducer, the scale factor of the integrating circuit, and the output voltage.

Angular velocity measured in radians per second, revolutions per second, or revolutions per minute can be determined by using the revolution counter mentioned above, which counted the revolutions per second. The wheel may be replaced by a variable-reluctance pickup. This arrangement is shown in Fig. 11-13. The teeth on a soft-iron rotor vary the reluctance in the

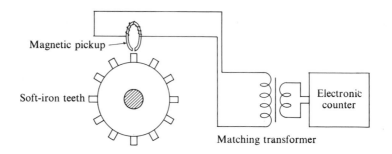

**Fig. 11-13.** *A variable-reluctance revolution counter*

air gap of the magnetic pickup, inducing an emf in the coil wound on the yoke. This produces $N$ pulses of emf per revolution, where $N$ is the number of teeth. Often, the rotor is designed with 60 teeth, producing 60 pulses of emf per revolution. When the counter reads the number of pulses in 1 sec, the count will be the revolutions per minute. The magnitude of the emf pulse is a function of the time rate of change of the flux which decreases with decrease in revolutions per minute. If the revolutions per minute are small, the emf will be insufficient to trigger the counter and will not operate below a given speed.

Another method of measuring revolutions per minute uses a permanent-magnet d-c generator. The generated voltage is proportional to the angular velocity. The emf is measured with a high-resistance voltmeter. These generators are called tachometer generators. The brushes on small tachometer generators often produce a maintenance problem, as their contact resistance may vary and produce appreciable error. To overcome this difficulty, special permanent-magnetic (Alnico) a-c generators have been designed. The output of the generator is rectified and measured with a d-c meter. At very low frequencies, it is difficult to smooth out the ripple frequency; therefore, the a-c tachometer generators are designed with many poles. One type has 96 poles which would generate 0.80 cycles per second at 1 rpm. This circuit is shown in Fig. 11-14.

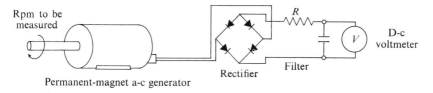

**Fig. 11-14.** *An a-c tachometer and revolutions-per-minute indicating circuit*

### 11-11. ACCELERATION MEASUREMENTS[3,4]

The acceleration in a given direction can be measured by restraining the motion of a mass except in the given direction. Then the force exerted by the mass in this direction is measured. The acceleration is proportional to the force exerted by the mass as

$$F = MA$$

or

$$A = \frac{F}{M} \tag{11-16}$$

where

$A$ = acceleration

$F$ = force

$M$ = mass, provided the mass is constant

The acceleration is the product of the constant scale factor $1/M$ and the force. A mass, with its movement in the direction of the acceleration constrained only by the conductors of an unbonded strain gage is shown in Fig. 11-15. These instruments can measure accelerations from a small fraction of the acceleration of gravity to thousands of times the acceleration of gravity. They have a frequency response better than 10,000 cycles per second.

### 11-12. VIBRATION MEASUREMENTS

There are many forms of vibration-measuring instruments. They may measure the frequency or the magnitude of the vibration. Acceleration-measuring instruments are used to measure the displacement, the velocity, and the acceleration of the vibrating body as a function of time. The output of the acceleration-measuring instrument is integrated with an integrating circuit to obtain the velocity of the vibration. The velocity is integrated by another integrating circuit to obtain the displacement of the vibration as a function of time.

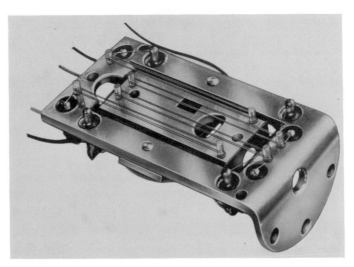

**Fig. 11-15.** *An unbonded strain-gage accelerometer (courtesy of Statham Instruments, Inc.)*

The frequency of the vibration can be determined by measuring the frequency of the output of an acceleration, velocity, or displacement with a standard frequency meter using a tuned resonant circuit, or by comparing this frequency with a known frequency using an oscilloscope. For frequencies in the range of a vibrating reed, a Fram tuned-reed frequency meter may be used. The reed with a frequency response equal to the frequency of the vibration will vibrate, indicating the frequency.

## 11-13. PRESSURE MEASUREMENTS [3,4,5]

A capacitor-type pressure-measuring instrument was described in Sec. 11-5. The most common pressure-measuring instruments use the Bourdon element shown in Fig. 11-16(*b*) or the bellows shown in Fig. 11-16(*a*) to produce a deflection which is a function of the pressure being measured. Strain gages and similar devices are used to measure the displacement. In some instruments the displacement of a very small diaphragm is measured with strain gages to obtain the pressure. The outputs of these instruments are often nonlinear, but, when correctly calibrated, they are very accurate and have good frequency response. These instruments are often sensitive to temperature and require a temperature correction.

There are several instruments designed to measure very low pressures approaching a perfect vacuum; these are called *vacuum gages*. A few of these instruments will be described here.

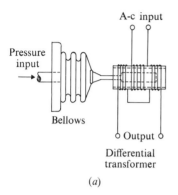

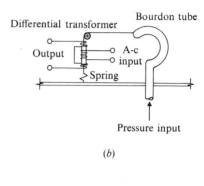

(a)

(b)

**Fig. 11-16.** *Pressure transducers*

The circuit of a *thermocouple vacuum gage* is shown in Fig. 11-17. The thermal conductivity of a gas is a function of the pressure of the gas, and the temperature of the heater element in this vacuum gage is a function of the heat produced in the element and the thermal conductivity of the surrounding gas at pressures below 1,000 $\mu$ (1/1,000 mm). The temperature of the heater element is measured with a thermocouple and a millivoltmeter.

The *Pirani vacuum gage* is also dependent upon the thermal conductivity of the surrounding gas. The temperature of the heater element is measured by the change of the resistance of the heater. This heater resistance is a leg of a bridge circuit. The unbalanced voltage across the bridge is calibrated to read the pressure. The circuit of the Pirani vacuum gage is shown in Fig. 11-18.

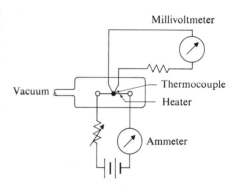

**Fig. 11-17.** *A thermocouple vacuum gage*

The circuit of an *ionization-type vacuum gage* is shown in Fig. 11-19. The ionization tube in this circuit is similar to a triode electron tube. The plate current is a function of the pressure of the gas in the tube when the potentials of the grid and the plate are constant. The range of this vacuum

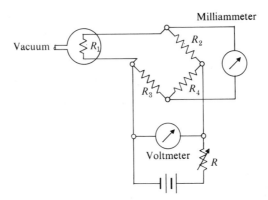

**Fig. 11-18.** *A Pirani vacuum gage*

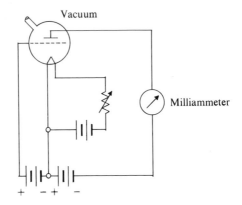

**Fig. 11-19.** *An ionization-type vacuum gage*

gage is from 10 to $10^{-6}\,\mu$ of mercury. It is very sensitive to vapors, and a liquid air trap is often used to prevent vapors from entering the tube.

## 11-14. THERMOCOUPLES[1,4,5]

The operation of a thermocouple was briefly described in Sec. 5-3, and the emf produced in a thermocouple circuit was given as

$$E = a\,\Delta t + b\,\Delta t^2 \tag{11-17}$$

where

$\Delta t$ = difference in temperature between the hot thermocouple junction and the reference junction of the thermocouple

$a$ = a constant

$b$ = a constant

and

$$a \gg b$$

A typical circuit of an iron-constantan thermocouple is shown in Fig. 11-20. The thermocouple junction is at the point where the temperature is being measured, and the reference junction is between the thermocouple and the millivoltmeter. At the metallic junction $a$, $b$, $c$, and $d$, an emf is produced

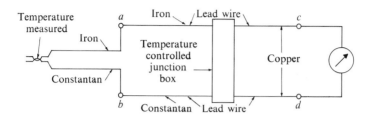

**Fig. 11-20.** *A typical circuit for measuring temperature with an iron-constantan thermocouple*

unless the lead material and the thermocouple wire have the same characteristics. Therefore, the leads from the thermocouple to the reference junction have the same characteristics as the thermocouple wire, and the leads from the reference junction to the millivoltmeter are copper. In modern instrumentation systems the reference-junction temperature is 150° to 200°F.

The common types of thermocouples are listed in Table 11-3, together with their range and temperature span for a 10-mv output.

The temperature of the thermocouple lags behind the temperature of the surrounding medium. This lag is a function of the size of the thermocouple wire and the material surrounding the wire. Many thermocouples are enclosed in a case to reduce their oxidation. These protective cases include an insulating material surrounding the thermocouple in a case of iron, steel, or Inconel. Other thermocouples are cast in ceramic materials such as Vycor (a glass) or porcelain. The response of a Chromel-Alumel No. 14 bare wire, a No. 14 Vycor covered wire, and a No. 14 calorized-iron-covered wire thermocouple, when they are suddenly plunged into dry air at 1,000°F, is shown in Fig. 11-21.

## 11-15. RESISTANCE THERMOMETERS[3]

The resistance thermometer uses the change in electrical resistance of a conductor to determine the temperature. The material used for the element of a resistance thermometer should have a continuous and stable relationship between the temperature and a high thermal coefficient of resistance. Metals used in resistance-thermometer elements include copper, with a resistivity of

Table 11-3

Characteristics of Thermocouples

| Thermocouple | Positive metal | Negative metal | Useful range (°F) | Temperature for 10-mv output with 32°F reference temperature (°F) | Average accuracy (%) |
|---|---|---|---|---|---|
| Copper-constantan | 100% Cu | 55% Cu, 44% Ni | −300 to 1,000 | 416 | ± 3/4 |
| Iron-constantan | 100% Fe | 55% Cu, 44% Ni | 0 to 1,300 | 368 | ± 1 |
| Chromel-alumel | 90% Ni, 9% Cr | 97% Ni, 3% Al | 600 to 1,800 | 475 | ± 3/4 |
| Platinum-platinum + 10% rhodium | 90% Pt, 10% Rh | 100% Pt | 1,200 to 2,900 | 1900 | ± 1/2 |
| Platinum-platinum + 13% rhodium | 87% Pt, 13% Rh | 100% Pt | 1,200 to 2,900 | 1767 | ± 1/2 |

9.4 ohms/mil-ft at 68°F and a temperature limit of 250°F; nickel, with a resistivity of 38 ohms/mil-ft at 68°F and a temperature limit of 600°F; and platinum, with a resistance of 59.1 ohms/mil-ft at 68°F and a temperature limit of 1,200°F. Most temperature thermometers have a lower temperature limit of −150°F, although platinum has been used to measure temperatures to −400°F.

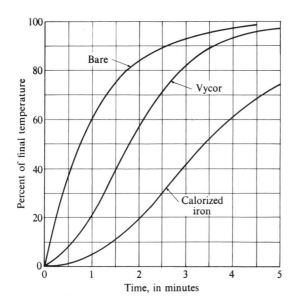

**Fig. 11-21.** *The response of a No. 14 wire Chromel-Alumel thermocouple with no coating, with Vycor coating, and with a calorized iron wall*

The Wheatstone bridge has three disadvantages when used to measure the resistance of a resistance thermometer: (1) The contact resistance of the adjustable standard resistor may be large enough to produce an error when measuring the change of resistance in the thermometer. (2) The leads from the thermometer element to the bridge may introduce an error owing to the change of their resistance produced by temperature changes. (3) The current through the thermometers produces a heating effect equal to the product of the current squared and the resistance of the element.

A double-slide-wire bridge is shown in Fig. 11-22. It has two slide-wire resistors $S_1$ and $S_2$ which are tied together so that the fraction of $S_1$ in series with the resistance $R_2$ is equal to the fraction of $S_2$ in series with resistance $R_3$. This fraction is defined as $f$. There are three equal leads from the thermometer to the bridge. The resistance of each of these leads is $R_L$. The resistance of the thermometer element is $R_T$. Then, for balanced conditions,

$$\frac{R_T + R_L}{fS_2 + R_3 + R_L} = \frac{R_1 + S_1 - fS_1}{fS_1 + R_2 + S_2 - fS_2}$$

If the right side of this equation is unity, the resistance of the thermometer element is

$$R_T = fS_2 + R_3 \qquad (11\text{-}18)$$

This condition is obtained when

$$R_1 + S_1 - fS_1 = fS_1 + R_2 + S_2 - fS_2$$

This is an identity when

$$R_1 - R_2 = S_1 = 0.5S_2 \qquad (11\text{-}19)$$

The bridge is designed using these values.

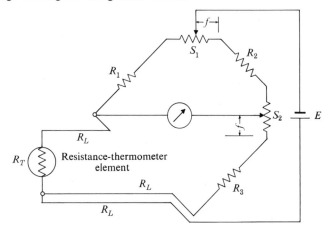

**Fig. 11-22.** *A double-slide-wire bridge and a resistance-thermometer element*

The heating effect due to the current through the resistive element of the thermometer is proportional to the power supplied to the resistive element. This power is the product of the current squared and the resistance $R_T$ of the element. Neglecting the resistance $R_L$ of the leads, the power is

$$P = \left(\frac{E}{R_T + R_1 + S_1 - fS_1}\right)^2 R_T \qquad (11\text{-}20)$$

The power $P$ is a function of $R_T$ and therefore is not constant. This will produce an error in the temperature measurement. This error is reduced by making $R_1$ very much larger than $R_T$. Then the variation of $R_T$ and $S_1 - fS$ will have minimum effect upon the power supplied to the element $R_T$.

Another simple bridge circuit with a resistance-thermometer element is shown in Fig. 11-23. It has a three-contact switch which can connect $R_O$, $R_{FS}$, or $R_T$ in the unknown branch of the bridge. In this circuit $R_O$ is a fixed resistance equal to the resistance of the resistance-thermometer element at zero degrees or some other reference temperature. When this resistance is connected in the unknown resistance branch of the bridge, the zero-adjustment potentiometer is adjusted until the recorder or converter reads zero or

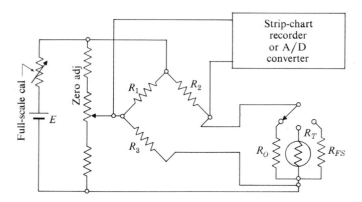

**Fig. 11-23.** *A resistance-thermometer element and temperature readout circuit*

the reference temperature. The fixed resistance $R_{FS}$ is equal to the resistance of the resistance-thermometer element at full-scale reading of the recorder or converter. When this resistance is connected into the unknown branch of the bridge, the full-scale calibrating resistor is adjusted until the recorder or converter reads full scale. Then the temperature is recorded with the resistance-thermometer element $R_T$ connected in the unknown arm of the bridge. The voltage output across the bridge is usually not a linear function of temperature and must be corrected by compensation in the circuit or in the readout system.

## 11-16. THERMISTORS AND THEIR CHARACTERISTICS[5,7,8]

Modern thermal resistors have been developed by sintering mixtures of metallic oxides such as manganese, nickel, cobalt, copper, iron, and uranium. These resistors have a high negative temperature coefficient of resistance. They are called "thermistors," a contraction of "thermal resistors."

Thermistors may be produced in several forms, as shown in Fig. 11-24. The beads can be made only a few thousandths of an inch in diameter, with the two fine lead wires placed parallel to each other and spaced 0.010 in. apart.

The beads may be coated with glass for protection. The disks may vary from 0.1 to 1 in. in diameter and from 0.020 to 0.5 in. thick. The rods are extruded through dies 0.053 to 0.17 in. in diameter.

Before discussing the applications, some of the characteristics of thermistors will be described.

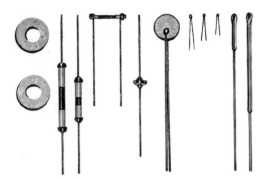

**Fig. 11-24.** *Typical thermistors (courtesy of Fenwal Electronics, Inc.)*

The mathematical expression for the relationship between the resistance of a thermistor and the absolute temperature of the thermistor is

$$\frac{R_{T1}}{R_{T2}} = e^{\beta} \left( \frac{1}{T1} - \frac{1}{T2} \right) \tag{11-21}$$

where

$R_{T1}$ = resistance of the thermistor at absolute temperature $T1$

$R_{T2}$ = resistance at absolute temperature $T2$

$e$ = base (2.718) of the natural logarithms

$\beta$ = a constant which depends on the material composing the thermistor

The *resistance-temperature characteristics* of two types of transistors and platinum are shown in Fig. 11-25. It will be noted that the type A thermistor changes from $10^4$ to less than 1 ohm/cir mil-ft, while platinum varies from $10^{-5}$ to $2.5 \times 10^{-5}$ ohm for a temperature change from 0° to 400°C. For the thermistor, the ratio of the resistance at these temperatures is $10^4$, and for platinum the ratio is 2.5.

The *voltage-current characteristics* of a thermistor are important. If the voltage applied to a thermistor is small, the current will be small, the voltage-current characteristics will obey Ohm's law, and the current will be proportional to the applied voltage; however, when the current in the thermistor is large enough to raise the temperature of the thermistor appreciably above the ambient temperature, the resistance of the thermistor will be decreased and more current will flow, further increasing the temperature and decreasing the resistance of the thermistor. This current will increase until the heat dissipation of the thermistor equals the electrical power supplied to the thermistor, and the resultant current will be greater than it would have been had the

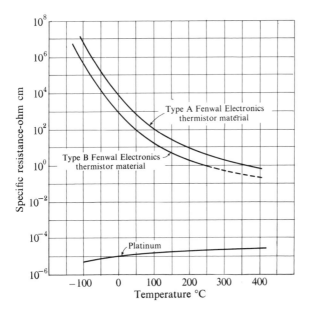

**Fig. 11-25.** *Resistance-temperature characteristics (courtesy of Fenwal Electronics, Inc.)*

thermistor remained at ambient temperature. Under normal operating conditions, this temperature is 200° to 300°C. The effect is illustrated in Fig. 11-26. The logarithm of the voltage is plotted as a function of the logarithm of the current, while the power and the resistance are read from the diagonal logarithmic scales. The current increases with increase in voltage until a maximum voltage is reached. Beyond this point the current increases with a decrease in voltage, and the thermistor has a negative resistance.

If a voltage is applied to a thermistor and a fixed resistor in series, the current will be determined by the total resistance of the circuit. When heating of the thermistor is sufficient to raise the temperature of the thermistor appreciably above the ambient temperature, the current will increase until the heat dissipation equals the electrical power supplied to the thermistor and equilibrium is obtained. The current as a function of time during this period of equilibrium is defined as the *current-time characteristics of the thermistor.* The current as a function of time is given for a resistor and thermistor with voltages of 30, 40, 50, 60, 70, and 80 volts applied to the circuit in Fig. 11-27. By choosing the types of thermistor, resistor, and voltage, time delays from 0.001 sec to several hours can be obtained.

## Applications of Thermistors[7, 8]

There are many ways in which thermistors may be used. A few of these will now be described.

*Temperature measurements* can be made by connecting a battery, a microammeter, and a thermistor in series, as shown in Fig. 11-28. The resistance of the thermistor may be 100,000 ohms or more, and that of the

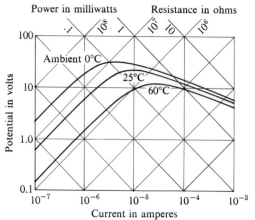

**Fig. 11-26.** *Voltage-current characteristics (courtesy of Fenwal Electronics, Inc.)*

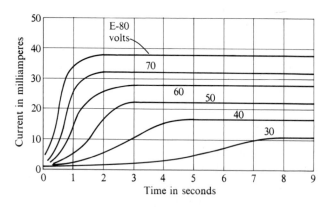

**Fig. 11-27.** *Current-time characteristics (courtesy of Fenwal Electronics Inc.)*

copper leads and the meter circuit is negligible. The only criteria required of this circuit are that the emf be constant and be limited to a value that will not raise the temperature appreciably above ambient, and that the microammeter be calibrated to read temperature. When a thermistor is used as a temperature sensing element in a bridge circuit as shown in Fig. 11-23, the sensitivity of the instrument is increased. This circuit can produce a sensitivity of 2°F at full scale.

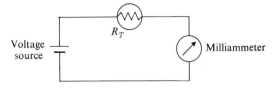

**Fig. 11-28.** *A simple circuit for measuring temperature*

The *difference of two temperatures* is measured by connecting two thermistors in the arms of a bridge circuit, as shown in Fig. 11-29. The output voltage of the bridge is a function of the temperature difference of the two thermistors.

Most elements have a positive temperature coefficient of resistance, and thermistors have a negative temperature coefficient of resistance. These thermistors, when shunted by a resistance, are used to compensate for the change of resistance produced by changes of temperature in a circuit. This *temperature compensation* is effectively used in complex electronic equipment, magnetic amplifiers, and instrumentation equipment.

The temperature-measuring circuits in Figs. 11-23 and 11-28 can be converted to *temperature-control circuits* by replacing the readout devices with a relay, as shown in Fig. 11-30. The variable resistors in these circuits determine the temperature at which the relays operate. The important criterion of these control circuits is that there be no appreciable rise above ambient temperature.

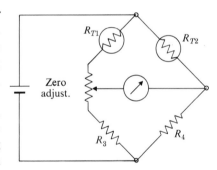

**Fig. 11-29.** *Two thermistor elements in a bridge circuit*

If the temperature does rise much above ambient, however, a *time-delay* circuit [Fig. 11-30(*a*)] is obtained. The resistance of the variable resistor will determine the time delay.

*High-frequency power* measurements are made using the circuit in Fig. 11-31. A 2,000-ohm thermistor and three 200-ohm fixed resistors form the bridge. The variable resistor in series with the bridge is varied until the bridge is balanced. Under these conditions the total resistance is 200 ohms, and the power supplied to the bridge is $200I^2$, where $I$ is the current measured by the ammeter. Then a high-frequency source is applied to the thermistor through the capacitors, and the variable resistance is adjusted until the bridge is balanced. The power to the bridge is computed, and the change in power is the high-frequency power supplied to the thermistor. Other values of resistance may be used, depending on the desired output resistance of the high-frequency source.

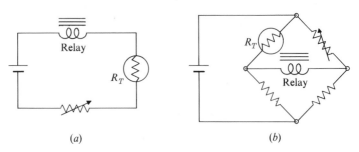

(a)                                        (b)

**Fig. 11-30.** *Temperature-control circuits*

A *thermal-conductivity instrument* is constructed by placing each of two bead thermistors in a small brass cavity and connecting them in the bridge circuit of Fig. 11-29. The emf applied to the bridge is sufficient to raise the temperature above 150°C. The bridge is balanced with air filling both cavities. Now, for example, if the air in one of the cavities is replaced by 100 percent carbon dioxide, which has a lower conductivity than air, the temperature of this thermistor will rise. This produces a change in resistance and an unbalance of the bridge. If the readout of this unbalanced bridge is set at 100 percent, the instrument will read the percent of carbon dioxide in the mixture in the cavity. This instrument is a *gas analyzer*.

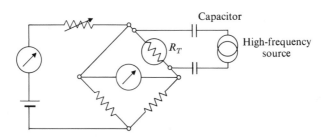

**Fig. 11-31.** *High-frequency power-measuring circuit*

A *flowmeter* is constructed with this same circuit. One thermistor bead is sealed in a brass block. The other is placed in a small pipe. When air flows through the pipe, the temperature of the thermistor is decreased because of conduction. The output of the bridge is calibrated to read the flow in the pipe. This instrument has been designed to measure flows as low as 0.001 cc/min, and one instrument can measure flow rates over a range of 100,000:1 by switching the resistance in series with the output meter.

When the sensing thermistor of the flowmeter is placed in free air, the instrument becomes an *anemometer* which measures the velocity of the air. It can be calibrated to measure, in miles per hour, velocities from a slight breeze to supersonic speeds.

If the sensing thermistor is sealed in an evacuated bulb, the instrument becomes a *vacuum gage.* It can be calibrated to measure from 1 to $10^{-5}$ mm of mercury.

## 11-17. RADIANT-ENERGY MEASUREMENTS[3,8]

The measurement of radiant energy has many applications. The choice of the measuring device depends on the frequency range of the radiant energy and the application. Some of these devices, with their wavelength range and their applications, are as follows:

*Thermal detectors* have an approximate wavelength range of 4 to 1,000 $\mu$. They include thermocouples, thermopiles, bolometers, pneumatics, thermal-image devices, and doped germanium and silicon cells. They are used in pyrometers, radiometers, infrared cameras, process-stream analyses, and automatic control devices.

*Photoconductive cells* have a wavelength range of approximately 1 to 10 $\mu$. They include lead selenide, lead telluride, indium antimonide, and doped germanium and silicon cells. They are used in pyrometers, radiometers, process-stream analyzers, microscopes, and infrared devices including search and tracking devices, telescopes, target detectors, and ranging devices.

*Photoelectric cells* have a wavelength range from approximately 0.2 to 2 $\mu$. They include photoemissive cells, photoconductive cells, photovoltaic cells, dielectric cells, thalofide cells, and phosphor cells. They are used for measuring radiant energy in the visible range for signal amplification using photomultiplier cells; and for spectroscopy, photography, thermoradiography, and display devices.

Some of these devices require special operating temperatures. Lead sulfide, lead selenide, lead telluride, and indium antimonide cells must have an operating temperature of 194°K, obtained with dry ice. Under some operating conditions germanium, silicon, and gold-dope germanium cells require a temperature of 20°K or less, obtained with liquid nitrogen, liquid hydrogen, or liquid helium. The latter has a temperature of 4°K.

Only a few of these radiant-energy measuring devices will be described. A more complete discussion will be found in References 2 and 8 at the end of this chapter.

### The Thermopile[2,3]

This device has several thermocouples in series. The hot junction is usually blackened to provide better absorption of radiant energy. This unit is a good detector of radiant energy. It is usually sealed in a transparent envelope, with the cold junctions sealed in the base. It is used in radiation pyrometers and infrared detectors. The thermopile and its envelope are shown in Fig. 11-32.

### The Bolometer[2,3,5]

The bolometer is a thin strip of blackened metal approximately 0.1 $\mu$ in thickness, 0.1 in. wide, and 0.5 in. long, with a glass film. The radiant energy increases the temperature of the metal strip, changing its resistance. This

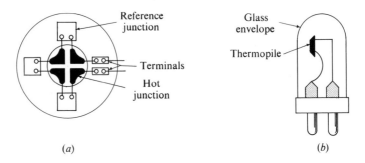

(a)  (b)

**Fig. 11-32.** *A thermopile and glass envelope*

change is measured with a bridge circuit. The strip may be coated with gold black or platinum black. Some bolometers use coated nitrocellulose film; others use columbium nitrate that becomes superconductive at the temperature of liquid hydrogen. Thermistors are also used as bolometers.

### Radiation Pyrometers[3,4,9,10]

The temperatures of bodies above the range of thermocouples are determined by measuring their radiant energy with a pyrometer. There are many kinds of pyrometers, but only the lens-type and mirror-type thermal pyrometers will be described here. The lens-type pyrometer has a lens which is used to concentrate the radiant energy on a thermopile, as shown in Fig. 11-33(a). This device is limited to the wavelengths of radiant energy that will pass through the lens. The mirror-type pyrometer uses a mirror instead of a lens to avoid this difficulty. This pyrometer is shown in Fig. 11-33(b).

**Photoemissive Cells[4,11]**

The photoemissive cell operates on the principle that incident radiant energy upon a sensitive surface produces an emission of electrons from its surface. These cells are also called phototubes. A typical phototube is shown

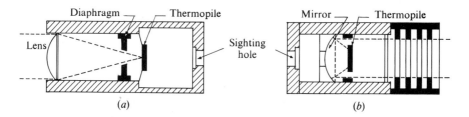

**Fig. 11-33.** *Lens-type and mirror-type pyrometers*

in Fig. 11-34($a$). The sensitive surface is the semicircular element which forms the *cathode* of the tube. The wire in the center of the tube is the *plate*. When the proper potential is applied between the cathode and plate, as shown in the circuit in Fig. 11-34($b$), the current in this circuit is a function of the radiant

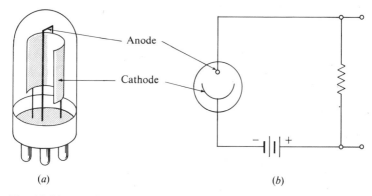

**Fig. 11-34.** *A phototube and a phototube circuit*

energy upon the cathode. The frequency response depends on the filtering action of the glass envelope of the tube. It is usually in the visual-light and infrared ranges.

This principle is used in photomultiplier tubes which use the principle of secondary emission. The plates of this tube are arranged so that the electrons striking the plate will produce further electron emission from the plates. This arrangement is shown in Fig. 11-35($a$), and a schematic of the operation of the tube is shown in Fig. 11-35(*b*). Further information about these tubes may be found in any modern electronics textbook.

### Photoconductive Cells[4]

Photoconductive cells operate on the principle that the resistance of some semiconductor materials changes when exposed to radiant energy in the visual-light and infrared ranges.

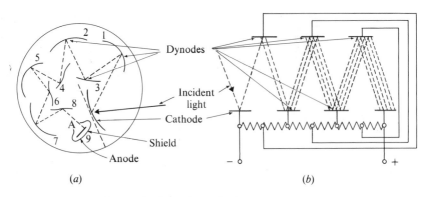

(a)          (b)

**Fig. 11-35.** *A photomultiplier tube and schematic*

These cells are constructed by depositing lead sulfide, lead selenide, or lead telluride on a small cell blank, as well as by crystal-growth processes forming semiconductor crystals such as indium phosphide, indium arsenide, indium antimonide, germanium, silicon, and doped germanium-silicon mixtures. Impurities are added to the pure zone-refined crystal during growth to produce doped crystals. The construction of these cells is schematically shown in Fig. 11-36.

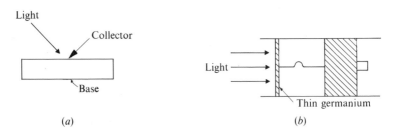

(a)          (b)

**Fig. 11-36.** *Photoconducting cells*

### Photovoltaic Cells[4,11]

The photovoltaic cell has a photosensitive barrier of high resistance deposited between two layers of conducting material which builds up a potential difference between the two layers when exposed to radiant energy in the visual-light and infrared ranges. In contrast to the photoemissive and photoconducting cells, the photovoltaic cells do not require an external power supply. Typical examples of these cells are the copper oxide on copper and the iron selenide on iron combinations. The semiconductor material may

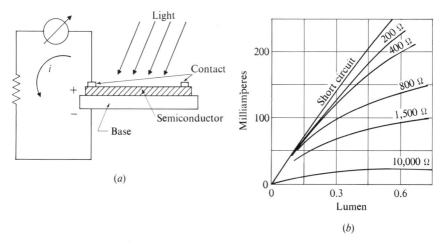

(a)

(b)

**Fig. 11-37.** *Photovoltaic-cell construction and the output as a function of lumens for various loads*

be covered with a thin layer of conducting lacquer. A sketch of the construction of a photovoltaic cell and a graph of the output of the cell as a function of the incident radiant energy, in lumens, for various load resistances is given in Fig. 11-37.

## 11-18. NUCLEAR INSTRUMENTATION [6,9]

A vast amount of instrumentation is used to measure the amount of radioactivity encountered in nuclear research and in tracking radiated alpha, beta, and gamma particles. The energy of these particles is absorbed by other molecules, producing a chemical change, ionization, or reactions that produce visual evidence of the presence of the particles. These processes are used to detect, count, and trace the movements of such particles.

The alpha particle is a helium nucleus with a mass of $62 \times 10^{-24}$ gm and a charge of $+3.2 \times 10^{-19}$ coulomb. It will penetrate about 0.002 cm of aluminum foil. The beta particle is an electron (or positron) with a mass of $9.03 \times 10^{-28}$ gm and a charge of $-1.6 \times 10^{-19}$ coulomb. Its penetration is about 100 times that of an alpha particle. Gamma particles, or gamma rays, have an electromagnetic radiation with a wavelength of approximately 0.03 to 3 angstrom (A; that is, $10^{-10}$ m). It can penetrate several centimeters of lead. These and other properties of these particles must be considered in the processes used for their detection and measurement. The discussion here will be limited to ionization chambers, proportional counters, Geiger counters, and scintillation counters.

### The Ionization Chamber[6,9]

The construction of a metal envelope filled with low-pressure gas with an electrode in the center is shown in Fig. 11-38(*a*), and the circuit used to measure the electron flow in the gas due to the particles produced by radioactivity

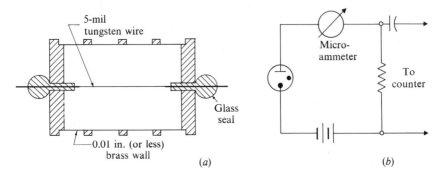

**Fig. 11-38.** *A gaseous-discharge chamber and circuit*

is shown in Fig. 11-38(*b*). The current that flows in the circuit is a function of the applied voltage. This relationship is shown in Fig. 11-39. It must be noted that this current is not constant but is a random pulse as a particle collides with a molecule of the gas. This pulse amplitude on a logarithmic scale is plotted as a function of voltage on a linear scale.

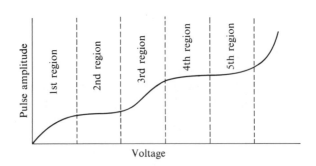

**Fig. 11-39.** *Voltage characteristics of a gas-discharge chamber*

In the first region of this graph, the pulse amplitude increases with voltage. The applied voltage is small, and the electrons produced by the collision of a particle with a molecule recombine with the positive ion to form a neutral ion before it can excite another molecule. Only a few of the electrons reach the anode, and the pulse amplitude is very small. The second region of this graph is flat. The anode voltage is large enough to collect all the electrons produced by particles colliding with molecules, but the electron velocity is not great enough to excite other molecules. This region is used in *ionization-chamber detectors*. These detectors operate on 100 to 500 volts. They have a unity gas amplification (no excitation of molecules by electrons released from other molecules). The main use of this transducer is to measure alpha particles. Air, carbon dioxide, nitrogen, argon, and methane gases are used in ionization chambers.

### The Proportional Counter[6,9]

Referring again to Fig. 11-39, the third region in this graph has an increase in the pulse amplitude with an increase in voltage. In this region the voltage applied to the elements of the ionization chamber gives the electrons or ions produced by particle collision sufficient velocity and kinetic energy to ionize other molecules. This produces more and more ions as the voltage is increased. The production of new ions by the collision of neutral molecules with other electrons and ions is called a *Townsend avalanche*. The ratio of the number of electrons produced by collision to the number of primary ions produced by radioactivity is the *gas-amplification factor*. A transducer that operates in this region is a proportional counter. Its circuit is shown in Fig. 11-38(*b*). It operates at voltages between 500 and 800 volts. Its gas amplification is $10^5$ to $10^6$. It is usually employed to detect alpha particles in the presence of beta and gamma particles. It can also separate alpha and beta particles. It uses methane with 10 to 20 percent argon gas. The thickness of the walls is used to filter or reject the alpha particles.

### The Geiger Counter[5,8]

The fourth region of the pulse-amplitude–voltage-characteristic curve in Fig. 11-39 is flat. It is of no use as a detector of radioactive particles.

The fifth region is used in Geiger counters. In this transducer the ionization chamber is called a Geiger-Müller tube. Often, this is shortened to Geiger tube. This tube usually requires 800 to 1,500 volts, although there are Geiger tubes that operate as low as 300 volts. Argon with a few percent organic vapor or a halogen is used in this tube. It is mainly used to detect beta and gamma particles. In this tube the Townsend avalanches are transmitted through the entire tube and are no longer confined to a small area. When this occurs the ionization in the tube continues until some means is provided to stop it. The process of stopping the ionization is known as *quenching*. There are two methods of quenching a Geiger tube: one means is *self-quenching*, with the use of some polyatomic vapor in the tube. The polyatomic vapors absorb the radiant energy produced by a Townsend avalanche and give off energy at a much longer wavelength. This prevents another Townsend avalanche from occurring until another particle enters the Geiger tube. The other method is *external quenching*, which necessitates some way of applying a negative potential to the anode of the tube for a few microseconds after an avalanche occurs. The time for a pulse to reach its maximum value varies from 2 $\mu$sec to milliseconds. It is a function of the resistance of the electrical circuit. The time from the beginning of a pulse to the time when all the positive ions have been moved away from the anode is the *dead time*. This varies from 5 $\mu$sec to milliseconds. The time from the end of one pulse to the beginning of another is the *recovery time*. Its counting rate is seldom greater than $10^3$ counts/sec.

### The Scintillation Counter[6,9]

The scintillation counter employs a photomultiplier to detect tiny flashes of light produced by alpha, beta, and gamma particles striking a suitable phosphor. A sketch of this transducer is shown in Fig. 11-40.

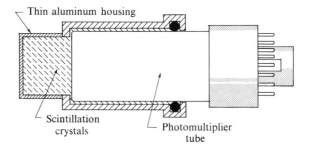

Thin aluminum housing

Scintillation crystals

Photomultiplier tube

**Fig. 11-40.** *A scintillation counter*

The phosphors used in these scintillation counters include the organic crystals of anthracene, stilbene, terphenyl, and naphthalene; inorganic crystals of zinc sulfide with a trace of silver and sodium iodide with a trace of thallium; a liquid of toluene with 3 to 5 gm/liter of terphenyl; and a plastic polystyrene or polyvinyl toluene with 3 percent terphenyl and 0.02 percent tetraphenyl butadiene. Pulses as short as $2 \times 10^{-9}$ sec have been recorded with these transducers. The output of the photomultiplier is applied to a high-speed electronic counter which counts each tiny flash of light generated in the scintillating phosphor.

## 11-19. MAGNETIC FLUX AND HYSTERESIS MEASUREMENTS [4,5,6]

A transducer that converts magnetic flux to an emf may consist of (1) a changing flux passing through a coil, (2) a conductor moving at right angles to the flux, or (3) the change in the electrical properties of the material. The standard circuit for measuring the change in flux produced by the change in mmf for determining the hysteresis loop of a sample of magnetic material is given in Fig. 11-41. The calibration coil is used to determine the flux-linkage

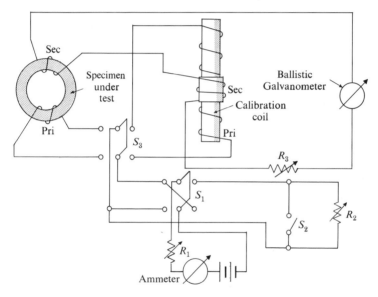

**Fig. 11-41.** *A circuit using a ballistic galvanometer for determining the hysteresis loop of a sample*

sensitivity of the circuit, as given in Sec. 3-26. The change in flux can then be determined by the maximum deflection of the galvanometer. The mmf is the product of the primary turns on the specimen and the current through this winding. The value of $R_1$ determines the maximum current applied to the primary winding during any given hysteresis loop. The value of $R_2$ determines the point to be measured on this loop, and $R_3$ controls the sensitivity of the galvanometer. Care must be taken to establish a stable loop before making any measurements, and to be sure that a complete forward cycle is made for each measurement.

This same hysteresis loop can be obtained with fair accuracy with a cathode-ray oscilloscope and the circuit given in Fig. 11-42. This circuit is called a *cathode-ray hysteresiscope.*

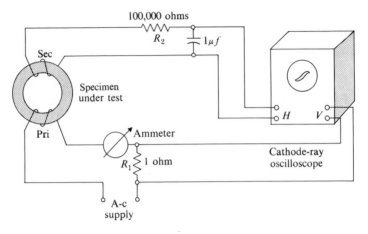

**Fig. 11-42.** *A cathode-ray hysteresiscope which uses a cathode-ray oscilloscope for tracing the hysteresis loop of a sample*

A *gauss meter* is shown in Fig. 11-43. The torque exerted on a small magnet by magnetic induction is balanced by the restoring torque of a spiral spring. As the instrument is turned in a counterclockwise direction, the pointer mounted on the same shaft as the magnet will indicate increasing gauss until a point is reached where the pointer suddenly returns to the zero stop position. The maximum gauss indicated by the pointer is the magnetic induction at the sensing point of the instrument. This instrument has an accuracy of 1 percent when special calibration methods are used, but commercial tolerances are commonly in the order of 5 percent.

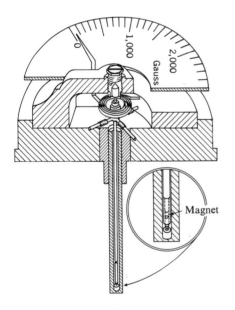

**Fig. 11-43.** *A gauss meter of the magnetometer type for measuring magnetic induction*

None of these instruments convert magnetic flux into a voltage acceptable to a modern instrumentation system. Figure 11-44 uses magnetic *mumetal wires* in a magnetic field. The impedance of the wires is a function of the magnetic field. This impedance is measured with an a-c bridge. This transducer produces an acceptable emf for the input to a modern instrumentation system. It is capable of an accuracy of 0.01 millioersted when measuring a constant field strength.

A similar instrument is shown in Fig. 11-45. It uses *bismuth spirals* in a bridge circuit. The resistance of the bismuth changes with the strength of the magnetic field. This instrument is capable of obtaining a full-scale reading of 500 to over 20,000 oersteds with a 50-ma bridge current.

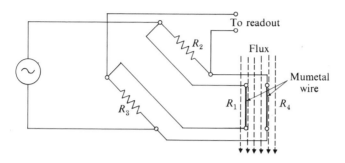

**Fig. 11-44.** *An a-c mumetal-wire bridge circuit for measuring small constant magnetic fields*

Another transducer uses the Hall effect in germanium. The circuit of this transducer is shown in Fig. 11-46. Leads 1 and 2 conduct current through a plate of germanium material. Leads 3 and 4 are at the same potential when there is no magnetic flux passing through the plate. When there is a magnetic

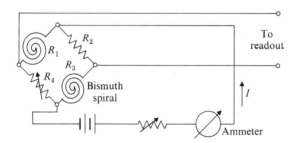

**Fig. 11-45.** *A bismuth-spiral bridge circuit for measuring magnetic fields*

flux through the plate, the emf between leads 3 and 4 is proportional to the product of the current and the field strength. Many materials exhibit the Hall effect, but in nearly all other materials it is so small that it cannot be used for measuring flux. Germanium has been produced with a Hall constant of $4 \times 10^{-5}$ volt-cm/amp-gauss. Crystals of germanium have been made as small as $1/16 \times 1/16 \times 0.025$ in. These crystals make by far the smallest probe available for measuring magnetic flux. These crystals should be operated with current densities not to exceed 2 amp/sq in.

### 11-20. $p$H MEASUREMENTS[2,3]

The degree of acidity or alkalinity is usually measured in terms of the hydronium ions $H_3O^+$ (the older theory used the hydrogen ion $H^+$) and the hydroxyl ion $OH^+$. The $p$H scale is generally used for measuring acidity or alkalinity of aqueous solutions. It is defined by the equation

$$pH = \log_{10} \frac{1}{h}$$

where $h$ is the $H_3O^+$ ion concentration. Water is neutral at 77°F and has a $p$H of 7.0. A $p$H of 0 corresponds to an acid of unit strength, and a $p$H of 14

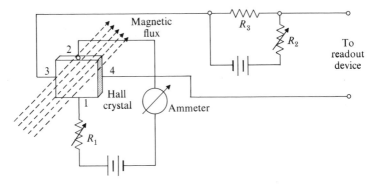

**Fig. 11-46.** *A circuit for measuring the magnetic field by use of the Hall effect*

corresponds to a basic solution of unit strength. It will be observed that a change of 1 unit in $p$H is a change of 10 in the ratio of concentration. The most common method of measuring $p$H is with a glass cell, called a measuring electrode, and a calomel cell, called a reference electrode. These electrodes are placed in the solution, and the emf generated between the two electrodes is measured with a potentiometer. A cross section of these cells and their external circuit is shown in Fig. 11-47.

The measuring electrode has a buffer solution of known $p$H permanently sealed in a very thin glass bulb. A platinum wire extends through the glass envelope and makes an electrical connection from the buffer solution to the external circuit. The thin glass envelope is part of the electrical circuit and may give the circuit a resistance as large as $10^9$ ohms.

The reference electrode has an inner container filled with a mixture of calomel (mercury and mercurous chloride). A wire connects this solution with the external circuit. The bottom of this container is packed with glass wool. A small capillary connects the portion of the inner container which is filled with glass wool to the external container which is filled with a saturated solution of potassium chloride. A porous filter connects this solution with the solution under test. Some of the potassium chloride slowly escapes from the electrode to the liquid being measured.

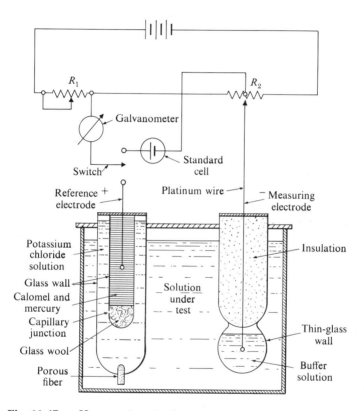

**Fig. 11-47.** *pH-measuring circuit*

The resistivity of the glass in the measuring electrode is a function of the temperature, and this parameter is compensated by connecting a resistance-thermometer element in series with the electrode. Both of the electrodes and the resistance thermometer must have suitable housings which can be immersed in the tank or stream of the liquid under test. The operating conditions for these electrodes are from 34° to 212°F at pressures up to 30 psi.

The potential produced by these electrodes is very small, as practically no current flows through the cell. This small potential requires amplification before it is measured with a potentiometer. The scale on the potentiometer can be made to read the *p*H being measured. Also the output of the amplifiers can be applied directly to a modern data-acquisition system.

## 11-21. TIME MEASUREMENTS[6,12,13]

The precise measurement of time and of very short time intervals is required in many types of instrumentation. These time-measuring systems

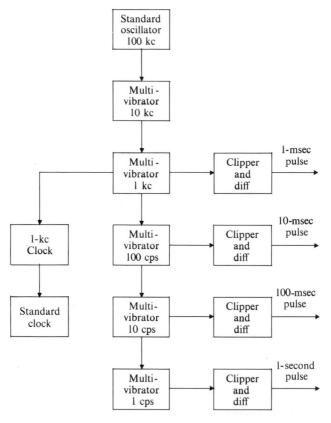

**Fig. 11-48.** *A standard quartz oscillator and time-pulse generator*

have been highly developed in connection with missile tracking, navigational radar, nuclear instrumentation, and acquisition and data-reduction systems. Precise measurements of time intervals less than 1/10 $\mu$sec are readily performed by electronic means.

Mechanical oscillatory-type spring-driven clocks and electrical synchronous-motor clocks are used for strip-chart and disk-chart drives. Synchronous motors are also used for magnetic tape drives, where the tape displacement per unit time must be a very precise value. To identify further the data with the time when it was acquired, magnetic tapes and strip-chart recorders employ a separate information channel to record a coded timing pulse which is synchronized with the recorded data. Then each increment of data is identified with an accurately measured time interval. A large data-acquisition system usually has a central clocking system. This clocking system sends out very short time pulses at precise time intervals. These are normally 1-msec, 10-msec, 100-msec, or 1-sec intervals. All the intervals may be generated by the same clock and identified by the width of the pulse. In some cases the exact time is given by a mark followed by the exact time given in a binary or a binary-coded decimal-number system written serially on the tape or chart. (These number systems are explained in Chap. 13.) The timing systems are not confined to these time intervals. In some high-speed computers the time interval between pulses is $1/10$ $\mu$sec, and with some solid-state devices a much shorter period is possible.

Electronics or transistor pulse generators are usually controlled with a quartz crystal oscillator. The controlling unit of this oscillator is a small quartz plate between two electrodes which produce a precise frequency when properly excited with an emf. The piezoelectric properties of the quartz plate maintain the frequency of the oscillator to within a few cycles in $10^8$ cycles. This is maintained over a period of several months.[13] The normal frequency range of these oscillators is from 50 to 100 kc. This can be reduced by electronic or transistor multivibrators. A block diagram of a crystal-controlled oscillator and frequency-reducing multivibrators and pulse generators is shown in Fig. 11-48.

When it is necessary to keep in step an instrumentation system that is spread over a wide area, such as a missile- or satellite-tracking system, the time signals from the Bureau of Standards radio stations WWV near Washington D.C., and WWVH at Mani, Hawaii, are used to set the timing at each location.

## PROBLEMS

**11-1.** A strain-gage bridge, as shown in Fig. 11-2($b$), has two fixed resistors $R_1$ and $R_2$ of 120 ohms each, and a variable resistance which is 120.00 ohms at zero strain and 120.63 ohms with a strain $e$. The gage factor is 2.04. Determine the strain in the beam at the point where the strain gage is attached.

**11-2.** The unstrained resistance of the four strain gages in the bridge circuit shown in Fig. 11-2($f$) is 120 ohms each. The gage factor is 2.04. The battery current is 0.05 amp. The strain is 0.00011. At balance, the input resistance to the potentiometer is infinite. Determine the voltage output of the bridge.

**11-3.** In Prob. 11-2, the bridge circuit in Fig. 11-2($f$) is replaced by the bridge circuit shown in Fig. 11-2($d$). $R_1$ and $R_3$ are each 120 ohms. Determine the voltage output of this bridge.

**11-4.** In Table 11-1, soft-iron wire of small diameter has a gage factor of $+4.2$. Determine the Poisson ratio of this wire.

**11-5.** Determine the sensitivity in volts per strain of the transducer given in Prob. 11-3.

**11-6.** Determine the resolution of the circuit in Prob. 11-3 if the potentiometer reads 100 $\mu$volts/division and 1/10 of a division can be estimated without difficulty.

**11-7.** The rated load on a strain-gage load cell produces a strain of 0.0012. The load cell has two strain gages connected as $R_1$ and $R_4$ in Fig. 11-4($c$). At full load, both of the strain gages are in compression, and the strain of each gage is 0.0012. The resistance of the unstrained gages is 120 ohms each. The gage factor is 2.04. The fixed resistors $R_2$ and $R_3$ are 120 ohms each. Determine the value of the calibrating resistor $R_C$ for calibrating this circuit for full-load conditions.

**11-8.** Four unbonded strain gages are connected as shown in Fig. 11.4. Each has an unstrained resistance of 350 ohms and a gage factor of 4.4. The accelerometer is rated at 900 ft/sec/sec. At this acceleration the strain of the gages is 0.0015. Determine the resistance of the calibrating resistor to calibrate this circuit for rated load.

**11-9.** A differential transformer, as shown in Fig. 11-6, has an output of 6 volts rms when the displacement is $16 \times 10^{-6}$ in. Determine the sensitivity of this instrument in volts/$\mu$in.

**11-10.** The voltmeter used to read the output voltage in Prob. 11-9 has a 10-volt scale with 100 divisions. Two tenths of a division can be estimated with ease. Determine the resolution of this instrument.

**11-11.** The differential transformer and the voltmeter in Probs. 11.9 and 11.10 are used as part of a pressure transducer by measuring the deflection of a diaphragm. The diaphragm is deflected $19.4 \times 10^{-6}$ in. by a pressure of 156 psi. Determine the sensitivity and resolution of this instrument.

**11-12.** In Fig. 11-8($b$) the diaphragms are 1.25 in. in diameter and 0.14 in. apart. A pressure of 125 psi on one diaphragm will produce an average deflection of 0.011 in. Without any pressure on the transducer the capacitance is 372 $\mu\mu$f. Determine the capacitance after 125 psi pressure is applied to one diaphragm.

**11-13.** The reluctance-type revolution counter shown in Fig. 11-13 has 100 teeth. The counter records 3,600 counts/sec. Determine the revolutions per minute of the shaft.

**11-14.** Describe the operation of a thermocouple vacuum gage.

**11-15.** Describe the operation of a Pirani vacuum gage.

**11-16.** Describe the operation of an ionization-type vacuum gage.

**11-17.** ($a$) List the advantages of a resistance thermometer compared with a thermocouple for measuring temperatures. ($b$) List the advantages of a thermocouple compared with a resistance thermometer.

**11-18.** ($a$) What is a thermistor? ($b$) Describe at least eight applications of this device.

**11-19.** List the instruments that would be used to measure the following temperatures, and give the reasons for their use: (*a*) 150° ± 5°; (*b*) 340° ± 2°; (*c*) 920° ± 10°; (*d*) 1,220° ± 20°; (*e*) 3,000°; (*f*) 5,200°F.

**11-20.** Describe a radiation pyrometer and list its applications.

**11-21.** Describe a bolometer.

**11-22.** (*a*) What is the difference between a photoemissive cell, a photoconductive cell, and a photovoltaic cell? (*b*) Give the applications of each of these cells.

**11-23.** Describe the operation and application of: (*a*) a proportional counter; (*b*) an ionization-chamber detector; (*c*) a Geiger counter; (*d*) a scintillation counter.

**11-24.** Define self-quenching, external quenching, dead time, and recovery time, as applied to a Geiger counter.

**11-25.** Explain the operation of a cathode-ray hysteresiscope.

**11-26.** Describe a gauss meter and give its accuracy.

**11-27.** Compare the operation of a mumetal-wire bridge and a bismuth spiral bridge.

**11-28.** How is the Hall effect used to measure the strength of a magnetic field?

**11-29.** (*a*) Define *p*H. (*b*) How is *p*H measured?

**11-30.** Why is time an important factor in most instrumentation problems?

**11-31.** Describe the operation of a quartz-controlled clock and pulse-generating system.

## REFERENCES

1. M. B. Stout, *Basic Electrical Measurements* 2nd ed., Prentice-Hall, Inc., Englewood Cliffs, N.J., 1960.

2. D. P. Eckman, *Industrial Instrumentation*, John Wiley & Sons, Inc., New York, 1950.

3. C. C. Perry and H. R. Lissner, *The Strain Gage Primer*, McGraw-Hill Book Company, New York, 1955.

4. I. F. Kinnard, *Applied Electrical Measurements*, John Wiley & Sons, Inc., New York, 1956.

5. W. C. Michels, *Electrical Measurements and Their Applications*, D. Van Nostrand Company, Inc., Princeton, N.J., 1957.

6. G. R. Partridge, *Principles of Electronic Instruments*, Prentice-Hall, Inc., Englewood Cliffs, N.J., 1958.

7. *Thermistor Manual*, Fenwal Electronics, Inc., Framingham, Mass.

8. D. M. Warschaner, *Semiconductors and Transistors*, McGraw-Hill Book Company, Inc., New York, 1959.

9. *Reference Data for Radio Engineers*, 4th ed., International Telephone and Telegraph Corporation, 1956.

10. H. L. Hackforth, *Infrared Radiation*, McGraw-Hill Book Company, Inc., New York, 1960.

11. J. D. Ryder, *Engineering Electronics*, McGraw-Hill Book Company, Inc., New York, 1957, Chap. 13.

12. F. E. Terman and J. M. Pettit, *Electronic Measurements*, McGraw-Hill Book Company, Inc., New York, 1952.

13. B. Chance, R. I. Hulsizer, E. F. MacNichol, Jr., F. C. Williams, *Electronic Time Measurements*, Radiation Laboratory Series, Vol. 20, McGraw-Hill Book Company, Inc., New York, 1949.

# Chapter 12

# ANALOG

## 12-1. INTRODUCTION

Analog quantities are continuous functions. The curve of the current as a function of time on a recording ammeter is a typical illustration of an analog record. An electrical analog computer is a network which operates upon the input voltages of the computer and produces output voltages which are the desired functions of the input voltages. Not only is it necessary that the computer produce the desired functions of the voltage inputs; it also must be easily changed to solve many types of problems. Often, the input and output voltages are functions of time, and a record of the solution of the problem is recorded on a multichannel recorder. Some of the basic circuits used in analog computers will now be described.

## 12-2. AVERAGING CIRCUITS[1,2]

In Fig. 12-1, several input voltages are supplied to an averaging circuit. When the resistance of the output circuit is infinite, the voltage $X_0$ across $R_0$

# ELECTRICAL

# COMPUTERS

is

$$X_0 = R_0(I_1 + I_2 + \ldots + I_n)$$

But

$$I_1 = \frac{X_1 - X_0}{R_1}$$

$$I_2 = \frac{X_2 - X_0}{R_2}$$

and

$$I_n = \frac{X_n - X_0}{R_n}$$

Then

$$X_0 = R_0\left(\frac{X_1 - X_0}{R_1} + \frac{X_2 - X_0}{R_2} + \ldots + \frac{X_n - X_0}{R_n}\right)$$

$$= R_0 \sum_{i=n}^{n} \frac{X_i}{R_i} - R_0 X_0 \sum_{i=n}^{n} \frac{1}{R_i}$$

$$X_0 = \frac{R_0 \sum_{i=1}^{n} \frac{X_i}{R_i}}{1 + R_0 \sum_{i=1}^{n} \frac{1}{R_i}} \tag{12-1}$$

when

$$R_0 \sum_{i=1}^{n} \frac{1}{R_i} \gg 1 \quad \text{and} \quad R_i = R_1 = R_2 = R_3, \text{etc.}$$

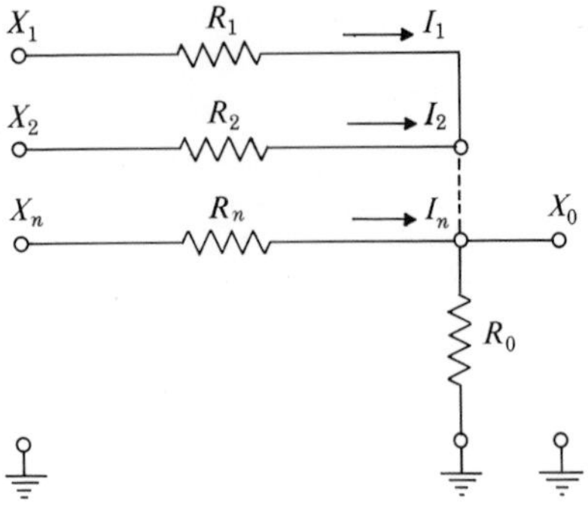

Fig. 12-1. *Averaging circuit*

$$X_0 \approx \frac{\sum_{i=1}^{n} X_i}{n} \tag{12-2}$$

which is the average of $\sum_{i=1}^{n} X_i$

## 12-3.  SUMMING CIRCUIT[1,2]

In the circuit shown in Fig. 12-2(a), $A$ is a very-high-gain d-c amplifier. Amplifiers of this type are called *operational amplifiers* in analog-computer circuits. The gain of the amplifier is $-A$, and the input voltage to the amplifier is $E$. It is assumed that the input impedance of the amplifier is infinite and that no current flows into the amplifier. The output voltage of the amplifier is

$$X_0 = -AE$$

Then the input voltage to the amplifier is

$$E = \frac{X_0}{-A}$$

and the input currents are

$$I_1 = \frac{X_1 + \dfrac{X_0}{A}}{R_1}$$

$$I_2 = \frac{X_2 + \dfrac{X_0}{A}}{R_2}$$

$$I_n = \frac{X_n + \dfrac{X_0}{A}}{R_0}$$

and

$$I_0 = \frac{X_0 + \dfrac{X_0}{A}}{R_0}$$

Then applying Kirchhoff's first law to point $E$ gives

$$\frac{X_0 + \dfrac{X_0}{A}}{R_0} = -\left(\frac{X_1 + \dfrac{X_0}{A}}{R_1} + \frac{X_2 + \dfrac{X_0}{A}}{R_2} + \ldots + \frac{X_n + \dfrac{X_0}{A}}{R_n}\right)$$

$$X_0\left[\frac{1}{R_0} + \frac{1}{A}\left(\frac{1}{R_0} - \frac{1}{R_1} - \frac{1}{R_2} - \ldots - \frac{1}{R_n}\right)\right] = -\left(\frac{X_1}{R_1} + \frac{X_2}{R_2} + \ldots + \frac{X_n}{R_n}\right)$$

$$X_0 = -\left(\frac{R_0}{R_1} X_1 + \frac{R_0}{R_2} X_2 + \ldots + \frac{R_0}{R_n} X_n\right) \qquad (12\text{-}3)$$

when $A \gg 1$

In Eq. (12-3), the output of the summing circuit is the negative of the sum of each input voltage multiplied by a factor which is equal to the ratio of the

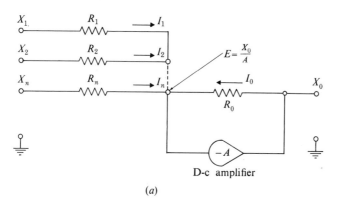

(a)

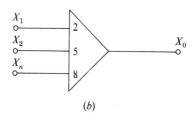

(b)

**Fig. 12-2.** *Summing circuit*

feedback resistance $R_0$ to the input resistance. For example, the sum of $2X_1 + 5X_2 + 8X_3$ would be obtained by setting $R_0 = 10^6$ ohms, $R_1 = 0.5 \times 10^6$ ohms, $R_2 = 0.2 \times 10^6$ ohms, and $R_3 = 0.125 \times 10^6$ ohms.

Then

$$X_0 = -\left(\frac{R_0}{R_1} X_1 + \frac{R_0}{R_2} X_2 + \frac{R_0}{R_3} X_3\right)$$
$$= -(2X_1 + 5X_2 + 8X_3)$$

where $X_1$, $X_2$, and $X_3$ are the input voltages.

The symbol shown in Fig. 12-2($b$) is used for a summing circuit. The number inside the triangle opposite each input is the coefficient of the input in the summation. Thus in Fig. 12-2($b$) the number by the input $X_1$ is 2, the number by the input $X_2$ is 5, and the number by the input $X_3$ is 8. Usually, $R_0$ is 1 megohm, and common resistors in this range have resistances of 0.1, 0.2, 0.5, 1.0, and 2 megohms. Therefore the coefficients that are available in the summing circuit are usually 10, 5, 2, 1, and 0.5.

It will be noted, from Eq. (12-3), that the output of a summing circuit is the negative of the sum of voltage inputs multiplied by their respective

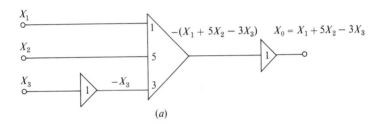

($a$)

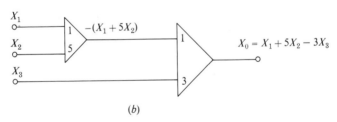

($b$)

**Fig. 12-3.** *Solution of* $X_0 = X_1 + 5X_2 - 3X_3$

coefficients. The output of a single-input summing circuit with a ratio of the feedback resistance to the input resistance of unity is the same as the input except for sign. Now consider the solution of the equation

$$X_0 = X_1 + 5X_2 - 3X_3$$

The block diagram of the circuit for the solution of this equation is shown in Fig. 12-3($a$). The first summing circuit to the left with an input of $X_3$ circuit has an output of $-X_3$. The inputs to the second summing circuit from the left are $X_1$, $X_2$, and $-X_3$. The coefficients of these terms introduced by the summing circuit are 1, 5, and 3, respectively, and the output of this circuit is $-(X_1 + 5X_2 - 3X_3)$. The output of the second summing circuit is the input to the third summing circuit which has a coefficient of unity. The output of the third summing circuit is $X_0 = X_1 + 5X_2 - 3X_3$.

A circuit which will solve this problem, using two summing circuits, is shown in Fig. 12-3(b). The first summing circuit to the left has two input voltages $X_1$ and $X_2$ with coefficients of 1 and 5, respectively, introduced by the summing circuit. The output of this summing circuit is $-(X_1 + 5X_2)$. This output voltage of the first summing circuit and $X_3$ are the input voltages to the second summing circuit which has coefficients of 1 and 3, respectively. The output of the second summing circuit is

$$X_0 = X_1 + 5X_2 - 3X_3$$

which is the desired solution.

## 12-4. INTEGRATING CIRCUITS [1,2,3]

A basic integrating circuit is shown in Fig. 12-4 with an input voltage $X_1$ and an output voltage $X_0$. The resistance $R$ is in series with the input, and the

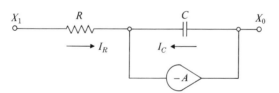

**Fig. 12-4.** *Basic integrating circuit*

feedback of the operational amplifier is through the capacitance $C$. The current in the resistance $R$ is

$$I_R = \frac{X_1 + \dfrac{X_0}{A}}{R}$$

and the voltage across the capacitance $C$ is

$$E_C = X_0 + \frac{X_0}{A} = \frac{1}{C} \int_0^T I_c \, dt = \frac{I_c}{CP}$$

where $P$ is the operator

$$P = \frac{d}{dt}$$

Then

$$PX = \frac{dX}{dt}$$

and

$$\frac{1}{P} X = \int X \, dt$$

Solving for the current through the capacitance $C$ gives

$$I_C = \left(X_0 + \frac{X_0}{A}\right) CP$$

Assuming that the input current to the operational amplifier is zero, then

$$I_R + I_C = 0$$

and

$$\frac{X_1 + \dfrac{X_0}{A}}{R} = -\left(X_0 + \frac{X_0}{A}\right) CP$$

Solving for $X_0$ gives

$$X_0 = \frac{-\dfrac{X_1}{R}}{\left(\dfrac{1 + A}{A}\right) CP + \dfrac{1}{AR}}$$

$$= \frac{-AX_1}{(1 + A)RCP + 1}$$

When $ARCP \gg RCP + 1$ or $A \gg 1$

$$X_0 \approx \frac{-X_1}{RCP}$$

$$= -\frac{1}{P}\left(\frac{X_1}{RC}\right) = -\frac{1}{RC}\int X_1 \, dt \qquad (12\text{-}4)$$

An integrating circuit with several input voltages is shown in Fig. 12-5($a$). The current in $R_1$ is

$$I_1 = \frac{X_1 + \dfrac{X_0}{A}}{R_1}$$

The current in $R_2$ is

$$I_2 = \frac{X_2 + \dfrac{X_0}{A}}{R_2}$$

Similarly, the current in $R_n$ is

$$I_n = \frac{X_n + \dfrac{X_0}{A}}{R_n}$$

and the current through the capacitor $C$ is

$$I_C = \left(X_0 + \frac{X_0}{A}\right) CP$$

By Kirchhoff's first law,

$$I_1 + I_2 + \ldots + I_n = 0$$

and

$$\frac{X_1 + \dfrac{X_0}{A}}{R_1} + \frac{X_2 + \dfrac{X_0}{A}}{R_2} + \ldots + \frac{X_n + \dfrac{X_0}{A}}{R_n} = -\left(X_0 + \frac{X_0}{A}\right) CP$$

When $A \gg 1$

$$\sum_{i=1}^{n} \frac{X_i}{R_i} = -CPX_0$$

or

$$X_0 = -\frac{1}{CP} \sum_{i=1}^{n} \frac{X_i}{R_i}$$

$$= -\frac{1}{P}\left(\frac{X_1}{CR_1} + \frac{X_2}{CR_2} + \ldots + \frac{X_n}{CR_n}\right) \tag{12-5}$$

Then this circuit integrates the negative sum of the individual input multiplied by the reciprocal of the product of the input resistance and the capacitance in

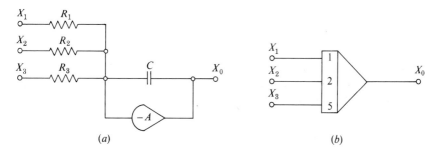

(a)  (b)

**Fig. 12-5.** *Summing and integrating circuit*

the feedback circuit. For example, let $R_1 = 1$ megohm, $R_2 = 10$ megohms, $R_3 = 0.1$ megohms, and $C = 1$ $\mu$f. Then

$$X_0 = -\int (X_1 + 0.1X_2 + 10X_3)\,dt$$

The symbol for this circuit in Fig. 12-5(*b*), where the numbers in the rectangle at the inputs are the $1/RC$ term for that input.

## 12-5. DIFFERENTIATING CIRCUITS[1,2,3]

A basic differentiating circuit is shown in Fig. 12-6. Assuming that the input current to the operational amplifier is zero, the current in the capacitor and the resistor is

$$I_C = \left( X_1 + \frac{X_0}{A} \right) CP$$

Then the voltage drop across the resistor is

$$X_0 - \frac{X_0}{A} = - \left( X_1 + \frac{X_0}{A} \right) RCP$$

When $A \gg 1$, then

$$X_0 = - RCPX_1 \tag{12-6}$$

This circuit is avoided in computer circuits for the following reasons: First, if the function $X_1$ had a sudden change in magnitude, such as a step function,

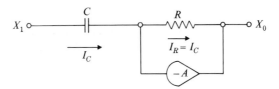

**Fig. 12-6.** *Differentiating circuit*

the derivative might become excessively large and overload the computer amplifiers which might follow the differentiating circuit. Second, the capacitive input to the amplifier is susceptible to noise.

## 12-6. SOLUTION OF LINEAR DIFFERENTIAL EQUATIONS[1,2]

Consider the ordinary second-order differential equation

$$P^2 X - 5PX - 2X = 0$$

The block diagram for the solution of this equation is shown in Fig. 12-7. To set up this circuit, the above equation is solved for the highest-order term, in this case

$$P^2 X = 5PX + 2X$$

Then $PX$ is equal to the integral of $5PX + 2X$. To obtain $PX$, $PX$ and $X$ are fed to the input of the first integrator on the left. The coefficients of the integrating circuit multiply $PX$ by 5 and $X$ by 2. Then the output of the integrator is $-PX$.

The capacitor in an integrator is usually 1 $\mu$f. Then the resistance for the $PX$ input in Fig. 12-7 is 0.2 megohm and the coefficient to $PX$ is

$$\frac{1}{R_1 C} = \frac{1}{(0.2 \times 10^6)(10^{-6})} = 5$$

Similarly, the resistance for the $X$ input is 0.5 megohm, and the coefficient of $X$ in this circuit is

$$\frac{1}{R_2 C} = \frac{1}{(0.5 \times 10^6)(10^{-6})} = 2$$

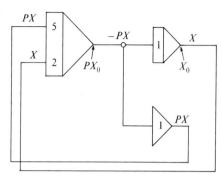

**Fig. 12-7.** *Block diagram of the circuit for the solution of a second-order differential equation*

Also, the $-PX$ input resistance, in both the integrator and the summing circuit, is 1 megohm, and the feedback resistance in the summing circuit is 1 megohm. These resistances are shown in Fig. 12-8.

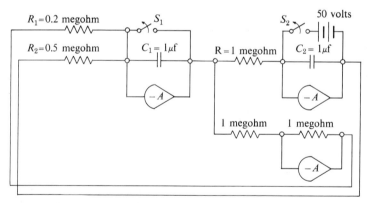

**Fig. 12-8.** *Circuit for the solution of the second-order differential equation in Fig. 12-7*

In the solution of this differential equation, no initial conditions were given. In this equation, if the driving force were zero with no initial value of $PX$ or $X$, there would be no solution, as the initial values of $PX$ and $X$ would be zero at time $t$ equals zero. The voltages across $C_1$ and $C_2$ would both be zero, giving a zero voltage for all values of $PX$ and $X$ after time $t$ equals zero. When the input conditions are $X$ equals 50 volts and $PX$ equals 0 volt at time $t$ equals zero, then the voltage across $C_2$ is 50 volts, and the voltage across $C_1$ is zero at time $t$ equals zero. These initial voltages are represented in Fig. 12-7 by $PX_0$ and $X_0$. In Fig. 12-8 these initial conditions are imposed upon the integrating circuits by the short circuit across $C_1$ through switch $S_1$ and a 50-volt battery in series with switch $S_2$ across $C_2$. At time $t$ equals zero, the switches $S_1$ and $S_2$ are opened, and the voltages at $X$ and $PX$ are the solutions of this problem as a function of time. Usually, $PX$ and $X$ are recorded on a strip-chart recorder.

A physical example of this problem is shown in Fig. 12-9. The mass $M$ is supported by a spring having a stiffness constant $K$ and a dashpot with a

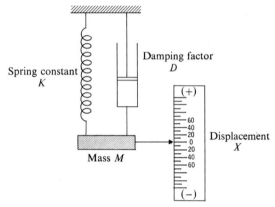

**Fig. 12-9.** *A physical system*

viscous damping $D$. $X$ is the displacement of the mass from its rest position. The equation of the forces in this system is

$$MP^2X + DPX + KX = 0$$

When $M = 1$, $D = 5$, and $K = 2$, this equation becomes

$$P^2X + 5PX + 2X = 0$$

The 50 volts across the capacitance $C_2$ at time $t$ equals zero represents a positive displacement of $X$ equal to $X_0$, which is the mechanical equivalent of 50 volts. At $t = 0$, the force holding the mass at $X_0$ is removed, and the mass movement is constrained only by the action of the spring and the dashpot. The voltage $X$ represents the instantaneous displacement of the mass, and the voltage $PX$ represents the velocity of the mass.

## 12-7. REPRESENTATION OF PHYSICAL FORCES[1,2]

The above problem illustrates that the summation of the forces acting on a mass is equal to the product of the mass and the acceleration. Thus

$$F = MA \tag{12-7}$$

or

$$A = \frac{F}{M} = P^2 X$$

Then the velocity is

$$v = \int A \, dt = PX \tag{12-8}$$

and the displacement is

$$X = \int v \, dt \tag{12-9}$$

The solution of these equations was illustrated in the example given in Sec. 12-6, where the forces acting on the mass in the rest position ($X = 0$) were the downward force of gravity and the upward force exerted by the stretched spring. These two forces were equal and opposite, and their sum was zero. Therefore, they were neglected in the above problem. Any additional force exerted by the spring is equal to

$$F_s = KX \tag{12-10}$$

The block diagram of the analog circuit for the solution of this simple equation is given in Fig. 12-10, where the circle with a letter or a number

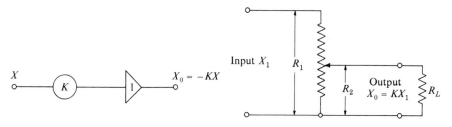

**Fig. 12-10.**  *Representation of the force exerted by a compressed spring*     **Fig. 12-11.**  *A coefficient potentiometer*

represents the potentiometer voltage divider shown in Fig. 12-11. The potentiometer is usually a 10-turn helical wire-wound potentiometer with good linearity and a vernier dial. The total resistance is usually from 10,000 to 100,000 ohms. If the resistance from the input terminal of the summing circuit to ground were very large, and the current into the summing circuit were zero, the voltage output of the potentiometer would be

$$KX_1 = X_1 \frac{R_2}{R_1}$$

where $K$, in this equation, represents the letter or the number enclosed in the circle in Fig. 12-10; $R_1$ is the total resistance of the potentiometer; and $R_2$ is the resistance from the sliding contact to ground. Then

$$K = \frac{R_2}{R_1} \tag{12-11}$$

and the letter in the circle, in this case $K$, must represent a number less than unity. Numbers inserted in a circle in analog-computer diagrams are less than 1, as they are the ratio of $R_2$ to $R_1$.

When the load current of the potentiometer is not zero

$$K = \frac{R_2 R_L}{R_1 R_2 + R_1 R_L - R_2^2} \tag{12-12}$$

where $R_L$ is the resistance of the load on the potentiometer.

The single-input summing circuit with the coefficient multiplier of unity in Fig. 12-10 has an output equal to the negative of its input. Then the output of the circuit is

$$X_0 = -KX_1 \tag{12-13}$$

which is the force on the mass exerted by the spring when the mass is moved a distance $X_1$ from the rest position.

The force due to viscous friction is

$$F_v = -DPX \tag{12-14}$$

where

$D = $ viscous-friction constant or damping constant

$PX = $ velocity

The circuit for the solution is the same as the circuit used to solve for the force exerted by the spring, except that the input to the circuit is $PX$ and the potentiometer is set to a resistance ratio $R_2/R_1$ equal to the damping constant $D$. This circuit is shown in Fig. 12-12.

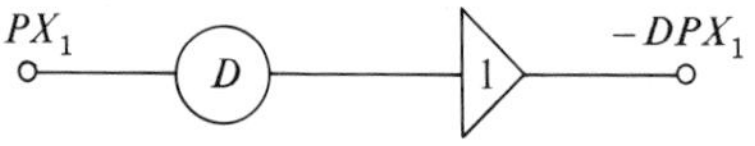

The circuit for representing the force due to *static friction* (*stiction*) and to *dry sliding* (*coulomb*) *friction* in a mechanical problem is not so simple as the circuit for viscous friction or for the deformation of a spring. The circuit

**Fig. 12-12.** *Representation of viscous friction*

shown in Fig. 12-13 can be used to represent these forces. In the input circuit, $R_1$, $R_0$, and the operational amplifier $A$ form a summing circuit with a gain of $R_0/R_1$, and this ratio is made very large.

$D_1$ and $D_2$ are limiters. When the voltage in the forward direction of the diode becomes positive, the diode conducts, the feedback resistance of the amplifier is reduced to a very low value, and the gain of the amplifier is nil. In this circuit the diodes $D_1$ and $D_2$ are biased by the voltage drop across the 25-K resistors, and the output of this summing circuit must exceed this voltage drop before one of the limiter diodes $D_1$ or $D_2$ conducts. This circuit limits the output voltage of the summing circuit to approximately 25 volts.

The output of this circuit is fed to the input of another summing circuit through two paths. One path is through a 0.5-megohm resistance with this input shunted by the diode limiters $D_3$ and $D_4$. One diode is biased by a voltage $+ F_s$ equal to the force of the static friction. The other diode is biased by a voltage $- F_s$. These diodes limit the voltage of this input to this summing circuit to $\pm F_s$. The other path is more complex. It first passes through a circuit that will not pass the signal on through the circuit until the input voltage to this circuit exceeds a value determined by the setting of the adjustment of the 10-K potentiometers. This represents the force that must be applied to the body before it will have appreciable motion determined by the settings on the 10-K potentiometers. This determines the dead zone.

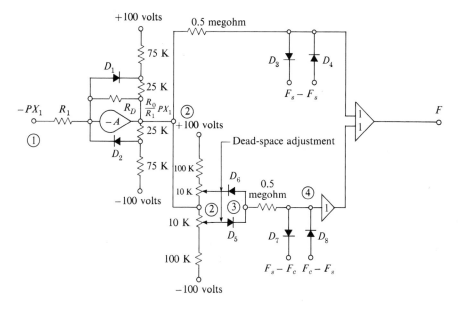

**Fig. 12-13.** *Representation of static and coulomb friction*

When the force exceeds this value, the body moves, and the static friction is replaced by sliding friction. Thus, when the input voltage at point 2 is greater than the voltage drop across the 10-K potentiometer, either diode $D_5$ or diode $D_6$ will conduct, and the input of this branch is transmitted through the 0.5-megohm resistance to point 4 and the input to another summing circuit. The input of this circuit is limited to $F_s - F_c$ or $F_c - F_s$ by the diodes $D_7$ and $D_8$. The output of this final summing circuit is either

$$(F_c - F_s) + F_s = F_c \qquad (12\text{-}15)$$

or

$$(F_s - F_c) - F_s = -F_c \qquad (12\text{-}16)$$

This is the force due to sliding or coulomb friction. When diodes $D_5$ and $D_6$ are not conducting, the output is $F_s$, but, when there is motion, $PX$ is sufficiently amplified to cause $D_5$ or $D_6$ to conduct, and the output is $\pm F_c$. The sign of $F_c$ will be such as to oppose the motion of the body. It will also be noted that the force $F_c$ is a constant. This force opposing the motion of the body is a function of the force normal to the two sliding surfaces and the degree of roughness of the two surfaces given by the coefficient of friction. Then

$$F_c = F_N C_F \tag{12-17}$$

where

$F_c$ = force opposing the motion of the body

$F_N$ = normal force

$C_F$ = coefficient of friction

## 12-8. AMPLITUDE AND TIME FACTORS[1,3]

An electrical analog computer is limited to a definite range of voltages. When the input voltage to an amplifier is excessively large, the amplifiers are overloaded, and distortion results. If the magnitude of the voltage is excessively small, the inherent noise of the computer will produce appreciable error in the quantity being measured. Therefore, it is desirable that the voltages in the computer be within certain limits. Similarly, it is desirable that the time or the frequency of the problem be compatible to the computer. If the time is too slow, the output voltages of the integrators will be small. If the time is too fast, phase shift may appear in the amplifiers, and the response of servo devices used in computing circuits and recording equipment may be too slow to follow the signal accurately. Thus it becomes necessary to modify the amplitude and the time of many problems to fit the characteristics of the computer.

The magnitudes of the quantities used in the problem to be solved are defined as *problem units*. These units are changed to units compatible with the computer. The units used in the computer are defined as *machine units*. The conversion from problem units to machine units is made with properly chosen *scale factors*. Thus

$$X = a_x x$$
$$Y = a_y y \tag{12-18}$$
$$Z = a_z z$$

where $X$, $Y$, and $Z$ are measured in machine units, $x$, $y$, and $z$ are measured in problem units and $a_x$, $a_y$, and $a_z$ are the scale factors.

Time is the independent variable, and the voltages representing the other quantities in the problem are the dependent quantities. The problem time is $t$ and the machine time or computer time is $\tau$. Then

$$\tau = \alpha_t t \tag{12-19}$$

where $\alpha_t$ is the time-scale factor. In some problems the magnitude of the time is operated upon arithmetically to produce the desired solution. For example,

$$\frac{dy}{dt} = y^2 + t - t^2$$

The $t$ given in the right side of the equation is not the problem time but a voltage that represents the problem time. The relation between the problem time and the voltage representing the problem time in the computer is

$$T = a_t t \qquad\qquad (12\text{-}20)$$

where $a_t$ is the scale factor, which must not be confused with the time-scale factor $\alpha_t$.

The voltage $T$ representing the time $t$ in a computer can be obtained by choosing a compatible scale factor $a_t$. For example, if 1 volt represented one unit of time, or 1 sec, then the circuit for producing the function $T$ is given in Fig. 12-14. The output of the single-input integrator with an initial voltage of zero and an input voltage of $-1$ volt after time $t$ is zero will give a voltage $T$ equal to the time $t$ in seconds after time is zero.

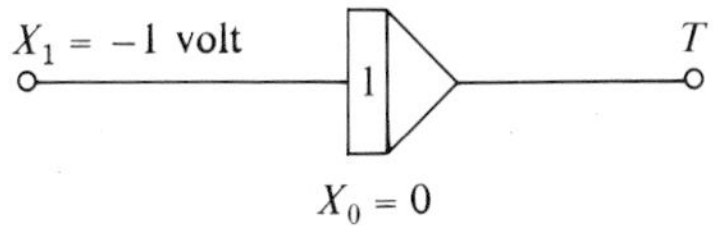

To illustrate the conversion from problem units to machine units, consider the problem

**Fig. 12-14.** *The circuit to produce a voltage which is a linear function of time*

$$p^2 x + 21px + 746x = \sin 2t$$

The initial conditions are

$$(px)_0 = 0; \qquad (x)_0 = 0 \quad \text{and} \quad t = 0$$

Let a unit of voltage be 50 volts and let all inputs be limited to a maximum of 2 units. The undamped natural angular velocity of this equation is

$$\omega_n = \sqrt{746} = 27.3 \text{ radians/sec}$$

and the undamped natural frequency is

$$f_n = \frac{27.3}{2\pi} = 4.37 \text{ cycles per second}$$

while the driving force has a frequency of

$$f_d = \frac{2}{2\pi} = 0.318 \text{ cycles per second}$$

Assuming that the response of the computer is limited to approximately 1 cycle per second, then the problem should be slowed down by a factor of 5. This is done by choosing a time-scale factor of 5. Then

$$t = \frac{\tau}{5}$$

Then

$$\frac{dx}{dt} = 5\frac{dx}{d\tau}$$

or

$$p = 5P$$

and

$$\frac{d^2x}{dt^2} = 25\frac{d^2x}{d\tau^2}$$

or

$$p^2 = 25P^2$$

With this new time, the problem equation becomes

$$25P^2x + 105Px + 746x = \sin 0.4\tau$$

To reduce the coefficients in this equation to the desired value, let

$$x = 500X$$

Then the machine equation is

$$0.05P^2X + 0.21PX + 1.492 = \sin 0.4\tau$$

The frequency of the driving force in this problem is

$$f_d = \frac{0.4}{2\pi} = 0.0638 \text{ cycles per second}$$

and the undamped natural frequency becomes

$$f_n = \frac{1}{2\pi}\sqrt{\frac{1.492}{0.05}} = 0.866 \text{ cycles per second}$$

The solution of the problem will be obtained from the machine solution by converting the machine solution to the desired function of $x$ and $t$ by the use of the scale factors and the time-scale factor.

## 12-9.  DIVISION WITH A SERVO CIRCUIT [1,2]

The division of one variable by another variable with an analog-computer circuit is not as simple as addition or integration. A typical analog divider using a servo circuit is shown in Fig. 12-15. The voltage $X_1$ is the voltage representing the dividend, and $X_2$ is the voltage representing the divisor. The voltage $X_2$ is applied to a single-input summing circuit having an amplifier gain of $A$. The input $-AX_2$ of this amplifier is applied to one end of the 10-turn, center-tapped, linear potentiometer $P_1$, and also to a single-input summing circuit with a gain of unity. The output of this circuit $+AX_2$ is connected to the other end of potentiometer $P_1$. The sliding contact of this potentiometer is connected to one input terminal of a high-gain servo amplifier, and the voltage $X_1$ is connected to the other input terminal. The voltage input to the servo amplifier is the difference between the voltage $X_1$ and the voltage across the resistance $R_2$ between the sliding contact and the grounded center tap of the potentiometer. The output of the amplifier operates a servomotor which turns the potentiometer in a direction that will reduce the input to the servo amplifier to zero. When this balanced condition exists, the

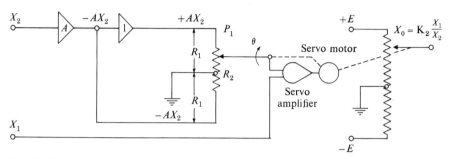

**Fig. 12-15.** *Division with a servo circuit*

voltage across $R_2$ equals voltage $X_1$. When the angle $\theta_m$ is the maximum angle which the sliding contact of the potentiometer will turn from its center tap, and the angle $\theta$ is the angle of the sliding contact of the potentiometer from its center tap under balanced conditions, the ratio of voltage $X_1$ to voltage $AX_2$ is

$$\frac{X_1}{AX_2} = \frac{\theta}{\theta_m} \tag{12-21}$$

or

$$\theta = \frac{\theta_m X_1}{AX_2} = K_1 \frac{X_1}{X_2} \tag{12-22}$$

where $K_1$ is the constant $\theta_m/A$.

Then the angular output $\theta$ is the quotient of $X_1$ divided by $X_2$ multiplied by the scale factor $K_1$.

When it is desired to express this quotient as a voltage, another center-tapped, linear potentiometer is added to the circuit and operated by the same servomotor as shown in Fig. 12-15. A fixed voltage $+E$ is applied to the terminal of this potentiometer which corresponds to the terminal $+AX_1$ of $P_1$ and a fixed voltage $-E$ is connected to the other terminal which corresponds to the terminal $-AX_1$ of $P_1$ with the center tap grounded. The voltage $X_0$ is the voltage from the sliding contact to ground on this potentiometer. Then

$$\frac{X_0}{E} = \frac{\theta}{\theta_m}$$

or

$$X_0 = \frac{\theta E}{\theta_m}$$

Substituting the value of $\theta$ in Eq. (12-22) in this equation gives

$$X_0 = \frac{E}{A}\left(\frac{X_1}{X_2}\right) = K_2 \frac{X_1}{X_2} \qquad (12\text{-}23)$$

where

$$K_2 = \frac{E}{A} \qquad (12\text{-}24)$$

The range of this dividing circuit is from $X_1/X_2 = -A$ to $X_1/X_2 = +A$. It will be observed that the sign of the quotient will be correct regardless of the sign of either $X_1$ or $X_2$. This is defined as a *four-quadrant* dividing circuit. If the dividing circuit were limited to only positive values of the divisor and the dividend, then it would be a *one-quadrant* dividing circuit.

## 12-10.  MULTIPLICATION WITH A SERVO CIRCUIT[1,2,4]

A servo circuit with an output voltage that is the product of the two input voltages when the output voltage is multiplied by the scale factor of the

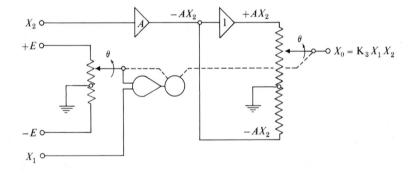

**Fig. 12-16.**  *Multiplication with a servo circuit*

circuit is shown in Fig. 12-16. In this circuit

$$\frac{X_1}{E} = \frac{\theta}{\theta_m} \qquad (12\text{-}25a)$$

Also

$$\frac{X_0}{AX_2} = \frac{\theta}{\theta_m} \qquad (12\text{-}25b)$$

Equating these values of $\theta/\theta_m$ gives

$$X_0 = \frac{A}{E} X_1 X_2 = K_3 X_1 X_2 \qquad (12\text{-}26)$$

where $K_3$ is the constant $A/E$.

Then the output of this circuit is the product of $X_1$ and $X_2$ multiplied by the scale factor $K_3$. This is also a four-quadrant circuit, as the sign of the product is correct regardless of the signs of $X_1$ and $X_2$. The maximum value of $\theta$ is $\theta_m$. Then at $\theta = \theta_m$, $X_1 = E$ and $X_0 = AX_2$, and when $\theta = -\theta_m$, $X_1 = -E$ and $X_0 = -AX_2$. The range of $X_1 X_2$ is $-EX_2$ to $+EX_2$.

If the third voltage input $X_3$ were applied to this circuit in Fig. 12-16 through an operational amplifier of gain $A$, and the output of this amplifier were fed to a single-input summing circuit with a gain of unity so that a voltage $+AX_3$ replaced $+E$ and a voltage $-AX_3$ replaced $-E$, the output would be

$$X_0 = K \frac{X_1 X_2}{X_3} \qquad (12\text{-}27)$$

where $K$ is a constant.

The accuracy of the servo circuits used for division and for multiplication depends upon the linearity of the potentiometers and the accuracy of the constant emf $E$. The major disadvantage of these circuits is the time required for the servomotor to rebalance the circuit when there is a sudden large change in input voltages.

## 12-11.  ELECTRODYNAMOMETER-TYPE MULTIPLIER AND DIVIDER CIRCUIT[1]

In Fig. 12-17, two electrodynamometer movements similar to the movements of a dynamometer-type meter are mounted on the same shaft. The torque produced by the first movement is

$$\tau_1 = k_1 I_1 I_2 \qquad (12\text{-}28)$$

where $k_1$ is a constant and $I_1$ and $I_2$ are the currents in the stator and rotor of the movement, as indicated in the figure. Similarly, the torque produced by the second movement is

$$\tau_2 = k_2 I_3 I_0 \qquad (12\text{-}29)$$

A sensing unit consisting of a mirror, a light source, and a split photocell will send a voltage signal to an amplifier. The output of the amplifier is the current $I_0$ in the second movement, which will maintain the shaft to a fixed position. Under this condition the torques on the two movements are equal and opposite.

Then

$$k_1 I_1 I_2 = -k_2 I_3 I_0$$

But

$$I_1 = \frac{X_1}{R_1}$$

$$I_2 = \frac{X_2}{R_2}$$

$$I_3 = \frac{X_3}{R_3}$$

and

$$X_0 = R_0 I_0$$

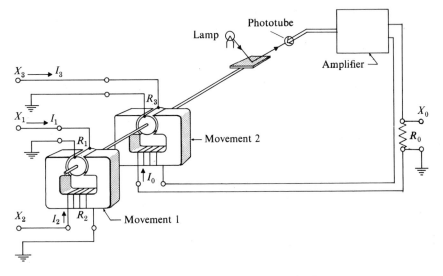

**Fig. 12-17.** *Electrodynamometer-type multiplying and dividing circuit*

where

$R_1$, $R_2$, and $R_3$ = resistances of the respective circuits

$R_0$ = external series resistance in the output of the amplifier

Then

$$k_1 \frac{X_1 X_2}{R_1 R_2} = -k_2 \frac{X_3 X_0}{R_3 R_0} \tag{12-30}$$

or

$$X_1 X_2 = -\frac{k_2 X_3 R_1 R_2}{k_1 R_3 R_0} X_0$$

$$= k_m X_0 \tag{12-31}$$

where

$$k_m = -\frac{k_2 X_3 R_1 R_2}{k_1 R_3 R_0} = \text{a constant}$$

when $X_3$ is held constant. Also, from Eq. (12-30),

$$\frac{X_1}{X_3} = -\frac{k_2 R_1 R_2}{k_1 R_0 R_3 X_2} X_0$$

$$= k_d X_0 \tag{12-32}$$

where

$$k_d = \frac{k_2 R_1 R_2}{k_1 R_0 R_3 X_2} = \text{a constant}$$

when $X_2$ is held constant.

The response of these units can be made better than 20 cycles per second with an accuracy better than 0.5 percent. The amplifier must have a very high gain and must be of the differential type which can deliver either positive or negative $I_0$ to the coil. Under these conditions the circuit is a four-quadrant device.

### 12-12. FEEDBACK DIVIDING AND MULTIPLYING CIRCUITS[1,2]

The feedback circuit for multiplication and division is based on an electronic amplifier with a gain that is independent of the input voltage but a function of a second voltage. Such an amplifier is represented by the rectangles marked with a $K$ in Figs. 12-18 and 12-19. In Fig. 12-18 this amplifier has an

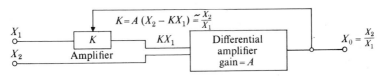

**Fig. 12-18.** *A feedback dividing circuit*

input voltage $X_1$ and an output voltage $KX_1$. This voltage is applied to a differential amplifier with inputs $KX_1$ and $X_2$ and an output $A(X_2 - KX_1)$. This voltage is used to control the gain $K$ of the first amplifier. Then

$$K = A(X_2 - KX_1)$$

or

$$K = \frac{AX_2}{1 + AX_1} \approx \frac{X_2}{X_1} \tag{12-33}$$

when

$$AX_1 \gg 1$$

Now add another amplifier with a gain of $K = X_2/X_1$ and an input voltage of $X_3$, as shown in Fig. 12-19. The output of this amplifier is

$$X_0 = \frac{X_2 X_3}{X_1} \qquad (12\text{-}34)$$

Thus multiplication and division can be obtained with this circuit.

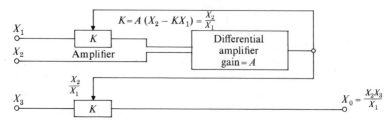

**Fig. 12-19.** *A feedback dividing and multiplying circuit*

There are many variations and types of circuits used for multiplication and division in electrical analog computers. The circuits described above are only an introduction to the possibilities that may be obtained. The major difficulty with this circuit is getting an amplifier with a gain equal to the voltage $K$.

## 12-13. NONLINEAR-POTENTIOMETER-FUNCTION GENERATOR[1]

In many instrumentation problems, nonlinear conditions arise. These may include the effect of magnetic saturation, the nonlinearity of the voltage produced by a thermocouple as a function of temperature, the air speed expressed in Mach number as a function of wind-tunnel pressures, trigonometric functions, etc. One simple method of solving these nonlinear functions is by the use of nonlinear potentiometers. A standard self-balancing potentiometer is used to produce a displacement proportional to the input voltage $X_1$, as shown in Fig. 12-20. This displacement also operates a nonlinear resistance which produces an output voltage $X_o$ which is the desired function of the input voltage $X_1$. This operation is illustrated in the following example. Let the input voltage $X_1$ vary from 0 to 10 volts. The desired function of this voltage is

$$X_o = 0.3 X_1 + 0.5 X_1{}^2 \qquad (12\text{-}35)$$

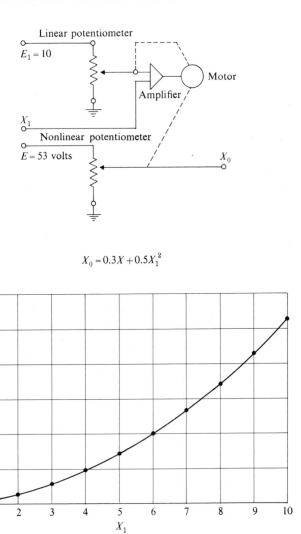

$$X_0 = 0.3X + 0.5X_1^2$$

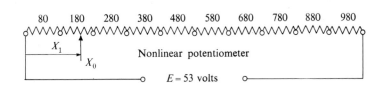

**Fig. 12-20.** *Nonlinear-potentiometer-function generator*

as shown by the curve in Fig. 12-20. The maximum output voltage

$$X_{o\,max} = (0.3)(10) + (0.5)(10^2)$$
$$= 53 \text{ volts}$$

A displacement proportional to $X_1$ is obtained with a self-balancing linear potentiometer using an amplifier and a servomotor, as shown in Fig. 12-20. A good approximation of the required resistance of the nonlinear potentiometer is obtained by shunting a linear potentiometer at 10 equally spaced taps with the correct resistances. The desired voltage above ground at each tap is computed from Eq. (12-35) and is listed in Table 12-1. The current is assumed to be 0.01 amp. The resistance $R$ is the resistance from each tap to ground, and the resistance $\Delta R$ is the resistance between adjacent taps. These resistances are computed and listed in Table 12-1. The circuit of the nonlinear potentiometer with the resistance between each tap is shown in Fig. 12-20.

**Table 12-1**

| $X_1$ | $X_o$ | $R$ | $\Delta R$ | $R_z$ |
|------|------|------|------|------|
| 0 | 0 | 0 | 0 | |
| 1 | 0.8 | 80 | 80 | 87 |
| 2 | 2.6 | 260 | 180 | 220 |
| 3 | 5.4 | 540 | 280 | 319 |
| 4 | 9.2 | 920 | 380 | 613 |
| 5 | 14.0 | 1,400 | 480 | 923 |
| 6 | 19.8 | 1,980 | 580 | 1,380 |
| 7 | 26.6 | 2,660 | 680 | 2,124 |
| 8 | 34.4 | 3,440 | 780 | 3,540 |
| 9 | 43.2 | 4,320 | 880 | 7,330 |
| 10 | 53.0 | 5,300 | 980 | 49,000 |

The maximum resistance between taps is 980 ohms. Then a 10,000-ohm, 10-tap potentiometer with 1,000 ohms between taps can be used with the correct shunt resistance externally connected between the taps for the nonlinear potentiometer. The shunt resistance $R_z$ between each pair of taps necessary to produce the desired nonlinearity is

$$R_z = \frac{R_p\,\Delta R}{R_p - \Delta R} \tag{12-36}$$

where $R_p$ is the resistance between the pair of adjacent taps of the potentiometer without the shunting resistors, and $\Delta R$ is the desired resistance. These values are given in Table 12-1. The difference between the desired function and the approximation obtained with this 10-tap potentiometer is the difference between the curve in Fig. 12-20 and the straight lines connecting the points on the curve.

An adjustable tapped potentiometer is shown in Fig. 12-21. This has the advantages that it can be adjusted to fit any desired curve, and that it is capable of having both positive and negative voltage outputs.

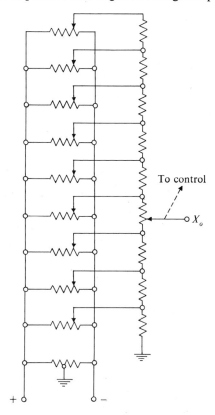

**Fig. 12-21.** *Adjustable tapped potentiometer*

When a fixed function is desired, a wire-wound potentiometer with the desired taper may be made. An example of this type of potentiometer is illustrated in Fig. 12-22, where the taper is shown for a continuous rotating potentiometer with a sine-cosine output function. The potentiometer shaft is rotated at the desired angular velocity with a servomotor when a sine-wave input voltage is desired, or it may be operated with a self-balancing potentiometer circuit, as shown in Fig. 12-20, when the desired output is

$$X_o = a \sin X_1$$

or, when the axis is shifted 90°,

$$X_o = b \cos X_1$$

It will be remembered that servo circuits are comparatively slow and are inadequate for fast analog computers, yet these circuits are very accurate, usually $\pm 0.5$ percent or better.

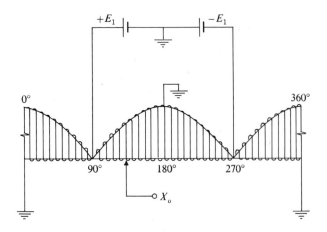

**Fig. 12-22.** *Sine-cosine, tapered potentiometer*

## 12-14. AN ELECTRONIC FUNCTION GENERATOR[2,4,5]

A circuit of a function generator that uses one integrating circuit, two summing circuits, four bridge circuits, and eight biased diode circuits is shown in Fig. 12-23. The input to the integrating circuit is a constant d-c voltage $V_{DC}$ that can be set at any value from $+100$ volts to $-100$ volts with respect to ground. The output of the integrator, when its multiplying coefficient is unity, is

$$V_R = V_I - \int_0^t V_{DC}\, dt = -V_{DC}t + V_I$$

where

$V_I$ = initial output of the integrator at $t = 0$

$t$ = time after $t = 0$ in seconds

$V_{DC}$ = d-c input voltage

It will be noted that the slope of $V_R$ as a function of time is constant when $V_{DC}$ is constant, is negative when $V_{DC}$ is positive, and is positive when $V_{DC}$ is negative. This voltage is defined as the *ramp voltage*.

Diodes 1, 3, 5, and 7 are biased with a positive voltage with respect to ground, and they conduct when $V_R$ is more positive than their bias voltages; diodes 2, 4, 6, and 8 are biased with a negative voltage with respect to ground,

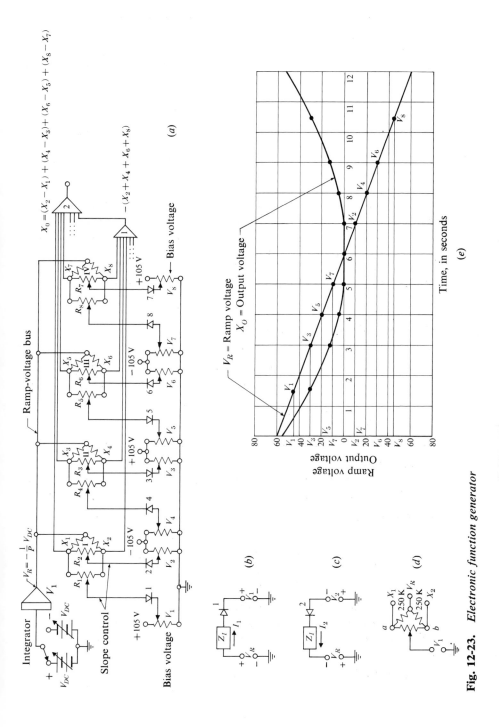

**Fig. 12-23.** *Electronic function generator*

and they conduct when $V_R$ is more negative than their bias voltage, as illustrated in Fig. 12-23($b$) and ($c$).

The circuit of bridge I when $V_R$ is greater than the bias voltage $V_1$ is shown in Fig. 12-23($d$). When the moving contact is at point $a$, the difference between the voltages $X_2$ and $X_1$ is

$$X_2 - X_1 = 0.5(V_R - V_1)$$

When the moving contact is at $b$, the difference between the voltages $X_2$ and $X_1$ is

$$X_2 - X_1 = -0.5(V_R - V_1)$$

Thus the difference between $X_2$ and $X_1$ can have any value $K_1(V_R - V_1)$ where $K_1$ is the bridge potentiometer coefficient of $R_1$, and in this bridge $K_1$ can have any value between 0.5 and $-0.5$ when diode 1 is conducting. When diode 1 is not conducting, $X_2 = X_1$ and the voltage difference is zero. Similar relations exist in each bridge circuit.

The output of integrator 1 is $-(X_2 + X_4 + X_6 + X_8)$ when the multiplying coefficients of its inputs are unity. The output of integrator 2 is

$$X_0 = (X_2 - X_1) + (X_4 - X_3) + (X_6 - X_5) + (X_8 - X_7)$$

when the multiplying coefficients of its inputs are unity. This can be expressed in terms of the ramp voltage $V_R$ and the bias voltages. Thus

$$X_0 = K_1(V_R - V_1) + K_2(V_R - V_2) + K_3(V_R - V_3) + K_4(V_R - V_4)$$
$$+ K_5(V_R - V_5) + K_6(V_R - V_6) + K_7(V_R - V_7) + K_8(V_R - V_8)$$
$$= \sum_{i=1}^{i=n} K_i(V_R - V_i)$$

The terms $K_i(V_R - V_i)$ exist only when $V_R$ has the same polarity as $V_i$ and is greater than or equal to $V_i$.

To illustrate the operation of this circuit, let the initial value of $V_R$ be $V_I = +60$ volts, and $V_{DC} = +10$ volts.

The bias voltages are as follows:

$$
\begin{array}{ll}
V_1 = 45 & V_2 = -10 \\
V_3 = 30 & V_4 = -20 \\
V_5 = 20 & V_6 = -30 \\
V_7 = 10 & V_8 = -45
\end{array}
$$

The bridge-potentiometer coefficients are $K_1 = K_3 = K_5 = K_7 = 0.4$ and $K_2 = K_4 = K_6 = K_8 = -0.4$. The break points in the output will occur when $V_R$ equals the above bias voltages. The initial value of the output voltage at $t = 0$ is

$$X_0 = K_1(V_R - V_1) + K_3(V_R - V_3) + K_5(V_R - V_5) + K_7(V_R - V_7)$$
$$= 0.4(60 - 45) + 0.4(60 - 30) + 0.4(60 - 20) + 0.4(60 - 10)$$
$$= 54 \text{ volts}$$

At $t = 1.5$ sec, $V_R = 45$ volts and

$$X_0 = K_3(V_R - V_3) + K_5(V_R - V_5) + K_7(V_R - V_7)$$
$$= 0.4(45 - 30) + 0.4(45 - 20) + 0.4(45 - 10)$$
$$= 30 \text{ volts}$$

At $t = 3$ sec, $V_R = 30$ volts and

$$X_0 = K_5(V_R - V_5) + K_7(V_R - V_7)$$
$$= 0.4(30 - 20) + 0.4(30 - 10)$$
$$= 12 \text{ volts}$$

At $t = 4$ sec, $V_R = 20$ volts and

$$X_0 = 0.4(20 - 10) = 4 \text{ volts}$$

At $t = 5$ sec, $V_R = 10$ volts and

$$X_0 = 0.4(10 - 10) = 0 \text{ volts}$$

At $t = 7$ sec, $V_R = -10$ volts and

$$X_0 = -0.4(-10 + 10) = 0 \text{ volts}$$

At $t = 8$ sec, $V_R = -20$ volts and

$$X_0 = -0.4(-20 + 10) = 4 \text{ volts}$$

At $t = 9$ sec, $V_R = -30$ volts and

$$X_0 = -0.4(-30 + 10) - 0.4(-30 + 20) = 12 \text{ volts}$$

At $t = 10.5$ sec, $V_R = -45$ volts and

$$X_0 = -0.4(-45 + 10) - 0.4(-45 + 20) - 0.4(-45 + 30) = 30 \text{ volts}$$

At $t = 12$ sec, $V_R = -60$ volts and

$$X_0 = -0.4(-60 + 10) - 0.4(-60 + 20) - 0.4(-60 + 30)$$
$$-0.4(-60 + 45)$$
$$= 54 \text{ volts}$$

At $t = 12$ sec, a timing pulse in a control circuit closes the initial-condition relay switch in the integrator circuit for an instant to rest the initial conditions, and the operation is repeated. The function generated with this circuit is shown in Fig. 12-23(e). Any desired curve can be approximated by varying bridge-potentiometer coefficients, the multiplying coefficients of the integrating circuit and the summing circuits, and the magnitude and polarity of the input voltage to the integrator $V_{DC}$.

## 12-15. RESOLVERS AND TRANSFORMATION FOR POLAR TO RECTANGULAR FORM[1,3]

A resolver is a transformer with two stationary windings placed 90 deg apart, and a rotor with one or more windings. The input to the resolver is an alternating current of constant frequency which is modulated by the voltage input. The construction of the resolver is similar to a servomotor. To illustrate the operation of the resolver, the circuit given in Fig. 12-24 will be described. The input voltage $X_1$ modulates an a-c emf. Then the magnitude of the a-c voltage supplied to the rotor is proportional to the input voltage $X_1$. The induced emf in the stator windings is a function of position of the rotor

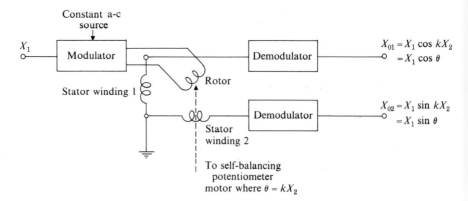

**Fig. 12-24.** *Resolver circuit for obtaining sine and cosine functions*

and the emf applied to the rotor. When the rotor is in the position at which the flux cutting stator winding 1 is a maximum, the induced emf in this winding is a maximum, and the induced emf in stator winding 2 will be zero. This position will be referred to as the zero-angle position, and the mechanical connection between the self-balancing potentiometer motor will be made so that the resolver is in this position when the angle $\theta$ is zero. Then, at $\theta$ equals zero, the voltage in stator winding 1 is a maximum value, and the voltage in stator winding 2 is zero. The windings on the stator and on the rotor are wound so that the flux in the stator windings is a sinusoidal function of the angular position of the rotor. The flux in the rotor is not a linear function of the current in the rotor winding, but the bias of the modulator keeps the envelope of the modulated a-c source on the straight portion of the magnetization curve. Then the magnitude of the demodulated signal of stator winding 1 is a linear function of the product of the input voltage $X_1$ and the cosine of $\theta$ and

$$X_{01} = kX_1 \cos \theta$$

Similarly, the demodulated signal of stator winding 2 is a linear function of the product of the input voltage $X_1$ and the sine of $\theta$ and

$$X_{02} = kX_1 \sin \theta$$

where $k$ is a constant. When the circuit is designed so that $k$ is unity,

$$X_{01} = X_1 \cos \theta$$

and

$$X_{02} = X_1 \sin \theta$$

Then $X_1$ has been resolved into its rectangular Cartesian coordinates,

$$X_1 = X_{01} + jX_{02}$$

from its polar form

$$X_1 = |X_1| \left/ \tan^{-1} \frac{X_{01}}{X_{02}} \right.$$

The same transformation from polar to rectangular Cartesian coordinates can be made by the use of two tapered potentiometers, as shown in

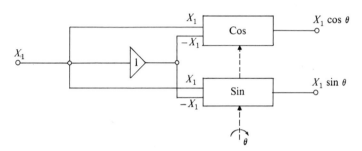

**Fig. 12-25.** *Transformation from polar to rectangular Cartesian coordinates using tapered sine and cosine potentiometers*

Fig. 12-22, on a common shaft with their sliding contacts displaced 90° from each other so that one potentiometer will produce a sine function while the other potentiometer will produce a cosine function. A block diagram of this arrangement is given in Fig. 12-25.

## 12-16. THE TRANSFORMATION OF RECTANGULAR CARTESIAN COORDINATES TO THE POLAR FORM[1]

The polar coordinates are given in terms of the vector radius $R$ and the angle $\theta$, as shown in Fig. 12-26, and written $R\underline{/\theta}$ where

$$R = \sqrt{x^2 + y^2}$$

and

$$\theta = \tan^{-1} \frac{y}{x}$$

From the triangle in Fig. 12-26, the following equations are obtained

$$x \sin \theta - y \cos \theta = 0 \tag{12-37}$$

$$x \cos \theta + y \sin \theta = R \tag{12-38}$$

Equation (12-37) is solved for $\theta$ by the upper sine and cosine function

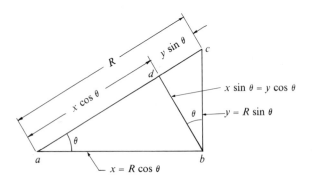

**Fig. 12-26.** *Rectangular and polar quantities*

generators and summing circuit in Fig. 12-27(a). The output of this circuit is $x \sin \theta - y \cos \theta$ which is amplified and applied to a servomotor. The servomotor produces the angle $\theta$ which will make the value

$$x \sin \theta - y \cos \theta = 0$$

which gives the angle $\theta$, the solution of Eq. (12-37). The servomotor also sets the two lower cosine and sine function generators to the correct value of angle $\theta$. These function generators and the lower summing circuit solve Eq. (12-38) for $R$. Thus, with inputs $x$ and $y$ the magnitudes of $\theta$ and $R$ are obtained.

The same solution is obtained using a resolver in Fig. 12-27(b). The instantaneous current input into the stator winding c-b flows from c to b when the instantaneous value of $y$ is positive, and the current in the stator winding a–b flows from a to b when $x$ is positive. The induced emf in the rotor windings produces a current flow from e to f and from e to d when $x$ is positive and from e to f and from d to e when $y$ is positive. Then the emf from e to f is $x \cos \theta + y \sin \theta = R$, and the emf from e to d is $x \sin \theta - y \cos \theta$. The latter emf is amplified and applied to a servomotor which turns the resolver until this emf is zero. This solves Eq. (12-37) for $\theta$. The emf from the rotor coil e to f is demodulated, giving the magnitude of $R$. This is only a brief introduction to the solution of nonlinear functions by analog methods. Many electronic devices are used to solve this function. For a more complete discussion of this subject, see the references listed at the end of this chapter.

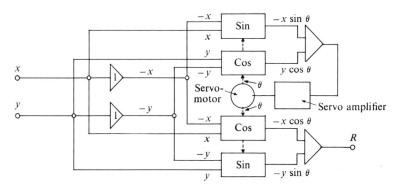

(a) Tapered potentiometers

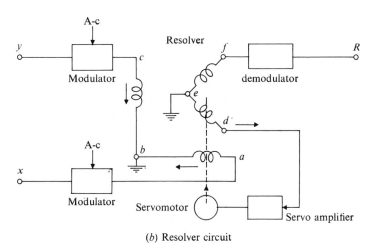

(b) Resolver circuit

**Fig. 12-27.** *Transformation from rectangular to polar quantities*

## 12-17. SOLUTION OF SIMULTANEOUS EQUATIONS[2,6]

Analog computers are often used for the solution of simultaneous differential equations such as

$$P^3 X + P^2 X - P^2 Y - 5Z = 2$$
$$P^3 Y + PZ - 2PX - 5Y = 0$$
$$P^2 Z + 5PX - 10Y + 3Z = 5$$

The initial conditions are

$$P^3 X_0 = P^3 Y_0 = P^2 X_0 = P^2 Y_0 = PZ = PX = 0$$
$$X_0 = 0, \qquad Y_0 = 5, \qquad Z_0 = 5$$

The first step in the solution of these equations is to solve for the highest-order terms in each equation. Then

$$P^3X = -(P^2X - P^2Y - 5Z - 2)$$
$$P^3Y = -(PZ - 2PX - 5Y)$$
$$P^2Z = -(5PX - 10Y + 3Z - 5)$$

The block diagram of the circuit for the solution of these equations is given in Fig. 12-28.

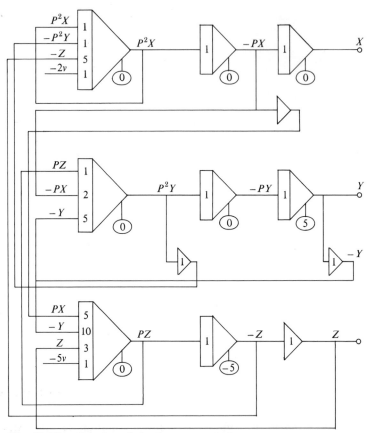

**Fig. 12-28.** *Solution of simultaneous equation*

## 12-18. COMMERCIAL ANALOG COMPUTERS[7]

There are many commercial analog computers available at the present time, varying in size from a small unit with only 10 operational amplifiers with capacitors, resistances, diodes, meters, potentiometers, and d-c voltage sources, to large computers which include more than 100 operational amplifiers, resolvers, coefficient potentiometers, high-speed servos, diodes, dividers, multipliers, function generators, power supplies, and removable problem patch boards for setting up the desired circuit. A Reeves Instrument Corporation electric analog computer is shown in Fig. 12-29. Often, the computer is equipped with a multichannel recorder to record the desired input and output voltages as a function of time.

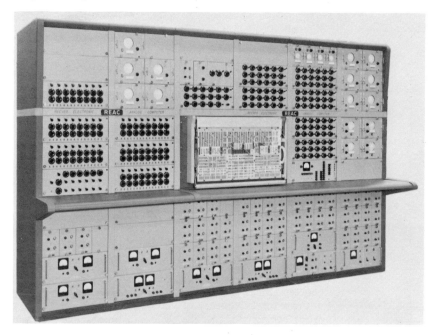

**Fig. 12-29.** *Reeves Analog Computer (courtesy Reeves Instrument Corporation)*

These examples of analog circuits are but a brief introduction to this subject. Much more information is available from the references given below.

### PROBLEMS

**12-1.** In Fig. 12-1, $R_1 = R_2 = R_n = 10,000$ ohms, $R_0 = 10,000$ ohms, $X_1 = 9$ volts, $X_2 = 4$ volts, and $X_n = 5$ volts. (*a*) Determine the error between the solution of $X_0$ by Eq. (12-1) and by Eq. (12-2). (*b*) Repeat, using $R_0 = 1$ megohm.

**12-2.** In Fig. 12-2, $X_1 = 2$ volts, $X_2 = 0.5$ volts, and $X_n = 4$ volts. $R_0 = 10^5$ ohms. Determine: (*a*) the values of $R_1$, $R_2$, and $R_n$ when $X_0 = X_1 + 2X_2 + 4X_3$; (*b*) the error in Eq. (12-3) when $A = 10$; (*c*) the error in Eq. (12-3) when $A = 100$; (*d*) the error in Eq. (12-3) when $A = 1,000$.

**12-3.** (a) Design a circuit which will have an output

$$X_0 = 2X_1 - 5X_2 + 10X_3 - 2 \text{ volts}$$

(b) When $R_0 = 10^5$ ohms, draw the block diagram of the circuit for solving part (a).

**12-4.** In Fig. 12-4, let $R = 1$ megohm and $C = 1$ $\mu$f. Determine the error in Eq. (12-4) when $X_1$ is 10 and the integration is between $t = 0$ and $t = 1$ sec for: (a) $A = 50$; (b) $A = 1,000$; (c) $A = 50,000$. (d) Repeat parts (a), (b), and (c) for the integration between $t = 0$ and $t = 10$ sec.

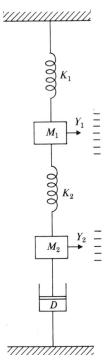

**12-5.** (a) Draw the block diagram for the solution of the differential equation

$$P^2 X + 5PX - 10X = 4$$

with the initial condition that $P^2 X = PX = 0$ and $X = +5$. (b) Draw the circuit and give the values of the components when each of the capacitors in the integrating circuits is 1 $\mu$f.

**12-6.** Prove that $K$ has the value given in Eq. (12-12) when the potentiometer in Fig. 12-11 has a load resistance $R_L$.

**12-7.** Write a machine equation for the problem equation.

$$2p^2x + 52\,px + 640x = 100$$

such that the natural frequency will be between 1 and 5 cycles per second and the largest coefficient in the machine equation will be unity. List the scale factors and the time-scale factor used to make this conversion.

**12-8.** Write a machine equation for the problem equation

$$5p^2x - 75px + 550 = 470 \cos 5t$$

such that the largest coefficient in the machine equation is between 1 and 2 and the larger of the driving-force frequency or the natural frequency of the system is between 1 and 2 cycles per second. List the scale and time factors used and determine the frequency of the driving force and the natural frequency of the machine equation.

**12-9.** Design a circuit using linear potentiometers with self-balancing servoloops to give an output voltage

**Fig. 12-30.** *Physical system for Prob. 12-15*

$$X_0 = k\frac{X_1 X_2}{X_3}$$

where $X_1$, $X_2$, and $X_3$ are input voltages. Evaluate the constant $k$ in terms of the circuit parameters.

**12-10.** The circuit in Fig. 12-17 is used to solve the equation

$$\frac{X_1 X_2}{X_3} = kX_0$$

Determine the value of $k$ in terms of the circuit parameters.

**12-11.** The circuit in Fig. 12-23 has the same bias voltages as given in the illustration in Sec. 12-14. $V_{DC} = 8$ volts, the initial voltage $V_I = -50$ volts, $K_1 = K_2 = K_3 = K_4 = 0.5$, and $K_5 = K_6 = K_7 = K_8 = -0.6$. Plot the ramp voltage and the value of $X_0$ as a function of time, in seconds.

**12-12.** Modify the circuit in Fig. 12-27(a) so that the value of $\theta$ will be measured in volts with a scale factor which will make 1 radian equal to 100 volts.

**12-13.** Draw the block diagram for the solution of the following simultaneous equations:

$$P^3X + P^2X - P^2Y + X - 5Y = 0$$
$$P^2Y + PX - 5Y - 4 = \sin X$$

**12-14.** Draw the block diagram for the solution of the following simultaneous equations:

$$P^2X + PX - PY - 5Z = 2$$
$$P^2Y + PY - PX + 5Y = 0$$
$$P^2Z - P^2X - PZ - Z = Y^2$$

**12-15.** The physical system in Fig. 12-30 has a spring constant $K_1 = 0.5$ newton/km, a spring constant $K_2 = 0.75$ newton/km, a mass $M_1 = 0.2$ in MKS units, a mass $M_2 = 0.15$ in MKS units, and a damping coefficient $D = 0.0012$ newton/meter/sec. (a) Write the problem equation for the motion of each mass. (b) Write the machine equation for each mass such that the natural frequency of each mass will be between 0.1 and 0.5 cycles per second and the largest coefficient in each equation shall be between 1 and 2. (c) The initial conditions of this problem are

$$P^2X_1 = PX_1 = 0$$
$$P^2X_2 = PX_2 = 0$$
$$X_1 = X_2 = 0.1 \text{ m}$$

Draw the block diagram for the solution of the motion of the two masses.

## REFERENCES

1. G. A. Korn and T. M. Korn, *Electronic Analog Computers*, 2nd ed., McGraw-Hill Book Company, Inc., New York, 1956.

2. C. L. Johnson, *Analog Computer Techniques*, McGraw-Hill Book Company, Inc., New York, 1956.

3. W. J. Karplus and W. W. Soroka, *Analog Methods in Computation and Simulation*, 2nd ed., McGraw-Hill Book Company, Inc., New York, 1959.

4. I. A. Grunwood, Jr., J. V. Holdam, Jr., and D. Macrae, Jr., *Electronic Instruments*, McGraw-Hill Book Company, Inc., New York, 1948.

5. J. N. Warfield, *Introduction to Electronic Analog Computers*, Prentice-Hall, Inc., Englewood Cliffs, N.J., 1959.

6. A. S. Jackson, *Analog Computation*, McGraw-Hill Book Company, Inc., New York, 1960.

7. R. M. Howe, *Design Fundamentals of Analog Computer Components*, D. Van Nostrand Company, Inc., Princeton, N.J., 1961.

# Chapter 13

# NUMBER

**13-1. DIGITAL VERSUS ANALOG SYSTEMS**[1]

In *analog* systems the function varies continuously, as represented by the magnitude of the function shown by the curve in Fig. 13-1, while *digital* values are discrete and vary in equal steps. Each digital number is a fixed sum of equal steps which is defined by that number. To convert an analog quantity into a digital number, such as the analog magnitudes in the curve in Fig. 13-1, the vertical displacement must be divided into equal parts (in this case, 10 parts), and each part has a length equal to 1 unit. From 0 to 0.5 is still 0, from 0.5 to 1.5 is 1, from 1.5 to 2.5 is 2, etc. Then from the origin to *a* is 4, from *a* to *b* is 5, from *b* to *c* is 6, etc. To obtain a more accurate conversion of these analog values to digital values, each of the 10 steps may be divided into 10 equal parts, giving a total of 100 steps instead of 10. These steps, in turn, may again be divided into 10 equal parts, giving a total of 1,000 steps instead of 100. This can be extended until any desired accuracy is obtained, but the digital number is still a sum of equal units. Magnitudes lying within one of these steps lose their identity and are all defined by the same number. Although analog computers perform mathematical operations with analog values, it is necessary to convert analog values to digital values in order to record them in written form and apply standard mathematical procedures to

322

# DIGITAL

# SYSTEMS

the written magnitudes. The analog form is very important in problems of analysis, but in the normal mathematical processes in the vocabulary of magnitudes, digital values are used. Also, digital computation is more economical when high precision is required.

## 13-2. BASIC THEORY OF DIGITAL NUMBERS[2,3]

The basis of any digital-number system is the choice of the symbols for the digits to be used in the system, beginning with 0, 1, 2, 3, etc. The number of these individual symbols used in the system is defined as the *radix* of the system. A common form of expressing the positive digital number $N$ is

$$N = d_n \ldots d_2 d_1 d_0 \cdot d_{-1} d_{-2} \ldots \tag{13-1}$$

where $d_n$, $d_2$, $d_1$, etc., are the individual digit symbols in the number. The magnitude of the number is

$$N = d_n R^n + \ldots d_2 R^2 + d_1 R^1 + d_0 R^0 + d_{-1} R^{-1} + d_{-2} R^{-2} + \ldots \tag{13-2}$$

where $R$ is the radix of the system. A digital-number system is identified by its radix. The *binary*-number system has a radix of 2, using the digital symbols 0 and 1. The *ternary*-number system has a radix of 3, using the digital

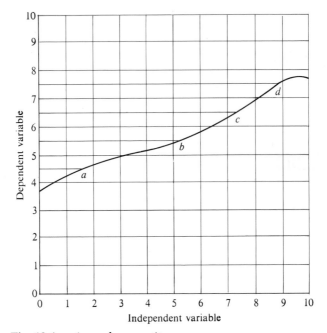

**Fig. 13-1.** *An analog quantity*

symbols 0, 1, and 2. The *octonary*-number system has a radix of 8. The *duodecimal*-number system has a radix of 12. The *sexadecimal*-number system has a radix of 16.

### 13-3. THE DECIMAL-NUMBER SYSTEM[2,3]

The most common digit system is the *decimal* system. It has a radix of 10 and is the system used in basic arithmetic and higher mathematics. To illustrate this system, let $d_3 = 3$, $d_2 = 5$, $d_1 = 1$, $d_0 = 7$, $d_{-1} = 4$, and $d_{-2} = 6$.

Then, by Eq. (13-2), the decimal number is

$$N = (3)(10^3) + (5)(10^2) + (1)(10^1) + (7)(10^0) + (4)(10^{-1}) + (6)(10^{-2})$$
$$= 3,000 + 500 + 10 + 7 + 0.4 + 0.06$$
$$= 3,517.46$$

This same expression is obtained by substituting $d_3$, $d_2$, $d_1$, $d_0$, $d_{-1}$, and $d_{-2}$ directly into Eq. (13-1). Equation (13-2) is useful in transposing from one system of numbers to another.

It will also be shown in the following sections that the decimal system is not the simplest system to use in many problems.

## 13-4. THE BINARY SYSTEM

The binary system, with only 2 digit symbols—0 and 1, is an off-on system which is well adapted to switching circuits. In this system the radix $R$ is 2, and the symbol for 2 in the binary system is 10. Other binary numbers with their equivalents in the decimal system are given in Table 13-1. The digit prefix to the integral powers of $R$ in Eq. (13-2) is either 0 or 1 and the powers of the radix 10 (2) are given in Table 13-2 together with their decimal equivalents.

**Table 13-1**

| Decimal | Binary | Ternary | Octonary | Duodecimal |
|---|---|---|---|---|
| 1 | 1 | 1 | 1 | 1 |
| 2 | 10 | 2 | 2 | 2 |
| 3 | 11 | 10 | 3 | 3 |
| 4 | 100 | 11 | 4 | 4 |
| 5 | 101 | 12 | 5 | 5 |
| 6 | 110 | 20 | 6 | 6 |
| 7 | 111 | 21 | 7 | 7 |
| 8 | 1,000 | 22 | 10 | 8 |
| 9 | 1,001 | 100 | 11 | 9 |
| 10 | 1,010 | 101 | 12 | # |
| 11 | 1,011 | 102 | 13 | $\pi$ |
| 12 | 1,100 | 110 | 14 | 10 |
| 13 | 1,101 | 111 | 15 | 11 |
| 14 | 1,110 | 112 | 16 | 12 |
| 15 | 1,111 | 120 | 17 | 13 |
| 16 | 10,000 | 121 | 20 | 14 |
| 17 | 10,001 | 122 | 21 | 15 |
| 18 | 10,010 | 200 | 22 | 16 |
| 19 | 10,011 | 201 | 23 | 17 |
| 20 | 10,100 | 202 | 24 | 18 |
| 21 | 10,101 | 210 | 25 | 19 |
| 22 | 10,110 | 211 | 26 | 1# |
| 23 | 10,111 | 212 | 27 | 1$\pi$ |
| 24 | 11,000 | 220 | 30 | 20 |

### Table 13-1—*continued*

| Decimal | Binary | Ternary | Octonary | Duodecimal |
|---------|--------|---------|----------|------------|
| 25 | 11,001 | 221 | 31 | 21 |
| 30 | 11,110 | 1,010 | 36 | 26 |
| 35 | 100,011 | 1,022 | 43 | $2\pi$ |
| 40 | 101,000 | 1,111 | 50 | 34 |
| 45 | 101,101 | 1,200 | 55 | 39 |
| 50 | 110,010 | 1,212 | 62 | 42 |
| 100 | 1,100,100 | 10,201 | 144 | 84 |
| 1,000 | 1,111,101,000 | 1,101,001 | 1,750 | $6\pi4$ |
| 10,000 | 10,011,100,010,000 | 111,201,101 | 23,420 | 5,954 |

### Table 13-2

### Binary-Number System, Powers of the Radix 2

| Binary | Decimal equivalent |
|--------|--------------------|
| $R^0 = 10^0 = 1$ | $2^0 = 1$ |
| $R^1 = 10^1 = 10$ | $2^1 = 2$ |
| $R^2 = 10^{10} = 100$ | $2^2 = 4$ |
| $R^3 = 10^{11} = 1,000$ | $2^3 = 8$ |
| $R^4 = 10^{100} = 10,000$ | $2^4 = 16$ |
| $R^5 = 10^{101} = 100,000$ | $2^5 = 32$ |
| $R^6 = 10^{110} = 1,000,000$ | $2^6 = 64$ |
| $R^7 = 10^{111} = 10,000,000$ | $2^7 = 128$ |
| $R^8 = 10^{1,000} = 100,000,000$ | $2^8 = 256$ |
| $R^9 = 10^{1,001} = 1,000,000,000$ | $2^9 = 512$ |
| $R^{10} = 10^{1,010} = 10,000,000,000$ | $2^{10} = 1,024$ |
| $R^{11} = 10^{1,011} = 100,000,000,000$ | $2^{11} = 2,048$ |
| $R^{12} = 10^{1,100} = 1,000,000,000,000$ | $2^{12} = 4,096$ |
| $R^{13} = 10^{1,101} = 10,000,000,000,000$ | $2^{13} = 8,192$ |
| $R^{14} = 10^{1,110} = 100,000,000,000,000$ | $2^{14} = 16,384$ |
| $R^{15} = 10^{1,111} = 1,000,000,000,000,000$ | $2^{15} = 32,768$ |

To illustrate the application of Eq. (13-2) to the binary system, let $d_3 = 1$, $d_2 = 1$, $d_1 = 0$, $d_0 = 1$, $d_{-1} = 0$, and $d_{-2} = 1$. Then, using Eq. (13-2), the magnitude of this number is

$$N = (1)(10^{11}) + (1)(10^{10}) + (0)(10^1) + (1)(10^0) + (0)(10^{-1}) + (1)(10^{-10})$$
$$= 1,000 + 100 + 0 + 1 + 0 + 0.01$$
$$= 1,101.01$$

By inserting the powers of 2 in the decimal system into this equation, the decimal equivalent of the binary number can be obtained. Thus

$$N = (1)(2^3) + (1)(2^2) + (0)(2^1) + (1)(2^0) + (0)(2^{-1}) + (1)(2^{-2})$$
$$= 8 + 4 + 0 + 1 + 0 + 1/4$$
$$= 13.25$$

The arithmetic processes of addition, subtraction, multiplication, and division in the binary system are the same as those used in the decimal system, except that only 2 digit symbols are used. To illustrate, in the binary system the flash cards for learning addition are

| 10 | 1 | 1 | 0 |
|----|----|----|----|
| +1 | +1 | +0 | +0 |
| 11 | 10 | 1 | 0 |

The flash cards for learning subtraction are

| 10 | 1 | 1 | 0 |
|----|----|----|----|
| −1 | −1 | −0 | −0 |
| 1 | 0 | 1 | 0 |

and the multiplication tables are

$$10 \times 1 = 10$$
$$1 \times 1 = 1$$
$$0 \times 1 = 0$$

Then the procedure for adding binary numbers is the same as for decimal numbers. To assist in becoming acquainted with the manipulation of numbers other than the decimal system, the following addition will be worked out in detail.

|   |   |   |   | Binary |   |   |   |   |   |   |   | Decimal |
|---|---|---|---|---|---|---|---|---|---|---|---|---|
|   | (1) |   |   |   |   | (1) |   |   |   |   |   |   |
|   | (1 | 0) |   |   |   | (1 | 0) |   |   |   |   |   |
| (1) |   | (1 | 1) | (1) |   | (1 | 0) | (1) |   |   |   |   |
| 1, | 1 | 1 | 1, | 1 | 0 | 1, | 0 | 0 | 0 |   |   | 1,000 |
|   |   |   | 1, | 1 | 0 | 0, | 1 | 0 | 0 |   |   | 100 |
|   |   |   | 1, | 1 | 0 | 0, | 1 | 0 | 0 |   |   | 100 |
|   |   |   | 1, | 1 | 0 | 0, | 1 | 0 | 0 |   |   | 100 |
|   |   |   | 1 | 0 | 0, | 0 | 1 | 1 |   |   |   | 35 |
|   |   |   | 1 | 0 | 0, | 0 | 1 | 1 |   |   |   | 35 |
|   |   |   |   |   | 1 | 1 | 1 |   |   |   |   | 7 |
| 1 | 0, | 1 | 0 | 1, | 1 | 0 | 0, | 0 | 0 | 1 |   | 1,377 |

The procedure for the above addition is as follows:

The sum of the numbers in the right-hand column is 11 (3). The right hand 1 is brought down below the summation line under this column, and the left-hand 1 is carried over to the next column to the left and placed above it, in parentheses, to be added with this column of figures. The sum of the numbers in the second column from the right is 100 (4). The 0 is placed below the summation line under this column, and the 10 is placed above the next two columns to the left to be added with those columns of figures. The sum of the numbers in the third column is 100 (4). The 0 is placed below the summation line under this column, and the 10 is carried over to the next two columns to the left. This procedure is continued until all the columns have been added, forming the sum of the binary numbers.

The procedure for multiplication in the binary-number system is the same as the decimal system. For example, the product of 111 and 101 is

| Binary | Decimal |
|:------:|:-------:|
| 111 | 7 |
| × 101 | × 5 |
| 111 | 35 |
| 1110 | |
| 100011 | |

The decimal equivalents are shown to the right of the binary numbers.

The procedure for subtraction of binary numbers is straightforward but may be a little more difficult to visualize. For example, the difference between the binary numbers 10,000 and 11 is

| Binary | Decimal |
|:------:|:-------:|
| 10,000 | 16 |
| − 11 | − 3 |
| 1,101 | 13 |

This may not be so evident as the other examples. It consists of subtracting binary number 1 from the 10 (2) to the left in the minuend leaving a 1, and forming a new 10 (2) in the next column to the right. This procedure is continued until a 10 (2) is formed in the column on the right and a 1 replaces the 0's on the left. Then 10 − 1 = 1, giving a 1 in the first column on the right in the answer. One for the 1 in the second column leaves 0 for this column in the answer. There is nothing to subtract from the remaining two 1's on the left, so they are brought down to make the answer 1,101. Thus

|   | (1) | (1) | (1) | (10) |
|:-:|:---:|:---:|:---:|:----:|
| 1 | 0, | 0 | 0 | 0 |
|   |   | − | 1 | 1 |
|   | 1, | 1 | 0 | 1 |

in the binary-number system.

Binary division follows the same procedure as division in the decimal system. For example, divide 100,011 by 101.

$$
\begin{array}{r}
111 \\
101\overline{)100011} \\
101 \\
\hline
111 \\
101 \\
\hline
101 \\
101 \\
\hline
\end{array}
$$

Other mathematical computations can easily be made in the binary-number system by using the same procedures as in the decimal system. For example, $100^{10}$, which is 4 squared, is

| Binary | Decimal |
|:---:|:---:|
| 100 | 4 |
| $\times\,100$ | $\times\,4$ |
| 10,000 | 16 |

## 13-5. THE CONVERSION FROM BINARY TO DECIMAL AND DECIMAL TO BINARY NUMBERS [1,2,3]

It has been shown that a binary number can be converted to a decimal number by expressing the binary number in the series form given in Eq. (13-2), then substituting the decimal powers of 2 in this equation. This method can also be used to convert binary to decimal numbers. For example, to convert the decimal number 1,377 to a binary number, the number is written in the series given in Eq. (13-2), thus,

$$N = 1(10^3) + 3(10^2) + 7(10^1) + 7(10^0)$$

Substituting the binary equivalent of these numbers into this equation gives

$$
\begin{aligned}
N &= 1(1,010^{11}) + 11(1,010^{10}) + 111(1,010^1) + 111(1,010^0) \\
&= 1(1,111,101,000) + 11(1,100,100) + 111(1,010) + 111(1) \\
&= 1,111,101,000 + 100,101,100 + 1,000,110 + 111 \\
&= 10,101,100,001
\end{aligned}
$$

Thus Eq. (13-2) can be used for converting binary numbers to decimal numbers and decimal numbers to binary numbers. Similarly, Eq. (13-2) can be used to convert a number in one system to its equivalent in another number system.

There are other methods of converting binary numbers to decimal numbers and decimal numbers to binary numbers. One method of converting binary integer numbers, or the portion of a number to the left of the binary point, to decimal numbers is as follows: Start with the left digit of the binary number. If the next digit is 0, double what you have; if it is 1, double what you have and add 1. Continue this procedure for each digit to the left of the binary point. This will give the decimal equivalent of the binary number. For example, to convert 10,101,100,001 in the binary system to a decimal number by this method requires the following steps:

Step 1. The first digit is 1 followed by 0, so double 1, giving 2.
Step 2. The next digit is 1, so double 2 and add 1, giving 5.
Step 3. The next digit is 0, so double 5, giving 10.
Step 4. The next digit is 1, so double 10 and add 1, giving 21.
Step 5. The next digit is 1, so double 21 and add 1, giving 43.
Step 6. The next digit is 0, so double 43, giving 86.
Step 7. The next digit is 0, so double 86, giving 172.
Step 8. The next digit is 0, so double 172, giving 344.
Step 9. The next digit is 0, so double 344, giving 688.
Step 10. The last digit is 1, so double 688 and add 1, giving 1,377 as the decimal equivalent of 10,101,100,001.

A method of converting a decimal integer, or the portion of a number to the left of the decimal point, to a binary number is as follows: Divide the decimal number by 2 and write down the quotient and the remainder, either 1 or 0. Divide this quotient by 2 and again write the new quotient and the remainder, either 1 or 0. Continue this procedure until the last quotient is 0, with either 1 or 0 remaining. The remainders written in the reverse order are the binary equivalent of the decimal number. Then the binary equivalent of 1,377 be found as follows:

| Decimal | Remainder | Binary |
|---------|-----------|--------|
| 2$\underline{/1,377}$ | | 10,101,100,001 |
| 2$\underline{/688}$ | 1 | |
| 2$\underline{/344}$ | 0 | |
| 2$\underline{/172}$ | 0 | |
| 2$\underline{/86}$ | 0 | |
| 2$\underline{/43}$ | 0 | |
| 2$\underline{/21}$ | 1 | |
| 2$\underline{/10}$ | 1 | |
| 2$\underline{/5}$ | 0 | |
| 2$\underline{/2}$ | 1 | |
| 2$\underline{/1}$ | 0 | |
| 0 | 1 | |

Writing these digits in order from bottom to top gives

$$1,377 \text{ (decimal)} = 10,101,100,001 \text{ (binary)}$$

A procedure for converting a decimal fraction, or the portion of a decimal number to the right of the decimal point, to a binary number is illustrated by the following numerical example: Let the decimal number 0.78 be converted to a binary number. Then multiply

$$\begin{array}{r} 0.78 \\ \underline{2} \\ 1.56 \end{array}$$

Then 1 is the first digit

$$\begin{array}{r} 0.56 \\ \underline{2} \\ 1.12 \end{array}$$

Then 1 is the second digit

$$\begin{array}{r} 0.12 \\ \underline{2} \\ 0.24 \end{array}$$

Then 0 is the third digit

$$\begin{array}{r} 0.24 \\ \underline{2} \\ 0.48 \end{array}$$

Then 0 is the fourth digit

$$\begin{array}{r} 0.48 \\ \underline{2} \\ 0.96 \end{array}$$

Then 0 is the fifth digit

$$\begin{array}{r} 0.96 \\ \underline{2} \\ 1.92 \end{array}$$

Then 1 is the sixth digit

$$\begin{array}{r} 0.92 \\ \underline{2} \\ 1.84 \end{array}$$

Then 1 is the seventh digit, and the binary equivalent of 0.78 to 7 binary significant figures is 0.1100011. This procedure can be stated as follows:

Step 1. Multiply the decimal fraction by 2. If the product is greater than or equal to 1, write 1 for the first digit of the binary equivalent to the right of the binary point. If the product is less than 1, write 0 for this digit.

Step 2. Multiply the number to the right of the decimal point in the product of the first step by 2. If this product is greater than or equal to 1, write 1 for the second binary digit to the right of the binary point. If this product is less than 1, write 0 for the second binary digit to the right of the binary point.

Step 3. Continue this procedure either until there are only 0's to the right of the decimal point or until the binary number has sufficient digits to produce the conversion to the desired accuracy.

The conversion of a binary fraction to a decimal fraction is similar to the conversion from a decimal fraction to a binary number. This procedure reduces to the following steps:

Step. 1. Multiply the binary fraction by 1010 which is a binary 10. The number to the left of the binary point in the product is the binary equivalent of the first decimal digit to the right of the decimal point in the decimal equivalent of the binary fraction.

Step 2. Multiply the digit to the right of the binary point in the product in the first step by 1010. The digits to the left of the binary point in this new product are the binary equivalent of the second digit to the right of the decimal point in the decimal equivalent of the binary fraction.

Step 3. Continue this procedure until the desired number of digits is determined. For example, determine the decimal equivalent of 0.1100011.

$$
\begin{array}{r}
0.1100011 \\
1010 \\
\hline
11000110 \\
11000110 \\
\hline
111.1011110
\end{array}
$$

Then 111 (binary) = 7 (decimal) for the first digit

$$
\begin{array}{r}
0.1011110 \\
1010 \\
\hline
10111100 \\
10111100 \\
\hline
111.0101100
\end{array}
$$

Again 111 (binary) = 7 (decimal) for the second digit

$$
\begin{array}{r}
0.0101100 \\
1010 \\
\hline
1011000 \\
1011000 \\
\hline
11.011100
\end{array}
$$

Then 11 (binary) = 3 (decimal) for the third digit

$$
\begin{array}{r}
0.0111000 \\
1010 \\
\hline
1110000 \\
1110000 \\
\hline
100.0110000
\end{array}
$$

Then 100 (binary) = 4 (decimal) for the fourth digit, or the decimal equivalent of 0.1100011 in the binary system is 0.7734 to 4 significant figures. If this were carried out 3 more figures, the exact equivalent would be 0.7734375. It is observed that the binary number 0.1100011 was the binary equivalent, to 7 significant figures, of the decimal number 0.78. Then the decimal number 0.78 has more information than the 7-digit binary number 0.1100011. It requires 8 significant figures to ensure that the binary number will round off a given 2-digit decimal number.

### Table 13-3

### Ternary-Number System, Powers of the Radix 3

| | Ternary | | | Decimal | |
|---|---|---|---|---|---|
| $R^0$ | $= 10^0$ | $= 1$ | $3^0$ | $= 1$ |
| $R^1$ | $= 10^1$ | $= 10$ | $3^1$ | $= 3$ |
| $R^2$ | $= 10^2$ | $= 100$ | $3^2$ | $= 9$ |
| $R^3$ | $= 10^{10}$ | $= 1,000$ | $3^3$ | $= 27$ |
| $R^4$ | $= 10^{11}$ | $= 10,000$ | $3^4$ | $= 81$ |
| $R^5$ | $= 10^{12}$ | $= 100,000$ | $3^5$ | $= 243$ |
| $R^6$ | $= 10^{20}$ | $= 1,000,000$ | $3^6$ | $= 729$ |
| $R^7$ | $= 10^{21}$ | $= 10,000,000$ | $3^7$ | $= 2,187$ |
| $R^8$ | $= 10^{22}$ | $= 100,000,000$ | $3^8$ | $= 6,561$ |
| $R^9$ | $= 10^{30}$ | $= 1,000,000,000$ | $3^9$ | $= 19,683$ |
| $R^{10}$ | $= 10^{31}$ | $= 10,000,000,000$ | $3^{10}$ | $= 59,049$ |
| $R^{11}$ | $= 10^{32}$ | $= 100,000,000,000$ | $3^{11}$ | $= 177,147$ |
| $R^{12}$ | $= 10^{40}$ | $= 1,000,000,000,000$ | $3^{12}$ | $= 531,441$ |
| $R^{13}$ | $= 10^{41}$ | $= 10,000,000,000,000$ | $3^{13}$ | $= 1,594,323$ |
| $R^{14}$ | $= 10^{42}$ | $= 100,000,000,000,000$ | $3^{14}$ | $= 4,782,699$ |
| $R^{15}$ | $= 10^{50}$ | $= 1,000,000,000,000,000$ | $3^{15}$ | $= 14,342,907$ |

## 13-6. THE TERNARY-NUMBER SYSTEM[1,3]

The ternary-number system, with a radix of 3, uses the digit symbols 0, 1, and 2. The number 3 in the ternary number system is 10. Other decimal equivalents of the ternary numbers are given in Table 13-1. The radix 10 (3) raised to the integral powers is given in Table 13-3. To illustrate the application of Eq. (13-2) to a ternary number, let $d_3 = 1$, $d_2 = 2$, $d_1 = 0$, $d_0 = 1$, $d_{-1} = 1$, and $d_{-2} = 2$. The magnitude of the ternary number is

$$N = (1)(10^{10}) + (2)(10^2) + (0)(10^1) + (1)(10^0) + (1)(10^{-1}) + (2)(10^{-2})$$
$$= 1,000 + 200 + 0 + 1 + 0.1 + 0.02$$
$$= 1,201.12$$

By inserting the power of 3 in the decimal system into the above equation, the decimal equivalent of the ternary number can be obtained. Thus

$$N = (1)(27) + (2)(9) + (0)(3) + (1)(1) + (1)(1/3) + (2)(1/9)$$
$$= 27 + 18 + 0 + 1 + 1/3 + 2/9$$
$$= 46.555\ldots$$

The procedures applied to the binary system can, with proper modifications, be applied to the ternary system. Addition, subtraction, division, and multiplication use the same procedures as decimal and binary and should create no difficulty in the performance of these operations.

The conversion from other number systems to ternary numbers and from ternary numbers to other number systems can be made by using the methods applied to the binary number system in Sec. 13-5. For example, when converting decimal integer numbers to ternary numbers, divide the decimal number by 3 and write down the remainder; then divide the quotient by 3 and write down the remainder, etc., until the last quotient is 0 and the remainder is either 0, 1, or 2. The remainders, beginning with the last, are the required ternary number. Thus

| Decimal | Remainder | Ternary number |
|---------|-----------|----------------|
| 3/1,377 |           | 1,220,000      |
| 3/459   | 0         |                |
| 3/153   | 0         |                |
| 3/51    | 0         |                |
| 3/17    | 0         |                |
| 3/5     | 2         |                |
| 3/1     | 2         |                |
| 0       | 1         |                |

Similarly, to convert a ternary integer number to decimal numbers, take the first digit to the left, and, if the second digit is 0, triple what you have; if it is 1, triple what you have and add 1; if it is 2, triple what you have and add 2. Continuing this procedure yields the decimal equivalent of the ternary number Thus the decimal equivalent of the ternary number 1,220,000 is determined as follows:

Step 1. The first digit is 1 and the second digit is 2; triple 1 and add 2, giving 5.

Step 2. The third digit is 2; triple 5 and add 2, giving 17.

Step 3. The fourth digit is 0; triple 17, giving 51.

Step 4. The fifth digit is 0; triple 51, giving 153.

Step 5. The sixth digit is 0; triple 153, giving 459.

Step 6. The last digit is 0; triple 459, giving 1,377 as the decimal equivalent.

With proper modifications, the above system of number conversion can be used for other systems.

### 13-7. THE OCTONARY-NUMBER SYSTEM[1,3]

Another number system that is of interest and is sometimes used is the octonary-number system, with a radix of 8, using the digit symbol 0, 1, 2, 3, 4, 5, 6, and 7. The number 8 becomes 10 in the octonary system. Other decimal equivalents of the octonary numbers are given in Table 13-1. The powers of 8 in octonary numbers and their decimal equivalents are given in Table 13-4.

### Table 13-4

### Octonary-Number System, Powers of the Radix 8

| *Octonary* | | | *Decimal* | |
|---|---|---|---|---|
| $R^0$ | $= 10^0$ | $= 1$ | $8^0$ | $= 1$ |
| $R^1$ | $= 10^1$ | $= 10$ | $8^1$ | $= 8$ |
| $R^2$ | $= 10^2$ | $= 100$ | $8^2$ | $= 64$ |
| $R^3$ | $= 10^3$ | $= 1,000$ | $8^3$ | $= 512$ |
| $R^4$ | $= 10^4$ | $= 10,000$ | $8^4$ | $= 4,096$ |
| $R^5$ | $= 10^5$ | $= 100,000$ | $8^5$ | $= 32,768$ |
| $R^6$ | $= 10^6$ | $= 1,000,000$ | $8^6$ | $= 262,144$ |
| $R^7$ | $= 10^7$ | $= 10,000,000$ | $8^7$ | $= 2,097,152$ |
| $R^8$ | $= 10^{10}$ | $= 100,000,000$ | $8^8$ | $= 16,777,216$ |
| $R^9$ | $= 10^{11}$ | $= 1,000,000,000$ | $8^9$ | $= 134,217,728$ |
| $R^{10}$ | $= 10^{12}$ | $= 10,000,000,000$ | $8^{10}$ | $= 1,073,741,824$ |

Applying Eqs. (13-1) and (13-2) to the octonary-number system, let $d_3 = 6$, $d_2 = 7$, $d_1 = 4$, $d_0 = 2$, $d_{-1} = 1$, and $d_{-2} = 5$. Then the magnitude of this number is

$$N = (6)(10^3) + (7)(10^2) + (4)(10^0) + (2)(10^0) + (1)(10^{-1}) + (5)(10^{-2})$$
$$= (6)(1,000) + (7)(100) + (4)(10) + 2(1) + (1)(0.1) + (5)(0.01)$$
$$= 6,742.15$$

By inserting the decimal numbers for the power of 8 into the above equations, the decimal equivalent of the octonary number can be obtained. Thus

$$N = (6)(512) + (7)(64) + (4)(8) + (2)(1) + (1)(1/8) + (5)(1/64)$$
$$= 3,554.1328125$$

The advantage of using the octonary-number system is the simplicity of converting from octonary to binary numbers. To convert from an octonary to a binary number, each digit in the octonary number is converted to a binary number. If the binary number has less than 3 digits, add 0's to the left of the binary number to make a total of 3 digits for each octonary digit, except for the octonary digit on the left, provided it is on the left of the octonary point. These binary digits, in order, form the binary equivalent of the octonary number. Thus, to convert 25,731 in the octonary system to a binary number,

| Octonary digits | Binary |
|:---:|:---:|
| 2 | 10 |
| 5 | 101 |
| 7 | 111 |
| 3 | 011 |
| 1 | 001 |

Then the binary number is 10,101,111,011,001. This procedure is valid for both integer and fractional numbers.

To convert from binary to an octonary number, mark off the binary digits in groups of 3 from the binary point and convert each group to an octonary number to form the octonary equivalent of the binary number. Thus, to convert the binary number 11,101,010,110,011 to an octonary number,

| Binary | Octonary |
|:---:|:---:|
| 11 | 3 |
| 101 | 5 |
| 10 | 2 |
| 110 | 6 |
| 11 | 3 |

The octonary number is 3,526.3.

## 13-8. THE DUODECIMAL-NUMBER SYSTEM [1,3,4]

The duodecimal number system has a radix of 12, requiring 12 digit symbols from 0 to 11. This is 2 more than in the decimal system; therefore, # will be used for digit 10 and $\pi$ will be used for digit 11. The decimal equivalents of this system are given in Table 13-1. The following relationships formed the basis for deriving this table:

| Decimal | Duodecimal |
|:---:|:---:|
| 0 | 0 |
| 1 | 1 |
| 12 | 10 |
| 144 | 100 |
| 1,728 | 1,000 |
| 20,736 | 10,000 |
| 248,832 | 100,000 |

It will be recognized that these numbers are $R$ raised to the integral powers. This system is useful in problems involving fractions, as will be shown in Sec. 13-13.

These examples of binary-, ternary, octonary-, and duodecimal-number systems are designed to give an insight into the theory of numbers and can be used as a basis for further work.

## 13-9.  THE BINARY-CODED DECIMAL SYSTEM

The binary-coded decimal system does not conform with Eqs. (13-1) and (13-2) but is a composite system using binary numbers from 0 to 1,001 to represent the decimal numbers 0 to 9. The advantage of this system in switching circuits will be shown in Chap. 14.

**Table 13-5**

**Binary-Coded Decimal System**

| Decimal | Binary-coded decimal | | | |
|---|---|---|---|---|
| 0 | 0000 | 0000 | 0000 | 0000 |
| 1 | 0000 | 0000 | 0000 | 0001 |
| 2 | 0000 | 0000 | 0000 | 0010 |
| 3 | 0000 | 0000 | 0000 | 0011 |
| 4 | 0000 | 0000 | 0000 | 0100 |
| 5 | 0000 | 0000 | 0000 | 0101 |
| 6 | 0000 | 0000 | 0000 | 0110 |
| 7 | 0000 | 0000 | 0000 | 0111 |
| 8 | 0000 | 0000 | 0000 | 1000 |
| 9 | 0000 | 0000 | 0000 | 1001 |
| 10 | 0000 | 0000 | 0001 | 0000 |
| 11 | 0000 | 0000 | 0001 | 0001 |
| 12 | 0000 | 0000 | 0001 | 0010 |
| 13 | 0000 | 0000 | 0001 | 0011 |
| 14 | 0000 | 0000 | 0001 | 0100 |
| 15 | 0000 | 0000 | 0001 | 0101 |
| 16 | 0000 | 0000 | 0001 | 0110 |
| 17 | 0000 | 0000 | 0001 | 0111 |
| 18 | 0000 | 0000 | 0001 | 1000 |
| 19 | 0000 | 0000 | 0001 | 1001 |
| 20 | 0000 | 0000 | 0010 | 0000 |
| 25 | 0000 | 0000 | 0010 | 0101 |
| 30 | 0000 | 0000 | 0011 | 0000 |
| 35 | 0000 | 0000 | 0011 | 0101 |
| 40 | 0000 | 0000 | 0100 | 0000 |

**Table 13-5**—*continued*

| Decimal | Binary-coded decimal | | | |
|---|---|---|---|---|
| 45 | 0000 | 0000 | 0100 | 0101 |
| 50 | 0000 | 0000 | 0101 | 0000 |
| 55 | 0000 | 0000 | 0101 | 0101 |
| 60 | 0000 | 0000 | 0110 | 0000 |
| 65 | 0000 | 0000 | 0110 | 0101 |
| 70 | 0000 | 0000 | 0111 | 0000 |
| 75 | 0000 | 0000 | 0111 | 0101 |
| 80 | 0000 | 0000 | 1000 | 0000 |
| 85 | 0000 | 0000 | 1000 | 0101 |
| 90 | 0000 | 0000 | 1001 | 0000 |
| 95 | 0000 | 0000 | 1001 | 0101 |
| 100 | 0000 | 0001 | 0000 | 0000 |
| 200 | 0000 | 0010 | 0000 | 0000 |
| 300 | 0000 | 0011 | 0000 | 0000 |
| 400 | 0000 | 0100 | 0000 | 0000 |
| 500 | 0000 | 0101 | 0000 | 0000 |
| 600 | 0000 | 0110 | 0000 | 0000 |
| 700 | 0000 | 0111 | 0000 | 0000 |
| 800 | 0000 | 1000 | 0000 | 0000 |
| 900 | 0000 | 1001 | 0000 | 0000 |
| 1,000 | 0001 | 0000 | 0000 | 0000 |
| 5,000 | 0101 | 0000 | 0000 | 0000 |
| 9,999 | 1001 | 1001 | 1001 | 1001 |

Table 13-5 shows the binary-coded decimal equivalents for the decimal numbers. The first group of 4 digits on the right in the binary-coded decimal numbers are the binary-number equivalent of the first digit on the right in the decimal number. The other groups of 4 digits from right to left are the binary equivalents of the decimal digits for the tens, hundreds, and thousands, respectively. In the binary system, 4 digits will represent 16 numbers, 0 to 15. In the binary-coded system, 6 of these numbers are lost, as 4 digits represent only 10 numbers, 0 to 9. This decreases the economy of the system, but it is extensively used to keep the numbers in a form that can easily be read in the decimal system and easily interpreted by the observer or recorded in decimal form.

## 13-10. THE REFLECTED BINARY-NUMBER SYSTEM[3,4]

The reflected binary-number system does not conform to Eqs. (13-1) and (13-2) or to common arithmetic operations. The criterion for the reflected binary system is that each succeeding number differs from the number preceding it and the number following it only by the change of 1 digit of the number. This system can take many forms. One of these is given in Table 13-6. The advantage of this system is that it avoids ambiguity in spatial analog-to-digital encoders. This will be illustrated in Chap. 14.

### Table 13-6

### Reflected Binary-Number System

| Decimal | Reflected binary | Decimal | Reflected binary |
|---------|------------------|---------|------------------|
| 0 | 0000 | 8 | 1100 |
| 1 | 0001 | 9 | 1101 |
| 2 | 0011 | 10 | 1111 |
| 3 | 0010 | 11 | 1110 |
| 4 | 0110 | 12 | 1010 |
| 5 | 0111 | 13 | 1011 |
| 6 | 0101 | 14 | 1001 |
| 7 | 0100 | 15 | 1000 |

### 13-11. THE CYCLIC-DECIMAL-NUMBER SYSTEM [2,3,4]

The cyclic-decimal-number system can be expressed in either Arabic digits or binary code. Table 13-7 lists the decimal numbers with their binary-coded cyclic-decimal and Arabic cyclic-number equivalents. The first 10 Arabic cyclic-decimal numbers, from 0 to 9, are the same as the decimal numbers. To preserve the criterion that successive integers differ, one from the next, by changing only 1 digit, the number 10 is 19, the number 11 is 18, the number 12 is 17, the number 13 is 16, etc., and the number 19 is 10, the number 20 is 20, the number 21 is 21, 99 is 90, 100 is 199, 199 is 100, and 200 is 200. Simple rules for determining the sequence of the digits in a cyclic-decimal-number system are as follows:

1. The sequence for any set of digits from 0 to 9 is the same as the decimal system when there is no number to the left, or when the number to the left is even or 0.

2. The sequence of any set of digits from 0 to 9 is the opposite to that of the decimal system when the number to the left of the sequence is odd.

The binary code for the cyclic-decimal numbers is not the same as that used in the binary or the binary-coded decimal numbers. It has 4 binary digits for each decimal digit. Each of these groups of 4 binary digits must never have all 1's or all 0's, and each number must differ from the preceding number and following number by only 1 digit. The condition of all 1's and all 0's is preserved for testing purposes. One combination that meets these criteria is

| | | | |
|---|---|---|---|
| Zero | 0001 | Five | 0101 |
| One | 0011 | Six | 0100 |
| Two | 0010 | Seven | 1100 |
| Three | 0110 | Eight | 1101 |
| Four | 0111 | Nine | 1001 |

This combination is used in Table 13-7. Other combinations are in commercial use. The application of this system will be given in Chap. 14.

**Table 13-7**

**Cyclic-Decimal-Number System**

| Decimal | Binary-coded cyclic decimal | | Cyclic decimal |
|---|---|---|---|
| 0 | 0001 | 0001 | 0 |
| 1 | 0001 | 0011 | 1 |
| 2 | 0001 | 0010 | 2 |
| 3 | 0001 | 0110 | 3 |
| 4 | 0001 | 0111 | 4 |
| 5 | 0001 | 0101 | 5 |
| 6 | 0001 | 0100 | 6 |
| 7 | 0001 | 1100 | 7 |
| 8 | 0001 | 1101 | 8 |
| 9 | 0001 | 1001 | 9 |
| 10 | 0011 | 1001 | 19 |
| 11 | 0011 | 1101 | 18 |
| 12 | 0011 | 1100 | 17 |
| 13 | 0011 | 0100 | 16 |
| 14 | 0011 | 0101 | 15 |
| 15 | 0011 | 0111 | 14 |
| 16 | 0011 | 0110 | 13 |
| 17 | 0011 | 0010 | 12 |
| 18 | 0011 | 0011 | 11 |
| 19 | 0011 | 0001 | 10 |
| 20 | 0010 | 0001 | 20 |
| 21 | 0010 | 0011 | 21 |
| 29 | 0010 | 1001 | 29 |
| 30 | 0110 | 1001 | 39 |
| 31 | 0110 | 1101 | 38 |
| 39 | 0110 | 0001 | 30 |
| 40 | 0111 | 0001 | 40 |
| 41 | 0111 | 0011 | 41 |
| 49 | 0111 | 1001 | 49 |

## Table 13-7—*continued*

| Decimal | Binary-coded cyclic decimal | | | Cyclic decimal |
|---|---|---|---|---|
| 50 | 0101 | 1001 | | 59 |
| 51 | 0101 | 1101 | | 58 |
| 59 | 0101 | 0001 | | 50 |
| 60 | 0100 | 0001 | | 60 |
| 61 | 0100 | 0011 | | 61 |
| 69 | 0100 | 1001 | | 69 |
| 70 | 1100 | 1001 | | 79 |
| 71 | 1100 | 1101 | | 78 |
| 79 | 1100 | 0001 | | 70 |
| 80 | 1101 | 0001 | | 80 |
| 81 | 1101 | 0011 | | 81 |
| 89 | 1101 | 1001 | | 89 |
| 90 | 1001 | 1001 | | 99 |
| 91 | 1001 | 1101 | | 98 |
| 99 | 1001 | 0001 | | 90 |
| 100 | 0001 | 1001 | 0001 | 190 |
| 101 | 0001 | 1001 | 0011 | 191 |
| 110 | 0001 | 1101 | 1001 | 189 |
| 111 | 0001 | 1101 | 1101 | 188 |

## 13-12. THE BIQUINARY CODE [5]

The biquinary-code decimal system uses 2 of a possible 7 digits for each decimal digit. These digits are grouped into one group of 2 digits called the binary units and one group of 5 digits called the quinary units. The binary units indicate whether the quinary unit is from 0 to 4 or from 5 to 9. There is only one of the binary-unit indicators and one of the quinary-unit indicators on at the same time. If the first binary and the third quinary indicators are on, the number is 2. If the second binary and the third quinary indicators are on, the number is 7.

| | Biquinary | |
|---|---|---|
| Binary units | Quinary units | Decimal Digits |
| 10 | 10000 | 0 |
| 10 | 01000 | 1 |
| 10 | 00100 | 2 |
| 10 | 00010 | 3 |
| 10 | 00001 | 4 |
| 01 | 10000 | 5 |
| 01 | 01000 | 6 |
| 01 | 00100 | 7 |
| 01 | 00010 | 8 |
| 01 | 00001 | 9 |

With this system, if both the binary units are the same, an error is indicated. Two 1's or all 0's in the quinary units indicate an error. This system is used in some of the IBM computers.

## 13-13. FRACTIONS

Most data-handling systems express noninteger quantities in the form given in Eqs. (13-1) and (13-2). Some systems use a radix, for quantities less than 1, which is different from that used for integers equal to or larger than 1, as some radices are superior to others for expressing common fractions. Table 13-8 gives the decimal equivalents of a few common fractions in binary, octonary, and duodecimal systems. It will be noted that all but the duodecimal system fail to express some of these fractions in rational numbers.

### Table 13-8

### Decimal Equivalent of Fractions

| Decimal fractions | Binary | Octonary | Duodecimal | Decimal |
|---|---|---|---|---|
| 1/64 | 0.000001 | 0.01 | 0.023 | 0.015625 |
| 1/32 | 0.00001 | 0.02 | 0.046 | 0.03125 |
| 1/16 | 0.0001 | 0.04 | 0.09 | 0.0625 |
| 1/12 | 0.0001010... | 0.05111... | 0.1 | 0.08333... |
| 1/8 | 0.001 | 0.1 | 0.16 | 0.125 |
| 1/6 | 0.001010... | 0.12222... | 0.2 | 0.16666... |
| 1/4 | 0.01 | 0.2 | 0.3 | 0.25 |
| 1/3 | 0.01010... | 0.24444... | 0.4 | 0.3333.... |
| 1/2 | 0.1 | 0.4 | 0.6 | 0.5 |

## 13.14. SUMMARY

The digital-number systems described in this chapter give the basic theory of these numbers. The applications of these number systems and additional coding systems will be described in the following chapters.

## PROBLEMS

**13-1.** Convert the following decimal numbers to binary numbers:
  (a) 328          (c) 4,582          (e) 23.91
  (b) 562          (d) 9,368          (f) 46.38

**13-2.** Convert the following binary numbers to their decimal equivalents:
(a) 11,001,101     (c) 11,101.011     (e) 11.11101
(b) 10,101,010     (d) 1,110.101     (f) 10.001101

**13-3.** Convert the following ternary numbers to their decimal equivalents:
(a) 22,101     (c) 212.11     (e) 21.222
(b) 21,120     (d) 102.22     (f) 11.212

**13-4.** Convert the following binary numbers to their ternary equivalents:
(a) 11,001     (c) 10.101     (e) 11,101.11
(b) 10,110     (d) 11.111     (f) 10,100.01

**13-5.** Convert the following decimal numbers to their ternary equivalents:
(a) 249     (c) 3,897     (e) 28.376
(b) 362     (d) 9,685     (f) 18.764

**13-6.** Convert the following octonary numbers to decimal equivalents:
(a) 746     (c) 3,576     (e) 2.374
(b) 243     (d) 35.76     (f) 7.645

**13-7.** Convert the following decimal numbers to their octonary equivalents:
(a) 942     (b) 35.98     (c) 87.496

**13-8.** Convert the following octonary numbers to their binary equivalents:
(a) 735     (b) 264.15     (c) 7.357

**13-9.** Convert the following binary numbers to their octonary equivalents:
(a) 11,111     (b) 11.11     (c) 101.101

**13-10.** Convert the following ternary numbers to their octonary equivalents:
(a) 210     (b) 2.11     (c) 221,102.12

**13-11.** Convert the following octonary numbers to their ternary equivalents:
(a) 744     (b) 56.37     (c) 75.75

**13-12.** Convert the following decimal numbers to their duodecimal equivalents and to their sexadecimal equivalents using $A$, $B$, $C$, $D$, $E$, and $F$ for 10, 11, 12, 13, 14, and 15, respectively:
(a) 397     (b) 45.45     (c) 297.83

**13-13.** Convert the following duodecimal numbers to their equivalent decimal numbers and binary numbers:
(a) 3π#     (b) π.#9     (c) 9π.3#

**13-14.** Make the following computations in binary numbers:
(a) 11,011 + 1,101 + 10,101 + 111.101 + 100.11
(b) 11,001,111 ÷ 101
(c) 100,001.11 − 10.11
(d) 11,110,001.01 − 1,111,101.11
(e) (11,101.011)(10,010.11)

**13-15.** Write the equivalent of the following decimal numbers in the binary-coded decimal, in the binary-coded cyclic decimal, and in the bi-quinary code:
(a) 58,922
(b) 29,654.73
(c) 625 × 10^6
(d) 0.732581
(e) 564.030

## REFERENCES

1. D. D. McCracken, *Digital Computer Programming*, John Wiley & Sons, Inc., New York, 1957.

2. Engineering Research Associates, *High-Speed Computing Devices*, McGraw-Hill Book Company, Inc., New York, 1950.

3. R. K. Richards, *Arithmetic Operations in Digital Computers*, D. Van Nostrand Company, Inc., Princeton, N.J., 1955.

4. M. Phister, Jr., *Logical Design of Digital Computers*, John Wiley & Sons, Inc., New York, 1958.

5. *IBM 650 Data-Processing System Manual of Operation*, International Business Machine Corporation, New York, 1955.

# Chapter 14

# ANALOG-TO-DIGITAL

## 14-1. INTRODUCTION[1]

The function of analog-to-digital converters is to change the analog output from a transducer or other voltage source into discrete digital quantities. These converters are also known as *encoders* and *digitizers*. The digital quantities are often indicated by lights or counters as they are obtained. They are also recorded in some form of memory unit, such as a tape, a punch card, or a magnetic drum, or written out on typewriters or tabulators to be used for analysis or for further computation. There are several commercial types of converters using different methods and circuits. They employ electromechanical, electronic, and transistor devices. These encoders usually use one of the following principles for converting an analog voltage output into digital form: (1) time-base encoders which measure the time of a sweep voltage at the instant the sweep voltage equals the analog voltage, the time being measured with a counter, and the final number counted during the sweep being the desired digital value; (2) feedback-voltage-comparison encoders which determine a digital comparison of the analog voltage to a given voltage; and (3) spatial encoders which utilize space displacement, such as the movement of a self-balancing potentiometer, to determine the digital value of the analog voltage.

346

# CONVERSION

The time-base and feedback-voltage-comparison systems can be made all electronic with a conversion speed greater than 100,000 readings/sec. The space encoder is usually an electromechanical device which is much slower.

The difference between analog and digital information, as discussed in Chap. 13, is that the analog output is a continuous function, while the digital output is a discrete number of units. The last digit of any digital number is rounded to $\pm 0.5$ of the last digit. The magnitude of the digit quantity is measured only at the instant the reading is taken. This is illustrated in Fig. 14-1. The continuous curve is the analog output, and the horizontal lines are the digital magnitudes observed at times 1 through 10. When one reading is taken, it persists until another reading is taken. The vertical range of this graph is from 0 to 100. If the readout device has the same range, 0 to 100, and a resolution of 1 count in 1,000, each reading would be read to the nearest tenth.

Encoders may be either a series or a parallel readout system. In the series output the digits are read in sequence or in a series of pulses; in a parallel readout all the digits are read at once. The parallel readout is usually faster than a similar series readout system.

## 14-2. NUMBER-INDICATOR SWITCHING SYSTEMS

An analog-to-digital encoder operates a system of switches to produce digital-number indications. These switches may be electromechanical, electronic, or transistor. They may turn lights off or on to indicate the digital number, or they may energize relays that operate card punches or tape recorders. The relay switches may send electrical pulses into a magnetic tape recorder, magnetic drums or magnetic-core memory circuits, or other memory devices where the digital numbers are stored for further use.

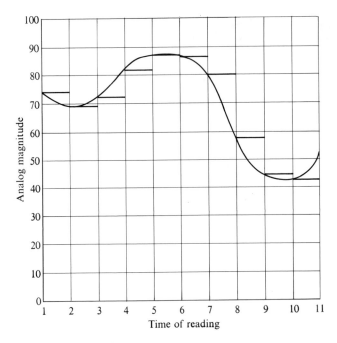

**Fig. 14-1.** *Digital samples of an analog quantity*

A decimal-number-system indicator with numbers from 0 to 999 is shown in Fig. 14-2(*a*). This circuit would require 30 switches and 30 indicating lights or relays, 10 for each decimal digit. Only 1 of the 10 switches for each decimal digit would be closed to energize the light which would indicate the number in each digit. Thus, to indicate the number 247, switches 23, 15, and 8 would be closed. The number of switches can be reduced by using a binary-coded decimal-number system, shown in Fig. 14-2(*b*). Here, only 5 indicators and switches are required for each digit in the decimal number. Again, if the number 247 were desired in this sytem, switches 13, 9, 2, 3, and 4 would be closed. This would indicate a 2 for the hundredths digit, 4 for the tenths digit, and the sum of 1, 2, and 4 for the units digit. This system has a saving of 15 switches over the decimal-number system, but it has the disadvantage of not having a distinct switch for each number of a given decimal digit.

A straight binary-number system can be indicated by the switching arrangement shown in Fig. 14-2(c). The numbers in the indicator from right to left are the powers of 2, or 0, 1, 2, 4, 8, 16, etc., in the decimal system. In the binary system the indicator numbers from right to left are 0; 1; 10; 100;

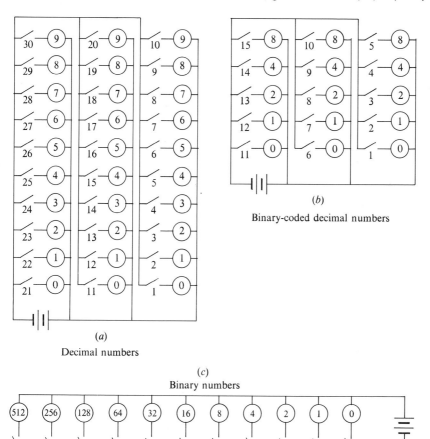

(b)

Binary-coded decimal numbers

(a)

Decimal numbers

(c)

Binary numbers

**Fig. 14-2.** *Switching circuits for indicating digital numbers*

1,000; etc. Thus, if switches to indicator lights 32, 8, and 1 were closed, it would indicate a decimal number equal to the sum of 1, 8, and 32, or 41. In the binary-number system this would be the sum of 1, 1,000, and 100,000, or 101,001. With the 11 switches shown, the equivalent of 0 to 1,023 in a decimal system could be indicated. The most efficient of these switching arrangements is the binary system, and the binary-coded decimal is more efficient than the decimal system. It will be kept in mind that all the encoding systems are essentially a means of closing switches which indicate the desired number.

### 14-3. DIODE MATRIX[1]

One number system may be converted to another number system by the use of a matrix circuit. For example, a binary-coded decimal number can be

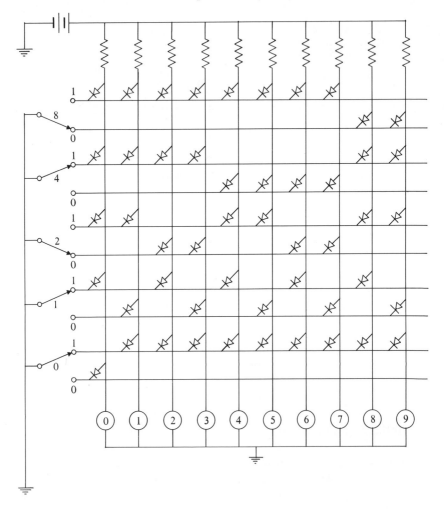

**Fig. 14-3.** *A matrix for converting binary-coded decimal numbers to decimal numbers*

converted to a decimal number with the diode-matrix circuit shown in Fig. 14-3. The switches 0, 1, 2, 4, and 8 are the inputs to the matrix, and the decimal indicators 0 through 9 are the output of the matrix. To energize an output indicator, the connection from the battery to the indicator must not be connected to ground through a diode rectifier, as the diode would short out the indicator. The 1 position of each input switch is connected through a diode rectifier to the indicators that must be off when the input switch is in this position. Similarly, the 0 position of each input switch is connected through a diode rectifier to the indicators that must be off when the switch is in this position. For example, the binary-coded decimal input for the number 7 requires that input switches 1, 2, and 4 be in the 1 position and input switches 0 and 8 be in the zero position. The 1 position of the input switch is connected to diodes that short-circuit indicator lights 0, 2, 4, 6, and 8, as there is no 1 in the binary-coded decimal number representing these numbers. Similarly, the 1 position of input switch 2 is connected to diodes that short-circuit indicator lights 0, 1, 4, 5, 8, and 9. The 1 position of input switch 4 is connected to diodes that short-circuit indicator lights 0, 1, 2, 3, 8, and 9. The 0 position of input switch 0 is connected to a diode that short-circuits indicator light 0, as this light must be off when input switch 0 is in the 0 position. Similarly, the 0 position of input switch 8 is connected to diodes that short-circuit indicator lights 8 and 9. Thus all indicator lights, with the exception of 7, have been short-circuited, and the readout is 7. It will also be observed that, if input switch 0 is omitted, the indicator 0 will be energized only when the input switches are all in the 0 position. Thus the 0 input switch can be eliminated. This logic can be applied to the conversion of other number systems.

To design a matrix circuit, mark all the junctions where the input switches must be closed to produce the desired readout, and place diodes across all the other junctions.

## 14-4. NUMBER INDICATORS

The output of analog-to-digital encoders is often fed directly into a memory circuit, yet it is desirable to have an indicator system which would indicate the exact digital number being read by the encoder. Several readout systems use the arrangement shown in Fig. 14-4. This consists of a frosted-glass plate with numbers etched on the frosted side. When the lights behind the numbers are energized, the light passes through the etched number and the number is easily read, whereas the other numbers are almost unreadable. Thus, if the number were 2,480, a light would appear behind the 2 in the thousandths column, behind the 4 in the hundredths column, behind the 8 in the tenths column, and behind the 0 in the units column. The lighted numbers would be read from left to right.

Another indicator uses a beam-switching-tube circuit. The beam-switching tube is shown in Fig. 14-5. There are 10 or more sets of electrodes in the tube. The proper electrode glows when the correct voltage is applied

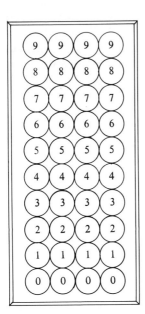

Fig. 14-4. *Digital-number indicator using etched glass and lights*

Fig. 14-5. *A beam-switching tube (courtesy of Sylvania Electric Products, Inc.)*

to it. Thus, by applying the proper voltage to the desired electrode, the tube reads the number marked on the periphery outside of the tube. The electronic circuits necessary to operate these beam-switching tubes are simple and economical. Only 10 of the electrodes of the beam-switching tube are used for each digit in the decimal number.

Another readout system uses 10 lucite sheets, with numbers from 0 to 9 etched on the face of the sheet. These sheets are stacked in order from 0 to 9. A light is placed on the edge of each sheet. The light passes through the lucite and comes out of the etched figure on the surface of the plate, indicating clearly the number being read. This indicator is illustrated in Figs. 14-6 and 14-7. Figure 14-6 shows a 4-digit lucite number-readout unit with the connections to the flashlight lamps which light each lucite sheet on top. Figure 14-7 shows a digital voltmeter using lucite number indicators.

**Fig. 14-6.** *A number-readout unit using lucite sheets and a digital voltmeter (courtesy of Non-Linear Systems, Inc.)*

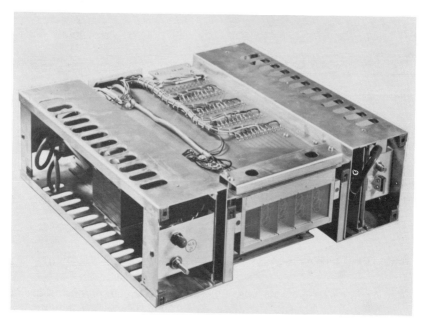

**Fig. 14-7.** *A digital voltmeter using a lucite readout unit, with cover removed (courtesy of Non-Linear Systems, Inc.)*

A fourth indicating device is a numerical-indicator tube. It is made by the Electronic Tube Division of Burroughs Corporation and consists of neon tubes as shown in Fig. 14-8. This neon tube has 10 plates shaped as a 0, 1, 2,

**Fig. 14-8.** *Number-indicator tube (courtesy of the Electronic Tube Division of Burroughs Corporation)*

3, and on to 9. When one of these plates is energized, the particular number appears in the tube, giving a direct number readout similar to the sheets of lucite in Fig. 14-6. Figure 14-9 shows a readout system using a number-indicator tube. They are called nixie tubes.

### 14-5. TIME-BASE ENCODERS[2]

A time-base encoder uses a linear sweep circuit producing a voltage which increases linearly with time from a fixed time reference unit it reaches a predetermined maximum voltage. At this instant the voltage drops to its original value. This value remains constant until the end of a definite time period, when it is triggered for another linear rise in voltage. This is graphically shown in Fig. 14-10. This linear sweep circuit and the analog voltage to be digitized are supplied to a gating circuit which is triggered when the two voltages are equal. A counter circuit is started at a fixed reference point of the linear sweep voltage, and it counts until the gating circuit is triggered.

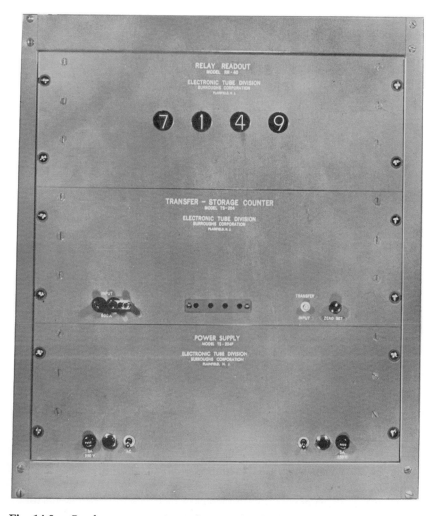

**Fig. 14-9.** *Readout system using indicator tubes* (*courtesy of the Electronic Tube Division of Burroughs Corporation*)

The instant that sweep voltage is equal to the analog voltage, the counter is stopped, and its count, in either binary or decimal form, is read. The gate is then reset, the counter returns to zero, and the cycle is ready to be repeated.

The numbers of readings per second obtainable with a time-base encoder depend on (1) the number of counts per second of the counter and (2) the resolution depending on the number of counts of the counter during the complete linear rise of the sweep voltage. If the counter produces $10^6$

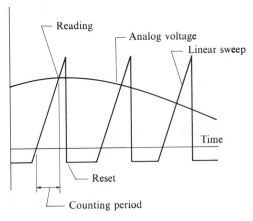

(a) Timing sweep diagram

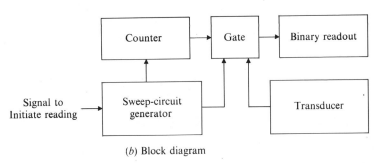

(b) Block diagram

**Fig. 14-10.** *Time-base encoder*

counts/sec and the resolution of the encoder is 1,023 counts, the maximum would be a little less than 1,000 readings/sec. If the resolution were only 128 counts, then the maximum number of readings would approach 7,800 readings/sec. If the counters were increased to $10^7$ counts/sec, the maximum number of readings would be increased by a multiple of 10. At these speeds each reading would be initiated by a programmer which would take the readings at the end of a definite period of time.

Inaccuracies in the time-base encoder are produced by errors or variations in the starting time, stopping time, and frequency of the counter, and by errors or variations in the linearity and slope of the sweep voltage. The advantages of the time-base encoder are simplicity of the circuit, ease of construction, and the fact that no logic circuitry is required. This latter feature will be described further in the discussion of spatial encoders later in this chapter.

### 14-6. FEEDBACK OR VOLTAGE-COMPARISON ENCODER

A feedback or voltage-comparison encoder which converts an analog voltage to a 3-digit decimal number is shown in Fig. 14-11. In this circuit three stepping switches are used, one for each digit in the number. Stepping

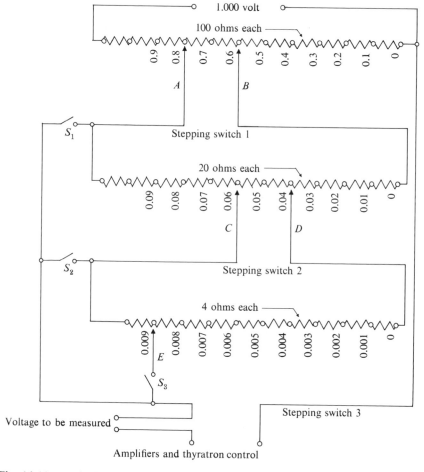

**Fig. 14-11.** *A feedback or voltage-comparison encoder*

switch 1 has 12 positions, with a 100-ohm resistance connected between each position, making a total resistance of 1,100 ohms. Contacts $A$ and $B$ are 2 spaces apart, making 200 ohms between these contacts. These contacts of switch 1 are connected to the first and last contacts of stepping switch 2. Switch 2 also has 12 contacts, with 20 ohms between each pair of contacts. Contacts $C$ and $D$ of stepping switch 2 are spaced 2 contacts apart, making a resistance of 40 ohms between these contacts. Contacts $C$ and $D$ of switch

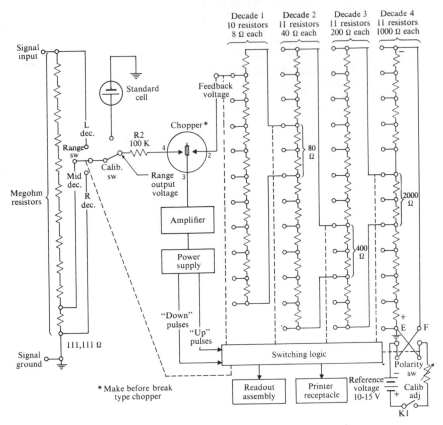

**Fig. 14-12.** *Digital-voltmeter circuit (courtesy of Non-Linear Systems, Inc.)*

2 are connected across the resistance comprising ten 4-ohm resistances connected between the 11 contacts of stepping switch 3. Thus contacts $C$ and $D$ of switch 2 have 40 ohms of switch 2 and 40 ohms of switch 3 in parallel across them, making a total of 20 ohms resistance, which is equal to the resistance between each of the other steps on switch 2. The total resistance between the first and the last contact of switch 2 is the sum of the nine 20-ohm resistances between the contacts outside of contacts $C$ and $D$, and 20 ohms between $C$ and $D$, making a total of 200 ohms across the first and the last

contact of switch 2. This resistance is in parallel with 200 ohms between contacts $A$ and $B$ of switch 1, making a total of 100 ohms between contacts $A$ and $B$ of switch 1. The total resistance between the first and the last contact of switch 1 is 1,000 ohms. This arrangement is known as the *Thomson–Varley potentiometer* circuit. In the initial condition contacts $B$, $D$, and $E$ are to the extreme right or 0 position. The relay contacts $S_1$, $S_2$, and $S_3$ are operated by the thyratron control unit. In the initial condition $S_1$ is closed, and $S_2$ and $S_3$ are open. To measure the unknown voltage applied to this circuit, the unknown voltage must be held constant; in other words, it must be "clamped" at a certain instant of time. Then switch 1 steps 1 point at a time to the left until the voltage on contact $A$ exceeds the measured voltage. Then stepping switch 1 is held at this position. Under these conditions contact $B$ of switch 1 is less than the input voltage, while contact $A$ exceeds the input voltage, and one tenth of the voltage across the top resistor is applied to the center resistor. Then contact $S_2$ is closed and contact $S_1$ is opened, and switch 2 moves step by step to the left until contact $C$ of switch 2 exceeds the applied voltage. Then stepping switch 2 is held at this position, contact $S_3$ is closed, and contact $S_2$ is opened. Under these conditions one tenth of the voltage across the center resistor is applied to the bottom resistor. Switch 3 then moves step by step to the left until contact $E$ exceeds the voltage being measured. Thus the voltage of contact $E$ on switch 3 is within 1 step of the voltage being measured. Stepping switch 1 has another contact which moves in step with contact $B$, which makes contact with another set of contacts giving a signal to the indicator of the most significant digit of a 3-digit decimal number. Thus, if contact $B$ were in position 0.6, the 0.6 indicator would be read on the readout system. Similarly, stepping switch 2 has another arm which moves in step with its contact $D$ which would connect the indicator to the second most significant digit corresponding to the position of contact $D$, and switch 3 has a contact corresponding to contact $E$ which makes contact with the indicator in the least significant digit.

This encoder has a resolution of 1 part in 1,000. It is very accurate and reliable, but it is comparatively slow. If the stepping switches operate at 30 steps/sec, it will require a maximum of 1 sec to read the unknown voltage to 3 significant figures. Of course, if the digits were less than 9, the time required would be correspondingly less. This same system of feedback-voltage-comparison encoding can utilize electronic devices which would perform the operation much faster, in the neighborhood of $10^7$ steps/sec. It is the most common commercial encoder.

### Digital Voltmeter

The Non-Linear Systems, Inc., digital voltmeter shown in Fig. 14-7 is an example of a feedback or voltage-comparison encoder. It uses a 4-digit self-balancing Thomson–Varley potentiometer circuit with amplifiers and controls. The fundamental circuit of this encoder is shown in Fig. 14-12. In this circuit the difference between the measured voltage and the potentiometer is chopped to produce an a-c signal which is much easier to amplify than the direct current, owing to the inherent drift in d-c electronic amplifiers. It also has a high-impedance range-selecting circuit and a standard cell for calibration of the circuit.

## 14-7. SPATIAL ENCODERS

The spatial encoder is the most direct method of converting analog to digital numbers. It uses spatial geometric configurations to represent the code of the numbers to be read. A very common form is the cylindrical disk, with the codes inset in concentric commutators on the disk. A brush connects

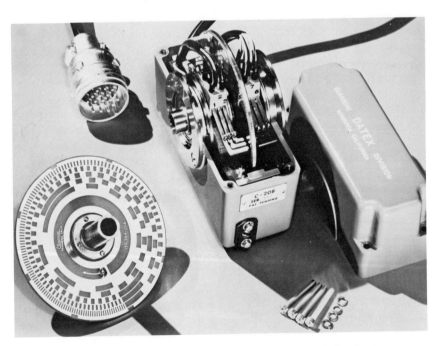

**Fig. 14-13.** *Spatial encoder (courtesy of G. M. Giannini and Co., Inc.)*

each concentric pattern with an external circuit which reads the patterns that are in contact with the brushes, thus interpreting the proper number into the readout system. The disk spatial encoder is used with self-balancing potentiometers, and the disk is driven by the self-balancing motor. The encoder reads the emf applied to the measuring circuit of the potentiometer. A potentiometer with a commutator spatial encoder is shown in Figs. 14-13 and 14-14.

Another spatial encoder uses a rectangular coding system, and the sweep of a cathode-ray tube reads the pattern on that particular line of the configuration. One encoder uses a code set in the sector of the sweep of the pointer of a d'Arsonval movement. The code at the position of the pointer is read by photoelectric cells which convert the position of the indicator into a

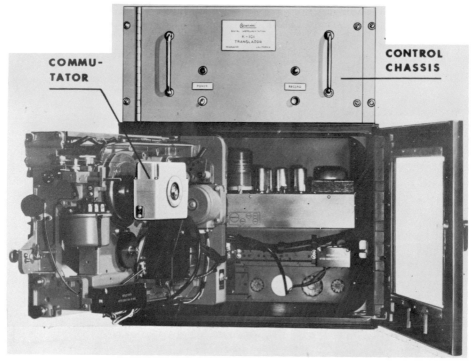

**Fig. 14-14.** *Spatial encoder attached to a potentiometer (courtesy of G. M. Giannini and Company, Inc.)*

digital number. Some encoders are subject to ambiguities requiring special logic circuits or special codes to prevent these ambiguities. Examples of these methods will be discussed below.

**Analog-to-Binary-Coded Decimal Spatial Encoder**

A disk-type spatial encoder which converts analog to binary-coded decimal numbers is shown in Fig. 14-15. This disk employs 8 separately encoded commutators, giving a readout of 0 to 99. In this circuit all the conducting commutator segments are connected to the positive side of the battery. In the position shown, the commutator segments make contact with the brush connected to readout circuits 20, 4, and 1, giving a total number indication of 25. If the disk were rotated in a clockwise direction 1 division or count, then the commutator segments would make contact with numbers

20, 4, and 2, making a total of 26 for the readout number. Now we rotate the disk in a counterclockwise direction 1/2 count. Suppose that the brush on the outside commutator ring makes contact with the commutator segment before the brush on the second contact ring ceases to make contact with that commutator segment. Then the number reading would be 20, 4, 2, and 1, indicating an output of 27, when it should be reading either 25 or 26. This is an *ambiguity*, which must be guarded against in this type of readout system.

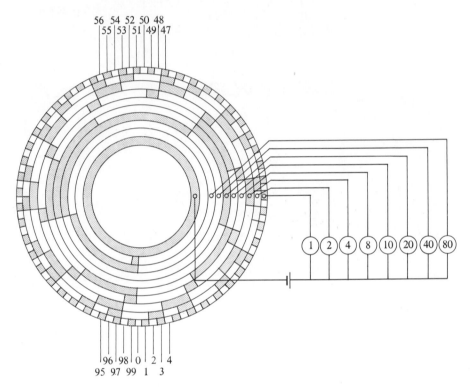

**Fig. 14-15.** *An analog-to-binary-coded decimal encoder*

Several systems have been devised to overcome this ambiguity. One of these utilizes an extra outer commutator segment, with commutators spaced in the regions where ambiguities may occur. When the brush on this outer ring makes contact, it automatically adds the proper increment of voltage to the unknown voltage to move the disk to a region of unambiguity. Other methods will be discussed in the next two subsections.

**V-Brush Binary Spatial Encoder[3]**

Referring to Table 13-1, it will be observed that in the binary-number system, when the least significant digit (abbreviated LSD) changes from 0 to 1 in the increasing-count direction, none of the other digits change. When the LSD changes from 1 to 0 in the increasing-count direction, the digit in the next significant digit changes. It will be noted that the next to the least significant (abbreviated NLSD) has the same relationship to the next least significant digit (abbreviated NNLSD) as the LSD has to the NLSD, etc. In other words, when the digit in the $N$th digit from the left changes from 1 to 0, the $N + 1$ digit also changes; when the $N$th digit from the left changes from 0 to 1, the $N + 1$ digit does not change. It will also be observed that when the $N$th digit is a 1, the $N + 1$ digit has not changed for a minimum of $2^N$ numbers. This logic can be visualized by referring to Fig. 14-16. Here are

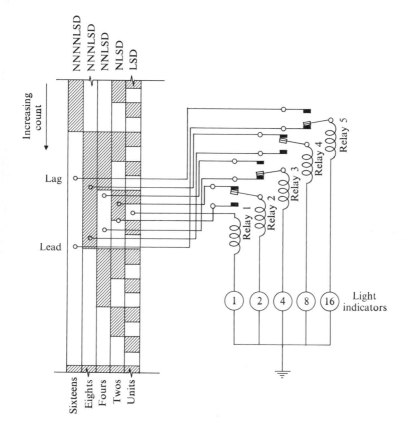

**Fig. 14-16.** *The circuit of a V-brush binary spatial encoder*

5 commutators, each representing a digit in a 5-digit binary number beginning with $2^0$ power on the right, or the LSD column; $2^1$ power in the next column to the left, or the NLSD column; $2^2$ in the next column to the left, or the NNLSD column; etc. The shaded portions of the commutators are

connected to the battery circuit. It will be observed that if the LSD reads 1, the NLSD will read the same as the previous count. Also, if the NLSD reads 1, the NNLSD will read the same as it did the previous count, etc. Likewise, if the LSD reads 0, the NLSD will be different from the previous count, and if the NLSD reads 0, the NNLSD will be different from the previous count.

Referring to Fig. 14-16, a single brush is placed on the LSD commutator and two brushes on the NLSD commutator, one brush 1/2 count behind the brush on the LSD commutator and one brush 1/2 count ahead of the brush on the LSD commutator; similarly, there are two brushes on the NNLSD commutator, one brush leading the leading brush on the NLSD

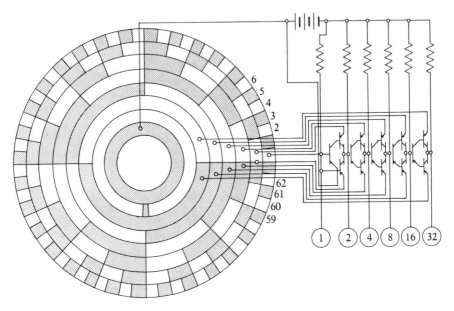

**Fig. 14-17.** *A V-brush spatial encoder with a transistor logic circuit*

commutator by 1/2 count and the other brush lagging the lagging brush on NLSD commutator by 1/2 count, etc. It will be observed that when the brush on the LSD reads zero, the lagging brush on the NLSD will read correctly, and when the brush on the LSD reads 1, the leading brush on the NLSD will read correctly. Similarly, when the output of the NLSD is 1, the leading brush on the NNLSD will read correctly. When the output of the NLSD is 0, the lagging brush on the NNLSD will read correctly. Therefore, the brush on the LSD can control the readings of the other commutating segments, provided that there is a logic circuit which will tell whether to read a leading or a lagging brush on the other commutating segments. Such a logic system is provided in the relay system in Fig. 14-16. If the brush on the LSD commutator reads 0, the relay in circuit 1 is not energized, and the lagging brush on the NLSD is connected to the relay and to indicator 2. When the brush on the LSD commutator reads 1, however, the relay in circuit 1 will be energized, connecting the leading brush of the NLSD to the relay in circuit 2. Similarly, when the brush in the NLSD commutator reads 1, it would energize the relay in circuit 2, connecting circuit 3 to the leading brush in the NNLSD commutator circuit, etc.

Figure 14-17 shows a disk converter with a transistor logic circuit taking the place of the electromechanical relays in Fig. 14-16. Inasmuch as this is a parallel readout system, the circuit can be energized with a pulse at that given instant, and the number on the disk would be read without stopping the disk and without ambiguities.

### Cyclic-Decimal Encoder

A disk-type spatial encoder using the cyclic-decimal-number system is shown in Fig. 14-18. This disk has the distinct advantage of having only one

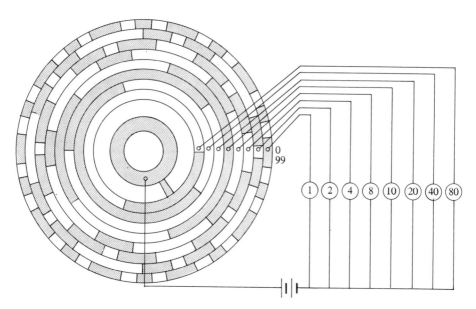

**Fig. 14-18.** *A spatial encoder using a binary-coded cyclic-decimal system*

disk-commutator change at a time, thus avoiding ambiguities. This system requires 4 commutator disks for each digit in the decimal number.

## 14-8. COMMERCIAL ENCODERS[4]

The Colman Engineering Company manufactures both analog-to-binary and analog-to-decimal encoders, under the trade name of Digitizer. The binary unit uses a disk with 6 coded zones giving a count of $2^6$ or 64 counts/ shaft revolution. This is geared to another disk having 4 coded zones. The

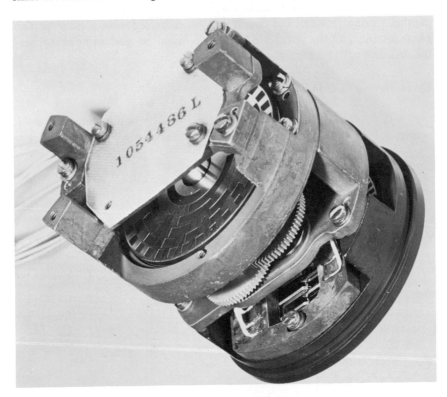

**Fig. 14-19.** *A librascope two-disk encoder (courtesy of Librascope, Inc.)*

gear ratio between the disks is 16:1. This gives $2^6$ times $2^4$ or $2^{10}$ or 1,024 counts, requiring 16 revolutions of the input shaft. This company also manufactures a unit which produces $2^{15}$ or 32,768 counts. The maximum speed of this unit is 1,200 rpm. It uses a V-brush arrangement to avoid ambiguity, and readout can be made at any desired instant. Colman also makes decimal units which are used to operate typewriters and tabulators. These units have an output of 10, 40, and 100 counts/shaft revolution and are available in 3-, 4-, or 5-decimal-digit units. They have a maximum speed of 1,800 rpm.

Librascope, Inc., manufactures a 19-digit binary converter. It uses a V-brush arrangement to avoid ambiguity. It can be read at a speed of 1,500 rpm. The brush output can be read in either series or parallel and can be equipped with a matrix for translation to decimal numbers. A two-disk Librascope encoder with the gear train between the disks and the brushes positioned on one disk is shown in Fig. 14-19.

The Electronic Corporation of America manufactures a shaft-position encoder using a cyclic-binary code. The disks consist of transparent and opaque areas in concentric rings, similar to the commutators on other encoders. These opaque and clear sections contain the cyclic-binary code which is read by means of a flash-type light source that passes through the coded disk onto light-sensitive cells which read out the desired number. A 13-digit system using a 4-in.-diameter disk provides an output of 8,192 discrete positions, and a 16-digit system on a 10-in.-diameter disk produces 65,536 discrete positions. This usually can be read at the rate of 600 times/sec. The duration of one reading is 6 $\mu$sec; therefore, it can be read accurately to 1,200 rpm without ambiguity of more than 1 count.

The Baldwin Piano Co. also makes an optical-disk shaft encoder, using opaque and transparent areas similar to a commutator. A view of this encoder, together with a breakdown of its assembly, is shown in Fig. 14-20.

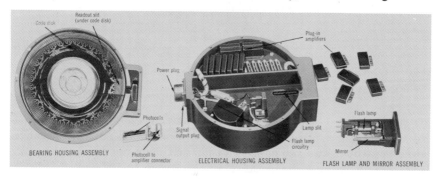

**Fig. 14-20.** *Transparent disk encoder* (*courtesy of the Baldwin Piano Co.*)

The small plug-in amplifiers shown in the figure have a voltage gain of more than 3,000. The clear areas produce a positive pulse, and the opaque areas produce a negative pulse. These units are made in several sizes, including a 13-digit, 6-in.-diameter encoder; a 16-digit, 9¼-in.-diameter encoder; and a 17-digit cyclic-binary code disk encoder. Baldwin also makes a 14-digit non-linear code disk, with a fifteenth track clear to provide for a light-source-intensity reference. These nonlinear codes include sine, cosine, and other trigonometric functions.

Farrand Controls, Incorporated, manufactures an analog-to-digital converter, known as the Inductosyn, employing an inductive system. It utilizes an inductive-type pickup; thus there are no brushes and no rubbing contact. It uses an error-detection device to prevent ambiguities and is capable of reading a 17 bit, or 131,072 counts/revolution.

The Giannini Datex Encoder uses a cyclic-decimal form with 12 commutator segments and 13 brushes, 1 brush providing the common return. This system produces 1,000 counts/revolution. It uses a relay matrix and a thyratron storage unit. Readings can be taken on the fly at the speed of 1 reading every 25 μsec. It also uses another system, with binary-coded decimals, which produces 1,000 counts/revolution; binary units that read 520, 1,024, or 2,048 counts/revolution; and a unit with a gear arrangement that reads 1 million counts.

The Consolidated Electrodynamics Corporation manufactures the SADIC, MilliSADIC, and MicroSADIC units, using the Thomson–Varley self-balancing potentiometer circuit. The basic MilliSADIC unit has an input of 99.9 volts and a full-scale output of 999 pulses. With the use of a preamplifier, it will take an input voltage of 1 volt and produce an accuracy of 0.5 percent. It is capable of taking more than 400 readings/sec. It has a visual digit-readout indicator using the binary-coded decimal system. A Flexowriter electric typewriter with a tape punch is used to record the processed data. The MicroSADIC reads 12 bits, either binary or binary-coded decimal, at 10,000 readings/sec. There are commercial analog-to-digital converters that convert up to $1\frac{1}{2}$ million readings/sec.

## 14-9. POSITIVE- AND NEGATIVE-READING ENCODERS

It will be noted that the above encoders have only positive numbers. If a disk is turned in a negative direction from 0, it would not read negative values but would read beginning with the maximum number on the disk. Thus, if both positive and negative numbers were to be read, the disk's numbers would begin with the most negative counts and proceed to 0, and then read positive numbers. The disk would also require another commutator which would indicate when the quantity read was positive or negative. It must be kept in mind that any encoder is limited by its total number of counts. If some of these counts are to be negative, they must be subtracted from the total number of positive counts that can be supplied by the encoder. If positive and negative values of voltage were to be read with a potentiometer with an encoder as positive and negative numbers, then the 0 point on the encoder would be 0 potential point on the potentiometer.

Another system of reading negative numbers uses a switching arrangement that reverses the polarity of the input when the input changes sign. It also energizes either a (+) or (−) sign before the number indicated. The digital voltmeter, Fig. 14-7, illustrates this type of instrument.

The Thomson–Varley potentiometer circuit shown in Fig. 14-11 reads negative numbers by reversing the polarity of the battery with a double-pole double-throw switch. The sign indicator is dependent upon the position of this switch.

## 14-10. SUMMARY

This chapter has outlined methods by which a voltage, a shaft rotation, or a space configuration may be converted into a digital number, and has shown the switching necessary to produce a system of relays or lights which will represent a digital number. It has also described lucite number indicators and number-indicator nixie tubes, and a diode matrix which will convert from one number system to another. The remaining chapters will discuss digital computation and the application of digital and analog systems in an integrated instrumentation system.

## PROBLEMS

**14-1.** Design a binary-coded decimal light indicator to represent the decimal number 1,999, using the 1, 2, 4, 8 code.

**14-2.** List the difference in the construction and operation of: (a) a time-base encoder; (b) a feedback or voltage-comparison encoder; (c) a spatial encoder.

**14-3.** Design an indicator switching circuit to give a light indication of binary numbers from 0 to the decimal number 2,047.

**14-4.** Determine the switches necessary to produce the decimal number 2,047 with each of the following systems: (a) decimal indicating lights; (b) binary-coded decimal indicating lights using the 1, 2, 4, 8 code; (c) binary indicating lights.

**14-5.** A binary-coded decimal system uses the binary numbers 1, 2, 3, 7. Design a diode matrix to convert this code to a decimal number.

**14-6.** A time-base encoder has a range of 0 to 1,999 counts. It requires 3 counts to reset the sweep circuit. The counter operates at 100 kc. Determine the number of readings per second that this system will perform.

**14-7.** The linearity of the sweep of a time-base encoder is 0.1 percent. Determine the range of this encoder when it has an accuracy of ±1 count.

**14-8.** Draw the circuit of a voltage-comparison encoder which will read the decimal number 9,999 if the total resistance of the Thomson–Varley potentiometer across the reference voltage is 50,000 ohms.

**14-9.** How does a digital voltmeter read either positive or negative voltages?

**14-10.** Draw the disk of a spatial analog-to-binary encoder that will have a range from −31 to +31 counts.

**14-11.** Design a V-brush logic circuit for a digital encoder with a range of 0 to 63.

**14-12.** Draw the disk of a binary-coded decimal spatial encoder using a 1, 2, 3, 6 code with a range of 0 to 199.

**14-13.** Design a reflected binary code from 0 to 31 and draw a pattern for a coded disk which will reproduce this code in a spatial encoder.


## REFERENCES

1. M. L. Klein, F. K. Williams, and H. C. Morgan, "Digital Automation," *Instr. and Automation*, December, 1955.

2. M. L. Klein, F. K. Williams, and H. C. Morgan, "Analog-to-Digital Conversion," *Instr. and Automation*, May, 1956.

3. F. K. Feingold, "Logic of V-Brush Analog to Digital Converters," *ISA Journal*, February, 1957.

4. M. L. Klein, F. K. Williams, and H. C. Morgan, "Practical Analog-Digital Converters," *Instr. and Automation*, June, 1956.

5. R. K. Richards, *Digital Computer Components and Circuits*, D. Van Nostrand Company, Inc., Princeton, N.J., 1957.

Chapter 1[

COMPUTER AN[

Modern digital computers perform high-speed digital computations. They are usually composed of the following units: input, memory or storage, arithmetic, control, error-checking, and output units.

A block diagram of these units is shown in Fig. 15-1. The units are combined to produce several thousand arithmetic operations per second upon digital data supplied to the computer, the results are tabulated in printed form. When the computed data are to be presented in graphical form, plotters which can plot the digital information are available, but these are usually considered as auxiliary equipment and not as part of the digital computer.

The input information is usually inscribed on punched cards, punched tape, or magnetic tape; it is read from these devices and stored in the memory unit of the computer. This operation is very slow compared with the computation operations of the computer.

The *memory units* include magnetic drums, magnetic cores, magnetic tapes, capacitive storage units, and transistor and electronic flip-flop circuits. These storage devices are described in the references at the end of the chapter. They all employ bistable states or conditions which represent binary digits. These states or conditions can be produced by *writing units* and read by *reading units* when the computer gives the command.

# THE DIGITAL

# DIGITAL-COMPUTER PROGRAMS

The *arithmetic units* and the *control units* take the information from the memory unit and perform the required sequence of operations to produce the desired computations. They are usually electronic, diode, or transistor circuits. The logical sequence of these operations is controlled by a clock-pulse generator that initiates the successive steps in the computation sequences.

The *error-checking units* are part of the switching and control system. They detect errors by a logic system called the *parity check* and also by duplicate data called the *redundance check*.

The *output unit* transfers the computed results to a permanent storage medium such as punched cards, punched tape, magnetic tape, or tabulated printed data. The overall operation of these units will be given in this chapter.

## 15-2. TYPICAL DIGITAL-COMPUTER OPERATION AND PROGRAMMING [1,2,4,5]

There are many small computers that could be used to illustrate a typical computer operation. The IBM 650 computer has been arbitrarily chosen, and its operation will be briefly described.

The input information for the IBM 650 computer is written on $3\frac{1}{4} \times 7\frac{3}{8}$-in. data cards. A sample of a data card is shown in Fig. 15-2. The punch locations on the data card comprise 12 rows and 80 columns. The top row is the (+) row. It is sometimes called the 12 or high-punch row. The next

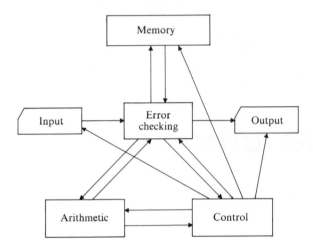

**Fig. 15-1.** *Block diagram of units of a digital computer*

row is the (−) row, sometimes called the 11, or $X$ row. The remaining 10 rows are numbered 0 through 9. These rows represent the arithmetic-system symbols +, −, 0, 1, 2, 3, 4, 5, 6, 7, 8, and 9. These symbols are produced by a single punch in each of the respective rows. One column is required for each symbol. The cards are designed to record 10-digit numbers.

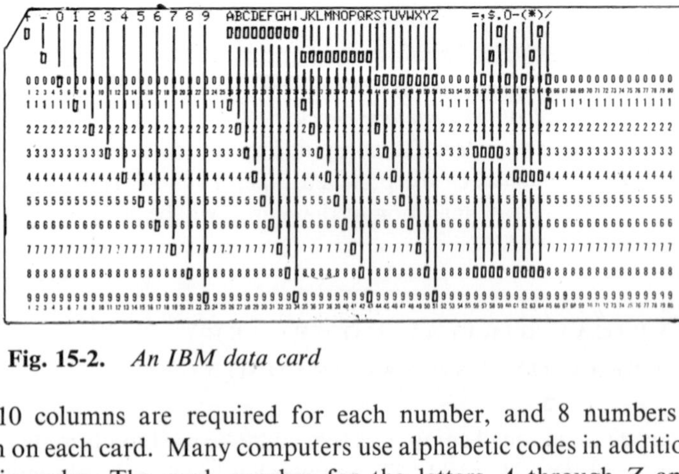

**Fig. 15-2.** *An IBM data card*

Then 10 columns are required for each number, and 8 numbers can be written on each card. Many computers use alphabetic codes in addition to the numeric codes. The card punches for the letters $A$ through $Z$ and other symbols that are used in this computer are shown in Fig. 15-2.

The cards are read with a set of brushes that complete electrical circuits when the holes in the card pass under the brushes. These electrical signals are transmitted to the drum storage unit of the computer.

Two types of information are read from the cards. The first is the *instructions* to be performed by the computer. The second is the *data* to be computed. Each instruction and sign is called a word. Then each word has 10 decimal digits and a sign. The 10-digit instruction word contains 3 parts. The first 2 digits on the left comprise the *operation code*. It gives the computer the operation to be performed. The next 4 digits from the left are the *data address*. It gives the computer the drum address of the data to be used in the computation to be performed. The last 4 digits on the instruction give the *drum address* of the next instruction. In the IBM 650 computer, *a sign must accompany each instruction or data number supplied to the computer*. The uses of these instructions will be illustrated later.

There are two methods for identifying the decimal point in a computer data number. The first method is the *fixed decimal point*. The *programmer* who prepares the instructions for the computer fixes the location of the decimal point in the data number by adding 0's to the left or to the right of the significant figures of the number until the number has 10 digits and the decimal point is in the right place, usually on the right or left side of the number. The second method is the *floating decimal point*. The significant figures of the number are written as an 8-digit decimal fraction. The last 2 digits give the power of 10 by which the decimal fraction is multiplied to obtain the desired data number. The number 50 represents the zero power of 10, and the numbers 51 to 99 represent the positive powers of 10 from 1 to 49, respectively. The numbers 49 to 1 represent the negative powers of 10 from 1 to 49, respectively. For example, the data number 24561.42 is written .2456142055 in the floating-decimal-point system. It is $.2456142 \times 10^5$.

The *drum storage unit*, which receives the information from the cards, is a cobalt–nickel-plated cylinder about 4 in. in diameter and 16 in. long. It has a 2,000-word storage area. Each word-storage area will store a 10-digit decimal number plus a sign. The decimal digits are written in biquinary code which requires 7 binary digits. These binary digits are often defined as *bits of information*. Then each of the 2,000 storage areas on the drum will contain 70 binary bits or storage spots where the 10-digit decimal number is stored and another binary bit or storage spot for the sign. This makes a total of 71 binary storage bits for each of the 2,000-word storage areas where a 10-digit decimal number and sign are stored. There are 40 columns, of 50 words each, around the drum, plus additional storage areas for identifying the position of the drum and for the read-and-punch buffer storage.

The flow of information through the computer is shown in Fig. 15-3. The sequence is from the card read by a punch-card reader to the drum through the read buffer. The computer instructions go from the drum to the *program register*, then to the *operation register* and *address register* through a *validity* or *error check*. These three registers control the operation of the computer and initiate the commands to the control units to perform the necessary operations.

The data words are transferred from the drum to the *arithmetic unit* of the computer through the *distributor* and a validity check. The last number that passes through the distributor remains written in the distributor until another number takes its place.

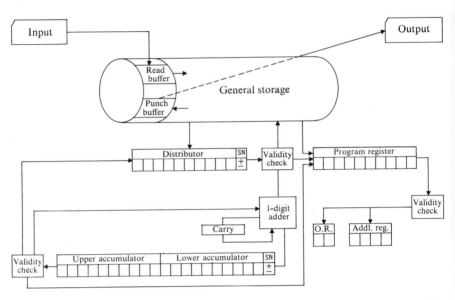

**Fig. 15-3.** *Block diagram of an IBM 650 digital computer* (*courtesy International Business Machines Corp.*)

The arithmetic unit consists of a 1-digit adder and an accumulator. The accumulator is divided into two parts. The upper accumulator has 10 digits. The lower accumulator has 10 digits and a sign. Then the total accumulator has 20 digits plus a sign. The information on the accumulator can be transmitted to the drum through the distributor, to the adder, or to the program register. The operation of an arithmetic unit will be discussed later, but first the overall operation of the computer will be outlined by listing the operations that the computer performs and then solving a problem using these operations.

**Computer Operations[6]**

The first 2 digits of an instruction word define the operation that the computer will perform when it receives this instruction. The typical operations of the IBM 650 computer and the numbers defining these operations are as follows:

00—No Operation. The data address is bypassed, and the machine goes to the instruction address given in this instruction number for a new operation, data address, and instruction address.

01—Stop. The computer stops.

10—Add to Upper. The contents of the data address on the drum are set in the distributor and added to the word in the upper accumulator. This sum is then placed in the upper accumulator. The word at the data address on the drum remains unchanged.

11—Subtract from Upper. The contents of the data address on the drum are set in the distributor and subtracted from the word in the upper accumulator. This difference is placed in the upper accumulator. The word at the data address on the drum remains unchanged.

14—Divide. A 20-digit dividend is placed in the entire accumulator, with one restriction: The absolute value of the divisor must be greater than the absolute value of the portion of the dividend in the upper accumulator. The divisor is specified by the data address in the instruction. The divisor is set in the distributor, the quotient is set in the lower accumulator, and the remainder appears in the upper accumulator. The number at the data address on the drum remains unchanged.

15—Add to Lower. The contents of the data address on the drum are set in the distributor and added to the number in the lower accumulator. This sum appears in the lower accumulator. If there is a carry, it will be added to the next digit in the upper accumulator. The number at the data address on the drum remains unchanged.

16—Subtract from Lower. The contents of the data address on the drum are set in the distributor and subtracted from the number in the lower accumulator, and the difference is stored in the lower accumulator. The contents of the upper accumulator could be affected by carries. The number at the data address on the drum remains unchanged.

19—Multiply. For this operation, the multiplier must be placed in the upper accumulator. The multiplicand is taken from the data address on the drum. It is set in the distributor and operates on the word in the upper accumulator to produce a 20-digit product which is set in the entire accumulator. For example, 0012345678+ multiplied by 8942711365+ will produce 0011040383 in the upper accumulator and 4959230470+ in the lower accumulator.

20—STORE LOWER. The word in the lower accumulator is set in the distributor and stored on the drum at the data address. The word in the lower accumulator remains unchanged.

21—STORE UPPER. The number in the upper accumulator is set in the distributor and stored on the drum at the data address. The word in the upper accumulator remains unchanged.

24—STORE DISTRIBUTOR. The number in the distributor is stored on the drum at the data address. The number in the distributor is undisturbed.

30—SHIFT RIGHT. The number in the entire accumulator is shifted right the number of spaces specified by the units digit of the data address of the shift instruction.

31—SHIFT RIGHT AND ROUND. The number in the entire accumulator is shifted right the number of spaces specified by the units digit of the data address of the shift instruction, and the right digit in the accumulator is set to the nearest 0.5. Thus, when the upper accumulator is 0015263849 and the lower accumulator is 1467837791, a shift to right 3 spaces and round would produce 0000015263 in the upper accumulator and 8491467838 in the lower accumulator.

35—SHIFT LEFT. The number in the entire accumulator is shifted left the number of spaces specified by the units digit of the data address of the shift instruction.

44—BRANCH IN NONZERO UPPER. If the upper accumulator is not 0, the next instruction is the number in the data address of the instruction. If the upper accumulator is 0, the next instruction is the instruction address of the instruction.

45—BRANCH ON NONZERO. If the entire accumulator is not 0, the next instruction is the data address of the instruction. If the entire accumulator is 0, the next instruction is the instruction address of the instruction.

46—BRANCH ON MINUS. If the sign is minus, the next instruction is the data address of the instruction. If the sign is not minus, the next instruction is the instruction address of the instruction.

47—BRANCH ON OVERFLOW. If the overflow circuit is operated, the next instruction is the data address of the instruction. If the overflow circuit has not been operated, the next instruction is the instruction-address of the instruction.

60—RESET AND ADD INTO UPPER. The entire accumulator is set to +0, and the number on the drum at the data address is set in the distributor and in the upper accumulator. The number on the drum remains unchanged.

61—RESET AND SUBTRACT INTO UPPER. The entire accumulator is set to +0, and the number on the drum at the data address is set in the distributor and is subtracted from the upper accumulator. This difference is set in the upper accumulator. The number on the drum remains unchanged.

64—DIVIDE AND RESET UPPER. A 20-digit dividend is placed in the entire accumulator, with one restriction: The absolute value of the divisor must be greater than the absolute value of the portion of the dividend that is in the upper accumulator. The divisor is specified by the data address in the instruction. The divisor is set in the distributor and the quotient is set in the lower accumulator. The remainder which appeared in the upper accumulator in operation 14 is cleared. Then the upper accumulator reads 0.

65—RESET AND ADD INTO LOWER. The entire accumulator is reset to +0, and the number in the data address on the drum is set in the distributor and in the upper accumulator. The number on the drum remains unchanged.

66—RESET AND SUBTRACT INTO LOWER. The entire accumulator is reset to +0. The number in the data address on the drum is set in the distributor and is subtracted from +0. The difference is set in the lower accumulator.

70—READ CARD. The card on the bottom of the stack in the card reader is read, and its contents are stored in the read buffer ready to be stored on the drum storage area at the next read operation, while the information that was stored in the read buffer on the previous read command is transferred to the drum address given in the data address of the instructions. Each card has a capacity of 8 words of 10 digits each, plus a sign. The first 10-digit number on the card is punched in columns 1 to 10. The following 7 numbers of 10 digits each are written in columns 11 to 80 on the card. All 8 numbers of 10 digits each are stored on the buffer when the card is read. When the next read command is given, all 8 numbers are stored on the drum. The first number that was on the card is written in the data address of the instruction. The remaining 7 numbers are written in the next 7 storage addresses on the drum. For example, the data address of a read operation is 0251. The first number on the card is written in the drum address 0251. The last number on the card is written in the drum address 0258. Only a given part of the drum will receive numbers from the read buffer. These are the addresses that end in 01 to 10 or 51 to 60.

71—PUNCH CARD. Similar to operation 70, this operation is in two steps: First, the data at the number on the drum at the data address of the instruction and the numbers at the following 7 addresses are read to the punch buffer. Second, the data in the punch buffer are punched into the card. As with the read area on the drum, only a given area of the drum can be read into the punch buffer. The addresses in this area end in 27 to 36 or 77 to 86.

## Preparing the Computer Program[6,7,8,9]

A program for solving a problem, using the above brief descriptions of the operations of the computer, will now be made. The problem is the solution of the equation

$$T = \frac{(A + B)C}{D}$$

This equation is to be solved for several sets of values of $A$, $B$, $C$, and $D$. Let $A$ be a 4-digit integer making a 10-digit word $000000XXXX$ for the computer input, where $X$ represents a significant figure. Similarly, $B$ is a 5-digit number written $00000XXXXX$ for the computer input, $C$ is a 3-digit number written $0000000XXX$ for the computer input, and $D$ is a 3-digit number written $0000000XXX$ for the computer input. Each data input card will contain these 4 numbers. $A$ is written in columns 1 to 10, $B$ in columns 11 to 20, $C$ in columns 21 to 30, and $D$ in columns 31 to 40. The output card will contain $A$, $B$, $C$, and $D$ written in the same columns as the input card, with $T$ written in columns 41 to 50. The words $A$, $B$, $C$, and $D$ on the input card must be stored in a drum location that will receive data from the read buffer. The address 0251 is chosen for storing $A$. Then $B$, $C$, and $D$ will be stored in drum addresses 0252, 0253, and 0254, respectively. The quantities $A$, $B$, $C$, $D$, and $T$ must be stored in sequence in the drum locations that can be transferred to the punch buffer. The address for storing $A$ is arbitrarily chosen as 0527. Then $B$, $C$, $D$, and $T$ must be stored in drum addresses 0528, 0529, 0530, and 0531, respectively. The addresses chosen for storing the instructions are 0000, 0010, 0020, etc. The instructions are spaced 10 spaces apart to allow one operation to be made before the next instruction is reached. In this process, if an operation requires more time than the time for the drum to advance 10 addresses, the drum must make a complete revolution before reading the new instruction. Expert programmers would space the instructions to give the minimum possible time between

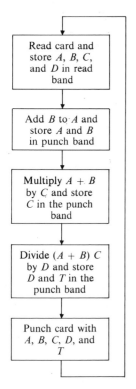

**Fig. 15-4.** *Flow chart of programming problem*

The flow chart boxes read:
- Read card and store $A$, $B$, $C$, and $D$ in read band
- Add $B$ to $A$ and store $A$ and $B$ in punch band
- Multiply $A + B$ by $C$ and store $C$ in the punch band
- Divide $(A + B) C$ by $D$ and store $D$ and $T$ in the punch band
- Punch card with $A$, $B$, $C$, $D$, and $T$

instructions. This is called *optimum programming*. This procedure will not be described here.

Now that the drum addresses for the input data, the instructions, and the output have been chosen, the sequence of operations for the solution of the problem can be prepared. The preparation of the sequence of operations is defined as *programming*. The first step in preparing a *program* is the construction of a *flow chart*. The flow chart for this problem is shown in Fig. 15-4. The first step in this flow chart is to read the card containing $A$, $B$, $C$, and $D$ and store these words in a read band of the drum. The second step is to compute $A + B$ and store $A$ and $B$ in a punch band on the drum. The third step is to compute $(A + B)C$ and store $C$ in the punch band on the drum. The fourth step is to divide this product by $D$, giving the answer $T$, and store $D$ and $T$ in the punch band on the drum. The fifth step is to punch out the answers on a card and return to the initial command, which starts the processing of a new set of data.

The instructions to be given the computer will now be prepared. They are listed in Table 15-1, which is the program listing the individual instructions. The first instruction is written 7002510010. It is stored on the drum at the address 0000. Operation 70 tells the computer to read a card and store the contents of the data card at addresses 0251 through 0258 on the drum. This places $A$, $B$, $C$, and $D$ on the drum. It then tells the computer to go to the drum address 0010 for the second instruction.

**Table 15-1**

| Location of instruction | Operation | Data address | Next instruction address | Upper accumulator | Lower accumulator | Dis- tributor |
|---|---|---|---|---|---|---|
| 0000 | 70 | 0251 | 0010 | ? | ? | ? |
| 0010 | 60 | 0251 | 0020 | $A$ | 0 | $A$ |
| 0020 | 24 | 0527 | 0030 | $A$ | 0 | $A$ |
| 0030 | 10 | 0252 | 0040 | $A + B$ | 0 | $B$ |
| 0040 | 24 | 0528 | 0050 | $A + B$ | 0 | $B$ |
| 0050 | 19 | 0253 | 0060 | 0 | $(A + B)C$ | $C$ |
| 0060 | 24 | 0529 | 0070 | 0 | $(A + B)C$ | $C$ |
| 0070 | 64 | 0254 | 0080 | 0 | $T$ | $D$ |
| 0080 | 24 | 0530 | 0090 | 0 | $T$ | $D$ |
| 0090 | 20 | 0531 | 0100 | 0 | $T$ | $T$ |
| 0100 | 71 | 0527 | 0000 | 0 | $T$ | $T$ |

The second instruction is 6002510020. Operation 60 tells the computer to set the entire accumulator to 0 and add the contents of the drum address 0251 to the upper accumulator. This places $A$ in the upper accumulator and in the distributor and 0 in the lower accumulator. It then tells the computer to go to the drum address 0020 for the third instruction.

The third instruction is 2405270030. Operation 24 tells the computer to store the contents of the distributor on the drum at the drum address 0527. The accumulator and contents of the distributor remain unchanged. It then tells the computer to go to the drum address 0030 for the fourth instruction.

The fourth instruction is 1002520040. Operation 10 tells the computer to add the contents of the drum address 0252 to the upper accumulator. This places $A + B$ in the upper accumulator and $B$ in the distributor; the lower accumulator remains 0. It then tells the computer to go to the drum address 0040 for the fifth instruction.

The fifth instruction is 2405280050. Operation 24 tells the computer to store the contents of the distributor in the drum address 0528. The contents of the accumulator and the distributor remain unchanged. It then tells the computer to go to the drum address 0050 for the sixth instruction.

The sixth instruction is 1902530060. Operation 19 tells the computer to multiply the upper accumulator by the contents of the drum address 0253. This places $(A + B)C$ in the lower accumulator as $A + B$ is only 6-digits at the most, and possibly only 5 digits, and $C$ is only 3 digits. Therefore, the product is a maximum of 9 digits. If the product had been greater than 10 digits, it would have extended into the upper accumulator, and a shift problem would have arisen. The word $C$ is placed in the distributor. It then tells the computer to go to the drum address 0060 for the seventh instruction.

The seventh instruction is 2405290070. Operation 24 tells the computer to store the contents of the distributor in the drum address 0529. The accumulator and distributor remain unchanged. It then tells the computer to go to the drum address 0070 for the eighth instruction.

The eighth instruction is 6402540080. Operation 64 tells the computer to divide the entire accumulator by the contents in the drum address 0254. This places the first 10 significant digits of the quotient $T$ in the lower accumulator; the remainder, which in operation 14 is placed in the upper accumulator, is removed, leaving 0 in the upper accumulator. The word $D$ is placed in the distributor. This instruction then tells the computer to go to the drum address 0080 for the ninth instruction.

The ninth instruction is 2405300090. Operation 24 tells the computer to store the contents of the distributor in the drum address 0530. The accumulator and the distributor remain unchanged. It then tells the computer to go to the drum address 0090 for the tenth instruction.

The tenth instruction is 2005310100. Operation 20 tells the computer to store the contents of the lower accumulator $T$ in the drum address 0531. The accumulator is unchanged, and $T$ is in the distributor. It then tells the computer to go to the drum address 0100 for the eleventh instruction.

The eleventh instruction is 7105270000. Operation 71 tells the computer to punch a card with 8 numbers, beginning at the drum address 0527. This places $A$, $B$, $C$, $D$, and $T$ on the punched card in the word positions 1 through 5, respectively. The accumulator and the distributor remain unchanged. It then tells the computer to return to the drum address 0000 for the next instruction. Then the computer will read another card with another set of values of *A*, *B*, *C*, and *D*, and the procedure will be repeated. A convenient method of stopping this computation is to place 3 or 4 blank cards in the card reader after the last set of data. When the computer receives the information from a blank card it will stop. This completes the program for the solution of this problem.

### The Preparation of Instruction Cards[6,8,10]

A total of 8 instructions may be placed on one punched card, but, for simplicity and for easy "debugging" of the program, only the 1-instruction-word-per-card routine for entering instructions on the drum will be described. The card for loading 1 instruction into the IBM 650 is shown in Fig. 15-5(*a*). Note that the following information is prepunched in the card: (1) The word 6919541953 is punched in columns 1 to 10. (2) The number 24 is punched in

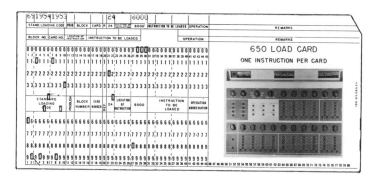

(a) A 650 IBM LOAD CARD WITH ONE INSTRUCTION
PER CARD

(b) A 650 IBM LOAD CARD WITH THE INSTRUCTIONS
WRITTEN IN THE CARD

**Fig. 15-5.** *An IBM 650 load card for 1 instruction per card (courtesy International Business Machines Corp.)*

columns 21 and 22. (3) The number 8000 is punched in columns 27 to 30. (4) Columns 10 and 30 also have the high punch on 12 punched. In this pre-punched card, the operator is required to punch only the drum address where the instruction is to be stored in columns 23 to 26 and the instruction to be stored on the drum in columns 31 to 40. Additional information may be stored on the card for identifying and sorting the cards. This is punched in columns 11 to 20, as listed on the card. Also, the abbreviation of the operation instruction may be written in columns 41 to 45. Figure 15-5(*b*) shows the 1-instruction-per-card load card with the first instructions of the above problem. Identification information is also punched in this card.

### Addresses other than Drum Locations

The number 8000 on the 1-instruction-per-card load card is the console *storage-entry address*. In addition to this address, the address 8001 is the distributor, 8002 is the lower accumulator, and 8003 is the upper accumulator. Thus, in referring to these components in an instruction, these addresses may be used.

### Auxiliary Equipment[2,5]

The IBM 650 computer requires an IBM 533 *read-punch unit*, an IBM 407 *tabulator*, and a keyboard-operated IBM *card-preparation* unit as auxiliary equipment. The punched cards are prepared on the card-preparation unit. They are read and the information is transmitted to the computer by the IBM 533 read-punch unit. This unit also receives information from the computer and punches it in IBM cards. The tabulator receives information from the read-punch unit in the form of data from punched cards; it then tabulates this information in printed form.

### Computer Controls[2,3,5]

The control console of an IBM 650 computer is shown in Fig. 15-6. The *display lights* read a 10-digit decimal number with sign in biquinary code. The 10 *storage-entry switches plus sign switch* under these lights can be referred to during the program by using the address 8000. They are also used, in conjunction with other controls, to enter information into the drum. The two sets of *operation lights* to the left under the storage-entry switches indicate the operation that is to be performed. The four sets of *address lights* to the right of the operation lights indicate the contents of either the instruction address or the data address, depending on the indication of the data-address or the instruction-address lights in the group of operating lights to the right of the data-address lights. The remaining operating lights indicate the status of the read, punch, accumulator, and program units. The *check lights* to the right of the operating lights indicate the validity of error at the different parts of the computer. The control switches from left to right, beginning under the operation lights, are: (1) *programmer*, stop or run switch; (2) *half cycle*, half or run switch; (3) four address selector switches; (4) *control*, address stop-run-manual operation switch; (5) *display* lower accumulator,

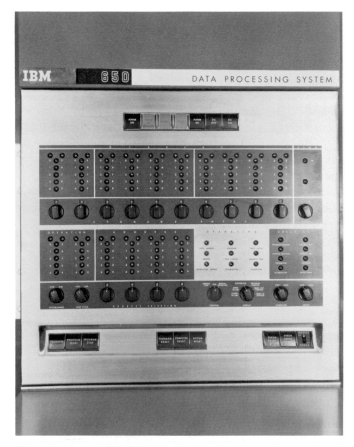

**Fig. 15-6.** *An IBM 650 control console (courtesy International Business Machines Corp.)*

upper accumulator, distributor, program register, readout storage, read-in storage switch; (6) *overflow*, stop or sense switch; and (7) *error*, stop, or sense switch. All but the read-in storage position on the display switch read the words at the above locations on the display lights. Any word may be entered into a drum address by use of the read-in storage-switch position in conjunction with the address-selection switches and the storage-entry switches.

The key-punch switches are clearly marked in Fig. 15-6.

There is another control on the IBM 650. It is a *patch panel*. The IBM 533 read-punch unit also has a patch panel. These will not be described here, but it should be noted that the patch panel must be connected correctly for the type of inputs and operations required in the problem.

**Procedure for Solving a Problem on the Computer**[6]

The procedure for solving a problem on the IBM 650 computer is as follows:

1. Be sure that the patch panel is connected correctly.

2. Obtain a drum zero card from the card library file and place it as the number-one card in your deck.

3. Follow the drum zero card with the instruction load cards.

4. Place a transfer card containing 000000 and location of the first instruction (in the above problem, this was 0000) in columns 1 to 10, behind the instruction load cards.

5. Place the data cards behind the transfer card.

6. Place several blank cards behind the last set of data cards.

7. Place this deck of cards, face down and 12 edge first, in the punch feed. Be sure that the punch feed has been cleared out.

8. Set the storage entry switch to 70 1951 8000.

9. Set the storage entry switch to run.

10. Set the control switch to run.

11. Set the display switch to accumulator, distributor or program register.

12. Set the half-cycle switch to run.

13. Set the program stop, overflow, and error switches as desired.

14. Push the computer reset.

15. Push the program start.

16. Push the read start on the IBM 533 read-punch unit.

17. Push the punch start on the IBM 533 read-punch unit.

The above description of a computer, its program, and its operation is brief and incomplete, but it should give an overall picture of the computer's function, without attempting to detail everything it can and cannot do; the goal of this section is not to make IBM 650 programmers but to give the reader a general idea of a computer.

All computers have libraries of subroutines that are prepared for solving special problems such as square roots, logarithms of numbers, trigonometric functions, matrices, etc. They also have program-assembly programs which will place the instructions in the optimum memory locations to obtain the fastest and most efficient operation. These are discussed in the references at the end of the chapter. A computer center, with tape inputs on the left and card read-punch unit and tabulator on the right, is shown in Fig. 15-7.

## 15-3. BOOLEAN ALGEBRA [3]

The operation of the switching circuits of a computer is more easily described in symbolic logic, which is expressed in a system known as Boolean algebra. This system uses two values, 1 and 0, similar to binary numbers. The 1 is defined as the true state and the 0 as the false state in logic systems, but, in circuit analysis, the 1 may be a closed circuit, a positive electrical potential, or an energized relay circuit, while the 0 may be an open circuit, a negative electrical potential or an unenergized relay.

**Fig. 15-7.** *A computer center with an IBM 650 computer and auxiliary equipment (courtesy of the Hercules Powder Co.)*

The operations performed by Boolean algebra are very different from those in ordinary algebra. The result of any Boolean algebra operation is either a 0 state or a 1 state. One basic Boolean algebra operation is defined as an AND operation, where $A$ AND $B$ produce a 1 state when $A$ is a 1 and $B$ is a 1. $A$ AND $B$ produce a 0 state when either $A$ or $B$ is 0 or when $A$ and $B$ are both 0. The expression for this operation is that of a product $AB$. It is expressed in a chart, defined as a *truth table* or a *function table*, which is given in Table 15-2. All the possible combinations of $A$ and $B$ are listed in the $A$ column and the $B$ column, and the results of the combinations are listed in the $AB$ column. It will be noted that the 0's and 1's under columns $A$ and $B$ form the binary numbers 00 to 11. This is a very effective method of writing all the possible combinations of a set of inputs. For example, the combination of the four inputs $A$, $B$, $C$, and $D$ would be the binary numbers 0 to 15, using all four spaces, as in a binary code. The circuits in Fig. 15-8 illustrate

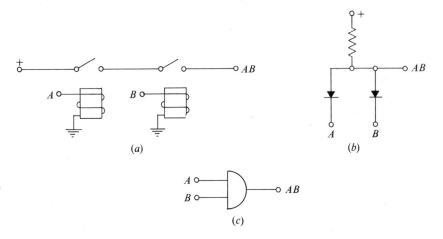

(a)    (b)

(c)

**Fig. 15-8.** AND *circuits*

typical AND circuits. Figure 15-8(a) is a relay AND circuit, and Fig. 15-8(b) is a diode AND circuit. The operation of these circuits can be checked with Table 15-2. The symbol for an AND circuit is given in Fig. 15-8(c).

| Table 15-2 | | | Table 15-3 | | |
|---|---|---|---|---|---|
| Function Table $A$ AND $B$ | | | Function Table for $A$ OR $B$ | | |
| $A$ | $B$ | $AB$ | $A$ | $B$ | $A + B$ |
| 0 | 0 | 0 | 0 | 0 | 0 |
| 0 | 1 | 0 | 0 | 1 | 1 |
| 1 | 0 | 0 | 1 | 0 | 1 |
| 1 | 1 | 1 | 1 | 1 | 1 |

Another basic Boolean algebra process is defined as an OR operation, where $A$ OR $B$ produces a 0 state when $A$ and $B$ are both 0, and a 1 state when either $A$ or $B$ is a 1 or when both $A$ and $B$ are 1's. The expression for this operation is that of a sum, $A + B$. The function table for this operation is Table 15-3. The circuits in Fig. 15-9 illustrate typical OR circuits. Figure 15-9(a) is a relay circuit which produces the quantity $A + B$. Figure 15-9(b) is a diode circuit which produces $A + B$. Figure 15-9(c) is the symbolic diagram of an OR circuit.

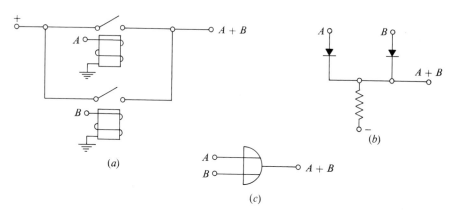

**Fig. 15-9.** OR *circuits*

Another basic Boolean algebra process is the NOT. It is expressed by a bar over the quantity which is not. Thus $\overline{A}$ is not $A$ or $\overline{A + B}$ is not $A + B$. $\overline{A}$ is defined as the complement of $A$. It is also defined as the conjugate of $A$ or the negation of $A$. $\overline{A + B}$ is the complement of $A + B$. When $A$ is 1, $\overline{A}$ is 0. When $\overline{A}$ is 1, $A$ is 0.

Then

$$A\overline{A} = 0 \qquad (15\text{-}1)$$

and

$$A + \overline{A} = 1 \qquad (15\text{-}2)$$

| Table 15-4 | | |
|---|---|---|
| **Function Table for $A\overline{A}$** | | |
| $A$ | $\overline{A}$ | $A\overline{A}$ |
| 0 | 1 | 0 |
| 1 | 0 | 0 |

| Table 15-5 | | |
|---|---|---|
| **Function Table for $A + \overline{A}$** | | |
| $A$ | $\overline{A}$ | $A + \overline{A}$ |
| 0 | 1 | 1 |
| 1 | 0 | 1 |

The function tables of these equations are Tables 15-4 and 15-5. Examples of circuits which produce a NOT are shown in Fig. 15-10. Figure 15-10(a) is a relay circuit with normally closed contact. Figure 15-10(b) is a P–N–P type of transistor circuit. It passes current when the base is made negative compared to the emitter. Then the output $\bar{A}$ is positive when the input $A$ is negative. When $A$ is positive, $\bar{A}$ will be negative. Figure 15-10($c$) shows the symbolic representation of a NOT circuit. Other transistor logic circuits are shown in Fig. 15-11.

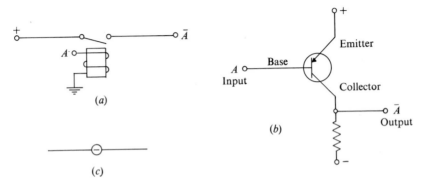

**Fig. 15-10.** NOT *circuits*

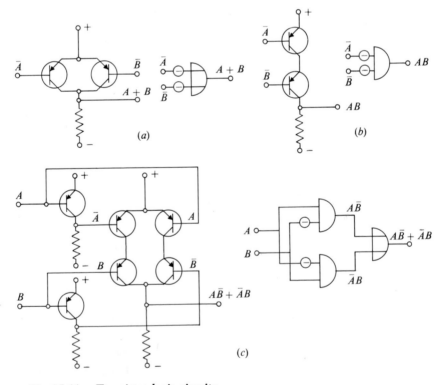

**Fig. 15-11.** *Transistor logic circuits*

## Boolean Algebra Theorems[2,3,4]

The following theorems in Boolean algebra are derived from the basic concepts that have been discussed. They can also be proved using function tables.

Theorem 1: $A + 0 = A$

Theorem 2: $A + 1 = 1$

Theorem 3: $A + A = A$

Theorem 4: $A0 = 0$

Theorem 5: $A1 = A$

Theorem 6: $AB + AC = A(B + C)$

Theorem 7: $(A + B)(A + C) = A + BC$

Theorem 8: $A(A + B) = A$

Theorem 9: $(A + B) + C = A + (B + C)$

Theorem 10: $(AB)C = A(BC)$

Theorem 11: $A + AB = A$

Theorem 12: $A + \bar{A} = 1$

Theorem 13: $A\bar{A} = 0$

Theorem 14: $\overline{ABC} = \bar{A} + \bar{B} + \bar{C}$

Theorem 15: $\overline{A + B + C} = \bar{A}\bar{B}\bar{C}$

Theorem 16: $\overline{AB + BC + CA} = \bar{A}\bar{B} + \bar{B}\bar{C} + \bar{C}\bar{A}$

Theorem 17: $AB + CD = (A + C)(A + D)(B + C)(B + D)$

Theorem 18: $A\bar{B} + \bar{A}B = (A + B)(\bar{A} + \bar{B})$

Theorem 19: $AB + A\bar{B} = A$

Theorem 20: $AA = A$

Theorem 21: $A + \bar{A}B = A + B$

Theorem 22: $\overline{(A + B)} = \bar{A}\bar{B}$

Theorem 23: $A(\bar{A}C) = 0$

Theorem 24: $A\bar{B} + \bar{A}B = \overline{AB + \bar{A}\bar{B}}$

The function table for Theorem 7 is given in Table 15-6. The digits in the column under $(A + B)(A + C)$ are the same as the digits in the column under $A + BC$. This proves that the two terms are equal.

## Table 15-6

### Function Table for Theorem 7

| $A$ | $B$ | $C$ | $A + B$ | $A + C$ | $(A + B)(A + C)$ | $BC$ | $A + BC$ |
|-----|-----|-----|---------|---------|------------------|------|----------|
| 0 | 0 | 0 | 0 | 0 | 0 | 0 | 0 |
| 0 | 0 | 1 | 0 | 1 | 0 | 0 | 0 |
| 0 | 1 | 0 | 1 | 0 | 0 | 0 | 0 |
| 0 | 1 | 1 | 1 | 1 | 1 | 1 | 1 |
| 1 | 0 | 0 | 1 | 1 | 1 | 0 | 1 |
| 1 | 0 | 1 | 1 | 1 | 1 | 0 | 1 |
| 1 | 1 | 0 | 1 | 1 | 1 | 0 | 1 |
| 1 | 1 | 1 | 1 | 1 | 1 | 1 | 1 |

**Minterms and Maxterms**

A *minterm* of $N$ variables is a Boolean product of these $N$ variables, with each variable either in its true form or in its complemented form. The possible minterms of the three terms $A$, $B$, and $C$ are $ABC$, $AB\bar{C}$, $A\bar{B}C$, $A\bar{B}\bar{C}$, $\bar{A}BC$, $\bar{A}\bar{B}C$, and $\bar{A}\bar{B}\bar{C}$. Often, it is desired to express a function as a sum of minterms. For example, the terms in this equation are not minterms:

$$f = AB + C + BC \tag{15-3}$$

This equation can be expanded to the sum of minterms by Theorem 19 which states that $AB + A\bar{B} = A$. Then

$$AB = ABC + AB\bar{C}$$

and

$$C = AC + \bar{A}C$$
$$= ABC + A\bar{B}C + \bar{A}BC + \bar{A}\bar{B}C$$

Then

$$BC = ABC + \bar{A}BC$$
$$f = ABC + AB\bar{C} + ABC + A\bar{B}C + \bar{A}BC + \bar{A}\bar{B}C + ABC + \bar{A}BC$$

But by Theorem 3, which states that $A + A = A$, all repeat terms can be omitted. Then

$$f = ABC + AB\bar{C} + A\bar{B}C + \bar{A}\bar{B}C + \bar{A}BC \tag{15-4}$$

*The sum of any combination of the products of n terms can be expanded into the sum of minterms.*

A maxterm of $n$ variables is a Boolean sum of these $n$ variables, with each variable either in its true form or in its complemented form. The possible maxterms of the three variables $A$, $B$, and $C$ are $A + B + C$, $A + B + \bar{C}$, $A + \bar{B} + C$, $\bar{A} + B + C$, $A + \bar{B} + \bar{C}$, $\bar{A} + \bar{B} + C$, $\bar{A} + B + \bar{C}$, and

$\bar{A} + \bar{B} + \bar{C}$. A function expressed in maxterms is the product of the maxterms.

A function expressed in the form

$$f = (A + B)(\bar{A} + C)(A + \bar{B}) \qquad (15\text{-}5)$$

is transformed to a sum of minterms by multiplying the three terms and using Theorems 13 and 20, which state that

$$A\bar{A} = 0 \quad \text{and} \quad AA = A$$

Then

$$(A + B)(\bar{A} + C) = A\bar{A} + AC + \bar{A}B + BC$$
$$= AC + \bar{A}B + BC$$

Then

$$(AC + \bar{A}B + BC)(A + \bar{B}) = AAC + A\bar{A}B + ABC + A\bar{B}C + \bar{A}B\bar{B} + B\bar{B}C$$
$$= AC + ABC + A\bar{B}C$$

Applying Theorem 19, which states that $AB + A\bar{B} = A$, gives

$$f = AC + ABC + A\bar{B}C$$
$$= ABC + A\bar{B}C \qquad (15\text{-}6)$$

The identity $(A + B)(\bar{A} + C)(A + \bar{B}) = ABC + A\bar{B}C$ can be proved with a function table. It illustrates the conversion from a product of sums to a sum of minterms. Thus it is possible to reduce any function to a sum of minterms. A more complete discussion of minterms and maxterms is found in Reference 3 at the end of the chapter.

## Diagrams and Simplification of Boolean Equations[2,3,4]

The diagrams for expressing Boolean equations in Fig. 15-12 are patterned after the Veitch diagrams and the Karnaugh maps. As the first step in representing an equation in a diagram, expand the equation into the sum of minterms. Next, make a diagram using the pattern shown in Fig. 15-12. The odd variables, counting the variables in the minterms from left to right, are placed in the tops of the columns in the diagram. The true and the complementary terms of a variable are in groups of two or four, etc., in the order shown in the diagram. Similarly, the even variables specify the rows. One is placed in each square where the variables specifying the row and the column of the location of the square have the same values, either true or complemented, as one of the minterms in the equation. For example, the first term of the equation in Fig. 15-12($d$) is $ABCDE$. These variables will be found in the top row and left-hand column. The 1 in the upper left-hand corner specifies this term. Similarly, the term $\bar{A}BCD\bar{E}$ is specified by the 1 in the upper right-hand corner.

The purpose of these diagrams is to reduce the equation to a fewer number of variables. This reduction is obtained by the use of Theorem 19, which states that $AB + A\bar{B} = A$. Applying this theorem, the terms represented by 1's in the first two columns in the top row of Fig. 15-12(c) gives

$$ABCD + AB\bar{C}D = ABD \tag{15-7}$$

The terms specified by the two 1's in the remaining columns of the top row are:

$$\bar{A}BCD + \bar{A}B\bar{C}D = \bar{A}BD \tag{15-8}$$

|   | $A$ | $\bar{A}$ |
|---|---|---|
| $B$ | 1 | 1 |
| $\bar{B}$ | 1 |  |

(a) $f = AB + A\bar{B} + \bar{A}B$

| | $A$ | $A$ | $\bar{A}$ | $\bar{A}$ |
| | $C$ | $\bar{C}$ | $\bar{C}$ | $C$ |
|---|---|---|---|---|
| $B$ | 1 |  |  | 1 |
| $\bar{B}$ | 1 |  | 1 |  |

(b) $f = ABC + A\bar{B}C + \bar{A}BC + \bar{A}\bar{B}C$

| | | $A$ | $A$ | $\bar{A}$ | $\bar{A}$ |
| | | $C$ | $\bar{C}$ | $\bar{C}$ | $C$ |
|---|---|---|---|---|---|
| $B$ | $D$ | 1 | 1 | 1 | 1 |
| $B$ | $\bar{D}$ | 1 | 1 |  |  |
| $\bar{B}$ | $\bar{D}$ |  |  |  | 1 |
| $\bar{B}$ | $D$ | 1 | 1 |  | 1 |

(c) $f = ABCD + ABC\bar{D} + AB\bar{C}D + AB\bar{C}\bar{D} + A\bar{B}\bar{C}D + A\bar{B}CD + \bar{A}B\bar{C}\bar{D} + \bar{A}\bar{B}\bar{C}\bar{D} + \bar{A}BCD + \bar{A}\bar{B}CD$

| | | $A$ | $A$ | $\bar{A}$ | $\bar{A}$ | $A$ | $A$ | $\bar{A}$ | $\bar{A}$ |
| | | $C$ | $\bar{C}$ | $\bar{C}$ | $C$ | $C$ | $\bar{C}$ | $\bar{C}$ | $C$ |
| | | $E$ | $E$ | $E$ | $E$ | $\bar{E}$ | $\bar{E}$ | $\bar{E}$ | $\bar{E}$ |
|---|---|---|---|---|---|---|---|---|---|
| $B$ | $D$ | 1 |  |  |  | 1 |  |  | 1 |
| $B$ | $\bar{D}$ |  |  | 1 |  |  |  |  |  |
| $\bar{B}$ | $\bar{D}$ |  |  |  |  |  | 1 | 1 |  |
| $\bar{B}$ | $D$ |  |  |  |  |  | 1 | 1 |  |

(d) $f = ABCDE + ABCD\bar{E} + A\bar{B}\bar{C}D\bar{E} + A\bar{B}C\bar{D}\bar{E} + \bar{A}B\bar{C}D\bar{E} + \bar{A}BCD\bar{E} + \bar{A}\bar{B}\bar{C}D\bar{E} + \bar{A}\bar{B}C\bar{D}\bar{E}$

**Fig. 15-12.** *Diagrams for Boolean equations*

Then the four terms in the top row can be reduced to

$$ABD + \bar{A}BD = BD \tag{15-9}$$

Thus adjacent terms can be reduced to a single term containing the common terms. After a little practice, a glance at the top row of Fig. 15-12(c) will reveal that the terms represented by these four 1's reduce to $BD$. Now consider the two terms represented by a 1 in the top row and second column and a 1 in the bottom row and the second column. They are

$$A\cancel{B}\bar{C}D + A\cancel{\bar{B}}\bar{C}D = A\bar{C}D \qquad (15\text{-}10)$$

Thus, opposite 1's in the same row or the same column are combined into a single term having the common variables. The four terms specified by the four 1's adjacent to each other, forming a square in the upper left-hand corner of Fig. 15-12($c$), are

$$ABC\cancel{D} + ABC\cancel{\bar{D}} + AB\bar{C}\cancel{D} + AB\bar{C}\cancel{\bar{D}} = AB\cancel{C} + AB\cancel{\bar{C}} = AB \qquad (15\text{-}11)$$

Then the terms specified by four adjacent 1's forming a square reduce to a single term of the common variables.

Now consider the four terms represented by the 1's in the four corners of Fig. 15-12($c$). They are

$$A\cancel{B}CD + A\cancel{\bar{B}}CD + \bar{A}\cancel{B}CD + \bar{A}\cancel{\bar{B}}CD = ACD + \bar{A}CD = CD \qquad (15\text{-}12)$$

The four terms specified by 1's in the four corners of a diagram reduce to a single term of the variables common to the four terms.

Now consider the four terms represented by the 1's in the first two columns of the top row and the first two columns of the bottom row. They are

$$AB\cancel{C}D + AB\cancel{\bar{C}}D + A\bar{B}\cancel{C}D + A\bar{B}\cancel{\bar{C}}D = A\cancel{B}D + A\cancel{\bar{B}}D = AD$$

Thus the four terms represented by two adjacent 1's on one side of a diagram and two adjacent 1's on the opposite side of the diagram reduce to a single term of the common variables of the four terms.

When the terms increase to form more than one 4-by-4 square, corresponding terms of one square can be combined with those in another square. Thus, in Fig. 15-12($d$), the terms in the top row are

$$\cancel{A}BCD\cancel{E} + ABCD\cancel{\bar{E}} + \cancel{\bar{A}}BCDE = BCD + ABCD + BCDE \qquad (15\text{-}13)$$

Now consider the reduction of the equation specified by Fig. 15-12($c$). The function reduces to

$$f_r = AB + BD + AD + CD + \bar{A}\bar{B}\bar{C}\bar{D} \qquad (15\text{-}14)$$

In Table 15-7, a function table for the equation of the diagram in Fig. 15-12($c$) and for Eq. (15-14) is considered. The 1's under $f$ and $f_r$ in each of these function tables fall in the same rows. This proves that the equations are equal. Note that a function table is an effective method of checking the results of Boolean computations.

**Table 15-7**

(a) $f = ABCD + ABC\bar{D} + AB\bar{C}D + AB\bar{C}\bar{D} + A\bar{B}CD + A\bar{B}\bar{C}D + \bar{A}BCD + \bar{A}B\bar{C}D + \bar{A}\bar{B}CD + \bar{A}\bar{B}\bar{C}\bar{D}$

| A | B | C | D | $ABCD$ | $ABC\bar{D}$ | $AB\bar{C}D$ | $AB\bar{C}\bar{D}$ | $A\bar{B}CD$ | $A\bar{B}\bar{C}D$ | $\bar{A}BCD$ | $\bar{A}B\bar{C}D$ | $\bar{A}\bar{B}CD$ | $\bar{A}\bar{B}\bar{C}\bar{D}$ | $f$ |
|---|---|---|---|---|---|---|---|---|---|---|---|---|---|---|
| 0 | 0 | 0 | 0 | 0 | 0 | 0 | 0 | 0 | 0 | 0 | 0 | 0 | 1 | 1 |
| 0 | 0 | 0 | 1 | 0 | 0 | 0 | 0 | 0 | 0 | 0 | 0 | 0 | 0 | 0 |
| 0 | 0 | 1 | 0 | 0 | 0 | 0 | 0 | 0 | 0 | 0 | 0 | 0 | 0 | 0 |
| 0 | 0 | 1 | 1 | 0 | 0 | 0 | 0 | 0 | 0 | 0 | 0 | 1 | 0 | 1 |
| 0 | 1 | 0 | 0 | 0 | 0 | 0 | 0 | 0 | 0 | 0 | 0 | 0 | 0 | 0 |
| 0 | 1 | 0 | 1 | 0 | 0 | 0 | 0 | 0 | 0 | 0 | 1 | 0 | 0 | 1 |
| 0 | 1 | 1 | 0 | 0 | 0 | 0 | 0 | 0 | 0 | 0 | 0 | 0 | 0 | 0 |
| 0 | 1 | 1 | 1 | 0 | 0 | 0 | 0 | 0 | 0 | 1 | 0 | 0 | 0 | 1 |
| 1 | 0 | 0 | 0 | 0 | 0 | 0 | 0 | 0 | 0 | 0 | 0 | 0 | 0 | 0 |
| 1 | 0 | 0 | 1 | 0 | 0 | 0 | 0 | 0 | 1 | 0 | 0 | 0 | 0 | 1 |
| 1 | 0 | 1 | 0 | 0 | 0 | 0 | 0 | 0 | 0 | 0 | 0 | 0 | 0 | 0 |
| 1 | 0 | 1 | 1 | 0 | 0 | 0 | 0 | 1 | 0 | 0 | 0 | 0 | 0 | 1 |
| 1 | 1 | 0 | 0 | 0 | 0 | 0 | 1 | 0 | 0 | 0 | 0 | 0 | 0 | 1 |
| 1 | 1 | 0 | 1 | 0 | 0 | 1 | 0 | 0 | 0 | 0 | 0 | 0 | 0 | 1 |
| 1 | 1 | 1 | 0 | 0 | 1 | 0 | 0 | 0 | 0 | 0 | 0 | 0 | 0 | 1 |
| 1 | 1 | 1 | 1 | 1 | 0 | 0 | 0 | 0 | 0 | 0 | 0 | 0 | 0 | 1 |

$(b)\ f_r = AB + BD + AD + CD + \bar{A}\bar{B}\bar{C}\bar{D}$

| A | B | C | D | AB | BD | AD | CD | $\bar{A}\bar{B}\bar{C}\bar{D}$ | $f_r$ |
|---|---|---|---|----|----|----|----|----|-----|
| 0 | 0 | 0 | 0 | 0 | 0 | 0 | 0 | 1 | 1 |
| 0 | 0 | 0 | 1 | 0 | 0 | 0 | 0 | 0 | 0 |
| 0 | 0 | 1 | 0 | 0 | 0 | 0 | 0 | 0 | 0 |
| 0 | 0 | 1 | 1 | 0 | 0 | 0 | 1 | 0 | 1 |
| 0 | 1 | 0 | 0 | 0 | 0 | 0 | 0 | 0 | 0 |
| 0 | 1 | 0 | 1 | 0 | 1 | 0 | 0 | 0 | 1 |
| 0 | 1 | 1 | 0 | 0 | 0 | 0 | 0 | 0 | 0 |
| 0 | 1 | 1 | 1 | 0 | 1 | 0 | 1 | 0 | 1 |
| 1 | 0 | 0 | 0 | 0 | 0 | 0 | 0 | 0 | 0 |
| 1 | 0 | 0 | 1 | 0 | 0 | 1 | 0 | 0 | 1 |
| 1 | 0 | 1 | 0 | 0 | 0 | 0 | 0 | 0 | 0 |
| 1 | 0 | 1 | 1 | 0 | 0 | 1 | 1 | 0 | 1 |
| 1 | 1 | 0 | 0 | 1 | 0 | 0 | 0 | 0 | 1 |
| 1 | 1 | 0 | 1 | 1 | 1 | 1 | 0 | 0 | 1 |
| 1 | 1 | 1 | 0 | 1 | 0 | 0 | 0 | 0 | 1 |
| 1 | 1 | 1 | 1 | 1 | 1 | 1 | 1 | 0 | 1 |

There are several methods of reducing Boolean equations to their simplest form. They will be found in the references at the end of this chapter.

## 15-4. ARITHMETIC PROCESSES[2,3,6]

The next portion of this chapter will discuss the logic and circuits used to perform arithmetic operations. These include the addition, subtraction, multiplication, and division of binary numbers. No attempt will be made to extend these processes to decimal operations, as the purpose of this chapter is to outline the basic concepts of a digital computer and arouse an interest in this field. The references at the end of this chapter develop the complete operation of modern computers.

**The Logic and Circuits Used to Add Binary Numbers**

Two binary numbers $X = X_N \ldots X_3 X_2 X_1$ and $Y = Y_M \ldots Y_3 Y_2 Y_1$ are to be added, where $X_1 X_2 X_3$ etc. are the binary digits of the number $X$, and $Y_1 Y_2 Y_3$ etc. are the binary digits of the number $Y$. The first phase of computing the sum of $X$ and $Y$ is to compute the sum of $X_1$ and $Y_1$. This yields the LSD, $S_1$, of the sum of $X$ and $Y$ and the carry digit $K_1$. The second phase is to compute the sum of $K_1$, $X_2$, and $Y_2$. This yields the NLSD, $S_2$, of the sum of $X$ and $Y$ and the carry digit $K_2$. Similarly, the third step computes the sum of $K_2$, $X_3$, and $Y_3$ to obtain $S_3$ and $K_3$. This procedure is continued until all the digits of $X$ and $Y$ have been added. If the last carry is 1, it becomes the most significant figure of the sum.

The function table giving the states of $S_1$ and $K_1$ for all the possible combinations of the states of $X_1$ and $Y_1$ is Table 15-8. The equation for $S_1$ is obtained by writing the sum of the minterms formed by the states of $X_1$ and $Y_1$ from Table 15-8 when $S_1$ is 1. $X_1$ and $Y_1$ are complemented when their

### Table 15-8

**The Sum and Carry Formed by the Addition of 2 Binary Digits**

| $X_1$ | $Y_1$ | $S_1$ | $K_1$ |
|-------|-------|-------|-------|
| 0 | 0 | 0 | 0 |
| 0 | 1 | 1 | 0 |
| 1 | 0 | 1 | 0 |
| 1 | 1 | 0 | 1 |

states are 0, and they are true when their states are 1. Thus, in the second row, the state of $S_1$ is 1, $X_1$ is 0, and $Y_1$ is 1. The minterm produced by this row is $\overline{X}_1 Y_1$. Similarly, the state of $S_1$ is 1, $X_1$ is 1, and $Y_1$ is 0 in the third row. The minterm produced by this row is $X_1 \overline{Y}_1$. $S_1$ is 0 in the remaining rows. Thus no minterms are formed for these rows. Then the equation for $S_1$ is

$$S_1 = X_1 \overline{Y}_1 + \overline{X}_1 Y_1 \tag{15-15}$$

Similarly, the equation for $K_1$ is

$$K_1 = X_1 Y_1 \tag{15-16}$$

The circuit for the solution of Eq. (15-15) is shown in Fig. 15-13($a$), and the circuit for the solution of Eq. (15-16) is shown in Fig. 15-13($b$). The combination of these circuits is shown in Fig. 15-13($c$). This circuit is called a *half*

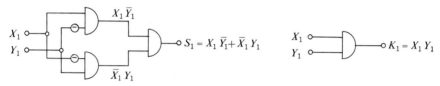

($a$) A circuit for the solution of Eq. (15-15)     ($b$) A circuit for the solution of Eq. (15-16)

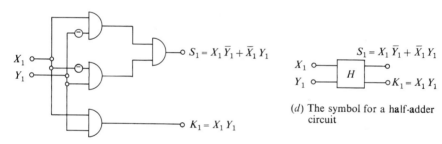

($c$) A half-adder circuit for the solution of both Eqs.
(15-15) and (15-16)

($d$) The symbol for a half-adder circuit

**Fig. 15-13.** *The circuits for obtaining the sum of 2 binary digits*

*adder,* to be explained later. The symbol used for this circuit is shown in Fig. 15-13($d$).

The function table giving the states of $S_2$ and $K_2$ obtained from the sum of $X_2$, $Y_2$, and $K_1$ is Table 15-9. Writing the equations for $S_2$ and $K_2$ from this function table gives

$$S_2 = X_2 Y_2 K_1 + X_2 \overline{Y}_2 \overline{K}_1 + \overline{X}_2 Y_2 \overline{K}_1 + \overline{X}_2 \overline{Y}_2 K_1 \tag{15-17}$$
and
$$K_2 = X_2 Y_2 K_1 + X_2 Y_2 \overline{K}_1 + X_2 \overline{Y}_2 K_1 + \overline{X}_2 Y_2 K_1 \tag{15-18}$$

## Table 15-9

### The Sum and Carry Formed by the Addition of 2 Binary Digits and a Carry

| $X_2$ | $Y_2$ | $K_1$ | $S_2$ | $K_2$ |
|-------|-------|-------|-------|-------|
| 0 | 0 | 0 | 0 | 0 |
| 0 | 0 | 1 | 1 | 0 |
| 0 | 1 | 0 | 1 | 0 |
| 0 | 1 | 1 | 0 | 1 |
| 1 | 0 | 0 | 1 | 0 |
| 1 | 0 | 1 | 0 | 1 |
| 1 | 1 | 0 | 0 | 1 |
| 1 | 1 | 1 | 1 | 1 |

## Table 15-10

### The Diagram for Eq. (15-17)

| | $X_2$ $K_1$ | $X_2$ $\bar{K}_1$ | $\bar{X}_2$ $\bar{K}_1$ | $\bar{X}_2$ $K_1$ |
|-----|-----|-----|-----|-----|
| $Y_2$ | 1 | | 1 | |
| $\bar{Y}_2$ | | 1 | | 1 |

## Table 15-11

### The Diagram for Eq. (15-18)

| | $X_2$ $K_1$ | $X_2$ $\bar{K}_1$ | $\bar{X}_2$ $\bar{K}_1$ | $\bar{X}_2$ $K_1$ |
|-----|-----|-----|-----|-----|
| $Y_2$ | 1 | 1 | | 1 |
| $\bar{Y}_2$ | 1 | | | |

The function diagram of Eq. (15-17) is shown in Table 15-10. There is no further reduction of this equation by this method. The circuit for this equation is given in Fig. 15-14(a). It will be noted that there are only two steps

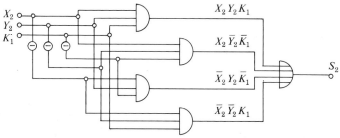

(*a*) A circuit for the solution of Eq. (15-17)

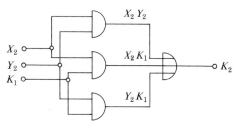

(*b*) A circuit for the solution of Eq. (15-19)

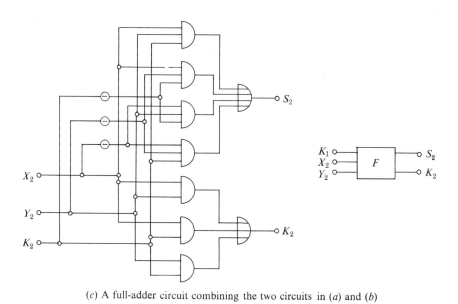

(*c*) A full-adder circuit combining the two circuits in (*a*) and (*b*)

**Fig. 15-14.** *The circuits for obtaining the sum of 2 digits and a carry*

from the input to the answer. This is defined as a *second-order* circuit. This equation can be further simplified by going to a higher-order equation, as will be shown later.

The function diagram of Eq. (15-18) is shown in Table 15-11. This shows that Eq. (15-18) reduces to

$$K_2 = X_2 Y_2 + X_2 K_1 + Y_2 K_1 \qquad (15\text{-}19)$$

The circuit for solving Eq. (15-19) is given in Fig. 15-14(*b*). The combination of the two circuits is shown in Fig. 15-14(*c*). This combination is a *full adder*. The block diagram of a full adder is shown in Fig. 15-14(*c*).

A higher-order full-adder circuit can be produced by rearranging Eqs. (15-17) and (15-19). Then

$$S_2 = K_1(X_2 Y_2 + \bar{X}_2 \bar{Y}_2) + \bar{K}_1(X_2 \bar{Y}_2 + \bar{X}_2 Y_2) \qquad (15\text{-}20)$$

By Theorem 24,

$$S_2 = K_1(\overline{\bar{X}_2 \bar{Y}_2 + \bar{X}_2 Y_2}) + \bar{K}_1(X_2 \bar{Y}_2 + \bar{X}_2 Y_2)$$
$$= K_1 \bar{S}_2' + \bar{K}_1 S_2'$$

From Eq. (15-18),

$$K_2 = X_2 Y_2 K_1 + X_2 Y_2 \bar{K}_1 + X_2 \bar{Y}_2 K_1 + \bar{X}_2 Y_2 K_1$$
$$= X_2 Y_2 + K_1(X_2 \bar{Y}_2 + \bar{X}_2 Y_2) \qquad (15\text{-}21)$$

The input $X_2$ and $Y_2$ to the first half adder in Fig. 15-15 produces the outputs

$$S_2' = X_2 \bar{Y}_2 + \bar{X}_2 Y_2 \quad \text{and} \quad K_2' = X_2 Y_2$$

The inputs $S_2'$ and $K_1$ to the second half adder in Fig. 15-15 produce outputs $S_2$ and

$$K_2'' = K_1 S_2'$$
$$= K_1(X_2 \bar{Y}_2 + \bar{X}_2 Y_2)$$

The inputs $K_2'$ and $K_2''$ to the OR circuit in Fig. 15-15 produce the output

$$K_2 = K_2' + K_2''$$
$$= X_2 Y_2 + K_1(X_2 \bar{Y}_2 + \bar{X}_2 Y_2)$$

Then the two half adders and the OR circuit of Fig. 15-15 are equivalent to the full-adder circuit of Fig. 15-14(*c*). The circuit in Fig. 15-15 requires 4 inverters and 18 diodes, while the circuit in Fig. 15-14(*c*) requires 3 inverters and 25 diodes, but Fig. 15-15 is a fifth-order circuit compared with a second-order circuit in Fig. 15-14(*c*).

A SERIAL ADDER.[1,2,3,4] The full-adder circuits in Figs. 15-14(*c*) and 15-15 require the presence of $K_1$ to obtain $S_2$ and $K_2$. Also $S_1$, $S_2$, etc., of the sum must be stored in the proper order. The circuit of a *serial adder* is shown in Fig. 15-16. The 9-digit binary number $Y$ in the memory storage is added to the 9-binary-digit number $X$ in the accumulator. The initial pulse produced by the command to add $X$ and $Y$ transfers $Y$ in the memory to the distributor through the gating circuit in Fig. 15-16. Then $Y$ in the distributor is added to $X$ in the accumulator. This operation is controlled by clocking pulses generated by the computer. The first clocking pulse, after the command to add $X$ and $Y$, gates $X_1$ and $Y_1$ to the full adder circuit, and the full adder

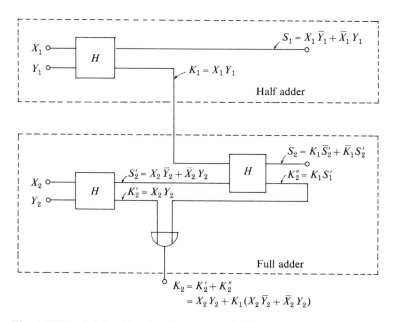

$K_2 = K_2' + K_2''$
$= X_2 Y_2 + K_1 (X_2 \overline{Y}_2 + \overline{X}_2 Y_2)$

**Fig. 15-15.** *A full-adder circuit using two half-adder circuits*

produces $S_1$ and $K_1$. The digits in the accumulator and in the distributor are shifted to the right 1 digit. $S_1$ is transmitted to the left digit of the accumulator. $Y$ is transmitted to the left digit of the distributor. $K_1$ is transmitted to the input of the full adder through a delay circuit $d$ so it enters the full adder at the beginning of the second phase of the addition when $X_2$ and $Y_2$ are gated to the input of the full adder by the second clocking pulse after the command to add $X$ and $Y$. These phases are repeated until the sum of $X$ and $Y$ is obtained in the accumulator, $Y$ is restored in the distributor, and $X$ is lost. This procedure is shown in Fig. 15-16.

The full-adder circuit used in the block diagram of Fig. 15-16 is shown in Fig. 15-17(a). It has two half adders and an OR circuit. The first phase of the addition is initiated by the first clock pulse which occurs at the same instant $X_1$ and $Y_1$ enter the first half-adder circuit. These three pulses form the input to the first adder and produce $K_1'$ and $S_1'$. $S_1'$ and $K_0 = 0$ enter the second half adder in synchronism and produce pulses $S_1$ and $K_1''$. It is assumed that there is no delay in the logic circuits (which is not true in actual

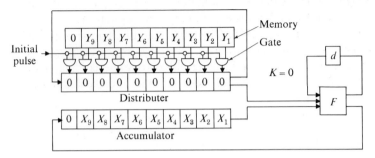

(*a*) Before phase 1

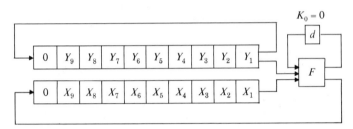

(*b*) Phase 1

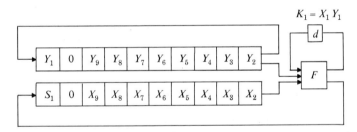

(*c*) Phase 2

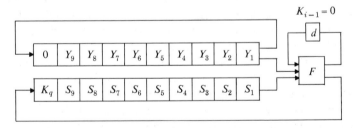

(*d*) After phase 10

**Fig. 15-16.** *The operation of a serial adder*

circuits). Then $K_1'$ and $K_1''$ enter the OR circuit and produce $K_1$. $K_1$ is propagated through a time-delay circuit to enter the second half-adder circuit in synchronism with $S_2'$ in the second phase of the addition. This procedure is repeated until the sum of $X$ and $Y$ is obtained. The chart of the sequence of

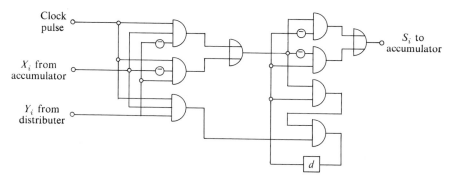

(a) A full-adder circuit with clock-pulse control

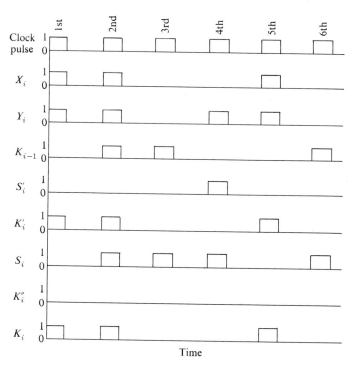

(b) A time chart of the pulses in (a) for the solution of $10011 + 11011$

**Fig. 15-17.** *A pulse-controlled full-adder circuit and time chart*

the timing sequence of the pulses in the circuit shown in Fig. 15-17($a$) for the addition of the binary numbers

$$X = \quad 10011$$
$$Y = \quad \underline{11011}$$
$$S = 101110$$

is given in Fig. 15-17($b$). This serial adder is comparatively slow. There are parallel adder circuits used in high-speed computers that add each pair of digits at the same time. These circuits are described in the references at the end of the chapter.

Computers that use a clocking pulse to control the operations are called *synchronous computers*. Computers that do not use a clocking pulse, but in which the end of one operation initiates the next operation, are called *asynchronous computers*. Most synchronous computers employ some asynchronous operations to increase their computation speed.

## The Logic and Circuits for Subtracting Binary Numbers[1,2,3,4]

The first phase of subtracting the binary number $Y = Y_N \ldots Y_3 Y_2 Y_1$ from $X = X_N \ldots X_3 X_2 X_1$ is to subtract the digit $Y_1$ from the digit $X_1$. When $Y_1$ is greater than $X_1$, the result is a borrow 1 from $X_2$. The result of this operation is given in the function table, Table 15-12, which gives the difference $D_1$ and the borrow $B_1$ for all combinations of the states of $X_1$ and $Y_1$. The equation for the difference $D_1$, taken from Table 15-12, is

$$D_1 = X_1 \overline{Y}_1 + \overline{X}_1 Y_1 \qquad (15\text{-}22)$$

and the equation for the borrow $B_1$ is

$$B_1 = \overline{X}_1 Y_1 \qquad (15\text{-}23)$$

### Table 15-12

### Subtracting $Y_1$ from $X_1$

| $X_1$ | $Y_1$ | $D_1$ | $B_1$ |
|-------|-------|-------|-------|
| 0 | 0 | 0 | 0 |
| 0 | 1 | 1 | 1 |
| 1 | 0 | 1 | 0 |
| 1 | 1 | 0 | 0 |

The circuit which produces $D_1$ and $B_1$ is shown in Fig. 15-18($a$). It is defined as a *half-subtract circuit*. The block diagram of a half subtractor is given in Fig. 15-18($b$).

The second phase in this operation is subtracting $Y_2$ and $B_1$ from $X_2$. The result of this operation is given in the function table, Table 15-13, which

## Table 15-13

### Subtracting $Y_2$ and $B_1$ from $X_2$

| $X_2$ | $Y_2$ | $B_1$ | $D_2$ | $B_2$ |
|-------|-------|-------|-------|-------|
| 0 | 0 | 0 | 0 | 0 |
| 0 | 0 | 1 | 1 | 1 |
| 0 | 1 | 0 | 1 | 1 |
| 0 | 1 | 1 | 0 | 1 |
| 1 | 0 | 0 | 1 | 0 |
| 1 | 0 | 1 | 0 | 0 |
| 1 | 1 | 0 | 0 | 0 |
| 1 | 1 | 1 | 1 | 1 |

gives the difference $D_2$ and the borrow $B_2$ for all combinations of the states of $X_2$, $Y_2$, and $B_1$. The equation for $D_2$, taken from Table 15-13, is

$$D_2 = X_2 Y_2 B_1 + X_2 \overline{Y}_2 \overline{B}_1 + \overline{X}_2 Y_2 \overline{B}_1 + \overline{X}_2 \overline{Y}_2 B_1 \tag{15-24}$$

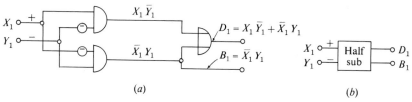

$(a)$ $\qquad\qquad\qquad\qquad\qquad\qquad (b)$

**Fig. 15-18.** *A half-subtract circuit*

Rearranging,

$$D_2 = B_1(X_2 Y_2 + \overline{X}_2 \overline{Y}_2) + \overline{B}_1(X_2 \overline{Y}_2 + \overline{X}_2 Y_2) \tag{15-25}$$

But, by Theorem 24,

$$D_2 = B_1(\overline{X_2 \overline{Y}_2 + \overline{X}_2 Y_2}) + \overline{B}_1(X_2 \overline{Y}_2 + \overline{X}_2 Y_2) \tag{15-25a}$$

Similarly, the equation for the borrow from $X_3$ is

$$B_2 = X_2 Y_2 B_1 + \overline{X}_2 Y_2 B_1 + \overline{X}_2 Y_2 \overline{B}_1 + \overline{X}_2 \overline{Y}_2 B_1 \tag{15-26}$$

## Table 15-14

### Diagram for Eq. (15-26)

|  | $X_2$ $B_1$ | $X_2$ $\overline{B}_1$ | $\overline{X}_2$ $\overline{B}_1$ | $\overline{X}_2$ $B_1$ |
|------------------|-------------|-------------|-------------|-------------|
| $Y_2$ | 1 |  | 1 | 1 |
| $\overline{Y}_2$ |  |  |  | 1 |

By constructing a function diagram of this equation as shown in Table 15-14, the equation can be reduced to

$$B_2 = \bar{X}_2 B_1 + \bar{X}_2 Y_2 + Y_2 B_1 \qquad (15\text{-}27)$$

Applying Theorem 24, Eq. (15-27) becomes

$$\begin{aligned} B_2 &= \bar{X}_2 Y_2 + X_2 Y_2 B_1 + \bar{X}_2 \bar{Y}_2 B_1 \\ &= \bar{X}_2 Y_2 + B_1 (X_2 Y_2 + \bar{X}_2 \bar{Y}_2) \end{aligned} \qquad (15\text{-}27a)$$

Applying Theorem 24 to the second term in this equation gives

$$B_2 = \bar{X}_2 Y_2 + B_1 (\overline{X_2 \bar{Y}_2 + \bar{X}_2 Y_2}) \qquad (15\text{-}28)$$

The circuit for solving Eqs. (15-24) and (15-27) is given in Fig. 15-19. This is a second-order *full-subtract circuit*. The same operation can be performed

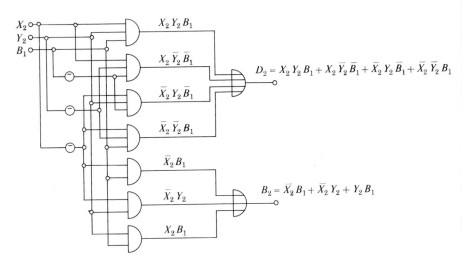

**Fig. 15-19.** *A second-order full-subtract circuit*

by two half-subtract circuits and an OR circuit, as shown in Fig. 15-20. Note that this circuit is obtained from Eqs. (15-25a) and (15-28). The same equations and circuits can be used for solving for $D_3$ and $B_3$, etc.

It will be observed that Eq. (15-20) for expressing $S_2$ in terms of $X_2$, $Y_2$, and $K_1$ is identical to Eq. (15-25) for expressing $D_2$ in terms of $X_2$, $Y_2$, and $B_1$. Also, Eq. (15-21) for $K_2$ expressed in terms of $X_2$, $Y_2$, and $K_1$ would be the same as Eq. (15-27a) for $B_2$ expressed in terms of $X_2$, $Y_2$, and $B_1$ if $X_2$ were complemented. A circuit using this logic is shown in Fig. 15-21. This will either add or subtract, depending on the circuits that are connected to the clocking pulse. When the clocking pulse is applied to $P_S$, the circuit adds. When the clocking pulse is applied to $P_D$ the circuit subtracts. When this circuit replaces the full adder in the serial-adder circuit in Fig. 15-16, it produces a serial add or subtract circuit.

SUBTRACTION USING THE COMPLEMENT OF THE SUBTRAHEND[1, 2, 3, 4]    The 2's complement of the binary number $N$ is defined as $2^n-N$, where $2^{n-1}$ is the most significant digit of the binary number. Then the difference between $M$ and $N$ is

$$M - N = M + (2^n - N) - 2^n \qquad (15\text{-}29)$$

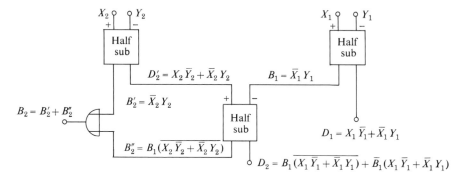

**Fig. 15-20.**   *A full-subtract circuit using two half-subtract circuits*

For example, let $M = 110110$ and $N = 101101$. The 2's complement of $N$ is

$$
\begin{aligned}
1000000 &= 2^n \\
-101101 &= N \\
\hline
10011 &= \text{2's complement of } N
\end{aligned}
$$

Now the difference between $M$ and $N$ is

$$
\begin{aligned}
110110 &= M \\
-101101 &= N \\
\hline
1001 &= M - N
\end{aligned}
$$

This difference is also obtained by adding $M$ and the 2's complement and subtracting $2^n$. Thus

$$
\begin{aligned}
110110 &= M \\
+10011 &= \text{2's complement of } N \\
\hline
1001001 &= M + \text{2's complement of } N \\
1000000 &= 2^n \\
\hline
1001 &= M - N
\end{aligned}
$$

The 1's complement of a binary number $N$ is defined as $2^n - 1 - N$. Then the 1's complement of $N = 101101$ is

$$\begin{array}{r} 111111 = 2^n - 1 \\ -101101 = N \\ \hline 10010 = \text{1's complement of } N \end{array}$$

It will be observed that the 1's complement of $N$ is obtained by changing each 1 in the number $N$ to 0 and each 0 in the number $N$ to 1. Then a 1's

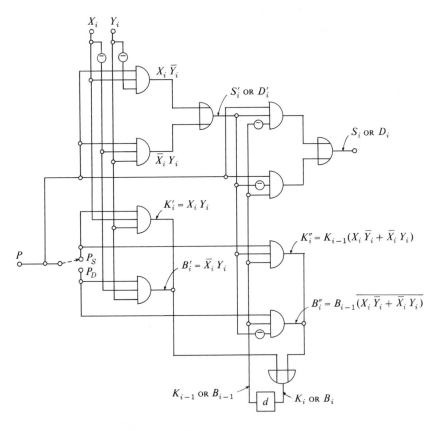

**Fig. 15-21.** *Add or subtract circuit*

complement circuit is a circuit which passes each digit of a binary number through a NOT circuit. This operation can be performed by either a serial operation or a parallel operation.

The difference between the two binary numbers $M$ and $N$ is

$$M - N = M + (2^n - 1 - N) - 2^n + 1 \qquad (15\text{-}30)$$

Using the values given above gives

$$110110 = M$$
$$+10010 = \text{1's complement of } N$$
$$\underline{+1 = \text{plus 1}}$$
$$1001001$$
$$\underline{1000000 = 2^n}$$
$$1001 = M - N$$

This operation could be performed by the serial adder if a NOT circuit were inserted between the distributor and the full adder and $K_0$ were reset to 1 instead of 0.

## Multiplication[1,2,3,4]

The product of two numbers is obtained by the process of addition. For example, the product of the binary numbers 111011 and 101011 is:

$$
\begin{array}{l}
111011 \text{ multiplicand} \\
\underline{101011} \text{ multiplier} \\
111011 \\
111011 \\
1110110 \\
\underline{1110110} \\
100111101001 \text{ product}
\end{array}
$$

This procedure may be started on the left and the subproducts shifted to the right. Thus

$$
\begin{array}{ll}
111011 & \text{multiplicand} \\
\underline{101011} & \text{multiplier} \\
111011 & \\
\phantom{1}111011 & \\
\phantom{11}111011 & \\
\phantom{111}111011 & \\
\underline{\phantom{111111}} & \\
100111101001 & \text{product}
\end{array}
$$

The latter method of addition will be used in the serial multiplying circuit shown in Fig. 15-22. This circuit has a 20-digit accumulator (divided into a

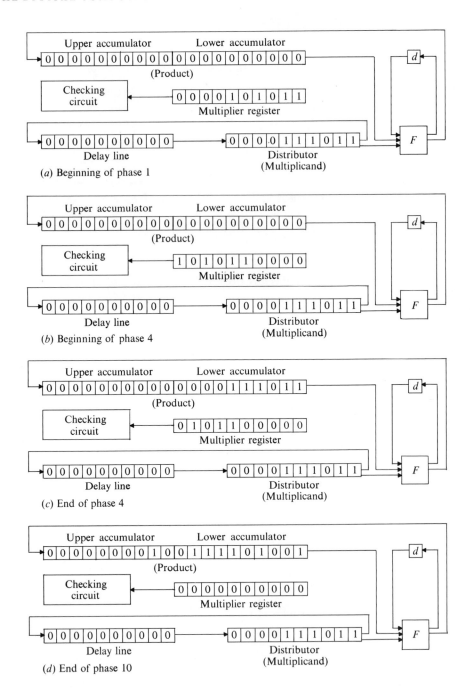

**Fig. 15-22.** *A serial multiplier*

10-digit upper accumulator on the left and a 10-digit lower accumulator on the right) and a 10-digit distributor which is gated to the memory circuit during the initial multiply command. This pulse transfers the multiplicand in the memory to the distributor. In a similar manner, the multiplier in the upper accumulator is gated to a special multiplier register, which is sometimes abbreviated to ier register, and the initial multiply command signal transfers the multiplier from the upper accumulator to the multiplier register. The multiplication procedure includes ten phases.

## PHASE 1

1. The left digit of the multiplier register is transferred into the checking circuit and the remaining digits are shifted one digit to the left.
2. If the digit in the checking circuit is 1, the multiplicand in the distributor is added to the entire 20-digit accumulator. A ten-unit delay line in the recirculating circuit of the distributor is necessary to return the multiplicand to its original position. After this sequence of operations is completed the computer goes to phase 2.
3. If the digit in the checking circuit is 0, the sequence goes to phase 2.

## PHASES 2 to 10

1. The left digit of the multiplier register is transferred into the checking circuit, and the remaining digits are shifted one digit to the left.
2. Accumulator is shifted one digit to the left.
3. If the digit in the checking circuit is 1, the multiplicand in the distributer is added to the entire 20-digit accumulator. Then the sequence goes to the next phase.
4. If the digit in the checking circuit is 0, the sequence goes to the next phase.

After ten phases, the product is in the entire accumulator. The distributor still contains the multiplicand, and the multiplier register is cleared to zeros.

The product in this example has the two most significant digits of the product in the upper accumulator and the remaining digits in the lower accumulator. It is necessary to transfer the desired portion, usually the ten most significant figures, of the product to either the upper or lower accumulator for further computation or tabulation. A two-digit shift to the right and round will put the ten most significant digits of the product in the lower accumulator, while an eight-digit shift to the right will put the ten most significant digits of the product in the upper accumulator, with the remaining digits in the lower accumulator.

## Division[1,2,3,4]

Division of a dividend by a divisor to obtain a quotient can be computed through successive subtractions. For example, dividing the binary dividend 1101101101 by the binary divisor 1011000000 gives

$$
\begin{array}{r}
1.001111101 \quad \text{quotient} \\
\text{divisor } 1011000000)\overline{1101101101.000000000} \quad \text{dividend} \\
1011000000 \\
\hline
10101101000 \\
1011000000 \\
\hline
10101010000 \\
1011000000 \\
\hline
10100100000 \\
1011000000 \\
\hline
10011000000 \\
1011000000 \\
\hline
10000000000 \\
1011000000 \\
\hline
10100000000 \\
1011000000 \\
\hline
1001000000 \quad \text{remainder}
\end{array}
$$

This operation is performed with a computer by placing the dividend in the 10 digits to the right in the 11-digit upper accumulator, resetting the 10-digit lower accumulator to 0's, and transferring the divisor in the memory to the 10-digit distributor through 10 gating circuits when the initial command-to-divide pulse is generated. Following this command, division is performed by the following phases:

PHASE 1

1. The 2's complement of the divisor is added to the upper accumulator, and the sum is stored in the upper accumulator.
2. If a 1 is formed in the left digit of the upper accumulator, which is defined as the $2^n$ digit: (a) 1 is placed in the right digit of the lower accumulator; (b) the computer then goes to phase 2.
3. If a 0 is formed in the $2^n$ digit of the upper accumulator: (a) 0 is placed in the right digit of the lower accumulator; (b) the divisor in the distributor is added to the upper accumulator (restoring the 10 digits on the right in the

upper accumulator to their value at the beginning of this phase); (*c*) the computer then goes to phase 2.

### PHASE 2 AND SUCCEEDING PHASES INCLUDING PHASE 10

1. Shift the entire accumulator 1 digit to the left and repeat phase 1. The block diagram of a serial divider to perform these operations is shown in Fig. 15-23. At the completion of the division, the quotient is in the lower accumulator, the remainder is in the upper accumulator, and the divisor is in

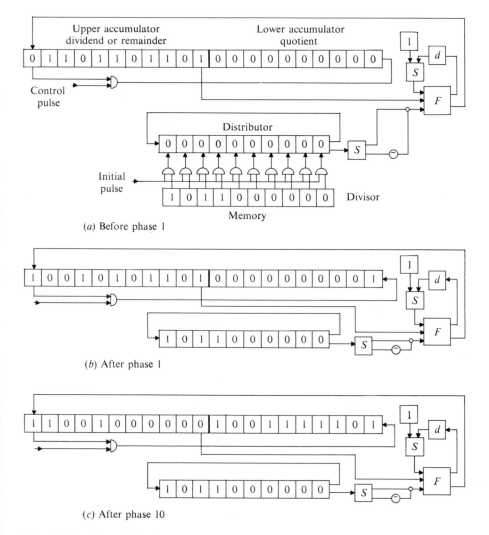

**Fig. 15-23.** *A serial divider*

the distributor. This operation will now be outlined phase by phase for the first four phases of the above example.

|  | $2^n$ digit | | |
|---|---|---|---|
| Phase 1 | 0 | 1101101101 | dividend |
| | | 0101000000 | add 2's complement of the divisor |
| | 1 | 0010101101 | 1 in $2^n$ digit, place 1 in quotient (lower accumulator) |
| Phase 2 | 0 | 0101011010 | shift 1 to left |
| | | 0101000000 | add 2's complement of the divisor |
| | 0 | 1010011010 | 0 in $2^n$ digit, place 0 in quotient |
| | | 1011000000 | add divisor |
| | 1 | 0101011010 | same as beginning of phase 2 |
| Phase 3 | 0 | 1010110100 | shift 1 to left |
| | | 0101000000 | add 2's complement of the divisor |
| | 0 | 1111110100 | 0 in $2^n$ digit, place 0 in quotient |
| | | 1011000000 | add divisor |
| | 1 | 1010110100 | same as beginning of phase 3 |
| Phase 4 | 1 | 0101101000 | shift 1 to left |
| | | 0101000000 | add 2's complement of the divisor |
| | 1 | 1010101000 | 1 in $2^n$ digit, place 1 in quotient |
| | 1 | 0101010000 | shift 1 to left |

The remaining six phases are left to the reader.

There are two single-pole double-throw switches marked $S$ in Fig. 15-23($a$). One is used to reset $K_{o-1}$ to 1, and the other is used to insert a NOT circuit in the output of the distributor when the 2's complement is formed.

The circuits that control the operation of the arithmetic unit and the error-checking devices will not be discussed. Ample information on these circuits may be found in the references listed at the end of this chapter.

### 15-5. SUMMARY

There are several modern computers, each with special features and advantages. Basically, a modern computer should have at least 8,000 words of core memory capable of being expanded to 32,000 words or more. It should have an add speed of 10 $\mu$sec or less and a multiplication or division speed of 100 $\mu$sec or less. The input and output of the computer should be magnetic tape with speeds equal to or greater than 120 in./sec and a packing density of 200 to 500 characters/in. The computer circuits should be solid state. The instructions and data are usually inscribed on punched cards, punched tape, or magnetic tape.

The computer may report the computated data on punched cards, paper tape, or magnetic tape. When the computed data are on magnetic tape, they are often transferred to punched cards and then to a tabulator for printing. These are *off-line* operations, and the computer should have sufficient *buffer circuits* to perform the operations without interfering with the computations. Some computing systems use satellite systems. For example, an IBM 7070 or 7074 may use an IBM 1401 computer for off-line operations. Similarly, a Control Data Corporation 160 computer may be used in a satellite system for off-line operations with a Control Data Corporation 1604 computer. These satellite computers are used for program checking and computing as well as off-line operations.

Computers used for large inventory problems may have auxiliary storage units to supplement the computer memory. These include magnetic tapes, magnetic drums, and *ramac* units. The ramac is similar to a juke box. Each record has thousands of magnetic memory word locations, each defined by a location or address number, stored on each side of the record. When a specified address is selected, the magnetic reading head goes to the record where the address is stored and makes a search for the required address. These units have 6 million words of storage per unit.

Some computers, such as the Larc and the Stretch, have clocking-pulse frequencies of $10^7$ cycles per second. These computers can make arithmetic operations taking only a fraction of a microsecond. Other computers, including the Philco S-2000, have no clocking pulse, and their complete operation is asynchronous.

Another important feature of any computer system is programming aids. Ease of programming is as important as computer operation. Perfection of programming aids requires not only the basic logic of the system but years of error corrections. Much is still needed in this field. It is also desirable to have a more uniform computer language so that the format of one computer may be acceptable to another. The use of solid-state circuitry has greatly advanced the reliability of computers. The present efforts being made to improve computer aids and to develop a universal computer language should bring even more advancement in the computer field.

## PROBLEMS

**15-1.** Write the program for solving

$$X = \frac{A^2 + AB + 2B^2}{A + B}$$

Let $A$ have 3 significant figures and $B$ have 4 significant figures. Store instructions in 0000, 0010, 0020, etc., and store data in 0251, 0252, etc. Store $A$, $B$, and $X$ in 0527, 0528, and 0529. Use single-entry instruction load cards and multientry data cards. Show the terms in the distributor and in the upper and the lower accumulators after each operation.

**15-2.** Write the program for solving the compound interest on $A$, compounding it semiannually at interest $B$ per year. The principal and the interest are to be tabulated at the end of each year over a period of $N$ years.

**15-3.** Make a function table of
$$f = AB + BC + \bar{A}B\bar{C} + \bar{A}\bar{B}C$$

**15-4.** Expand the equation in Prob. 15-3 to a sum of minterms.

**15-5.** Make a function diagram of the equation
$$f = ABC + A\bar{B}C + AB\bar{C} + \bar{A}BC + \bar{A}B\bar{C}$$
and reduce this equation to its simpler form.

**15-6.** Prove the answer to Prob. 15-5 with function tables of $f$ for the above equation and the simplified form of this equation.

**15-7.** Transform the equation
$$f = (A + B + \bar{C})(\bar{A} + B + C)(A + \bar{B} + \bar{C})$$
to a sum of minterms.

**15-8.** Draw the circuit for the solution of the following equation:
$$f = A(B + C) + \bar{A}(\bar{B} + C) + (\bar{A} + B)(A + \bar{C})$$

**15-9.** (a) Write the equations for $A_2$, $B_2$, and $C_2$ from the following function table. (b) Draw the function diagram for each equation. (c) Simplify each equation. (d) Draw the circuit for solving each equation.

| $A_1$ | $B_1$ | $C_1$ | $A_2$ | $B_2$ | $C_2$ |
|-------|-------|-------|-------|-------|-------|
| 0 | 0 | 0 | 1 | 1 | 1 |
| 0 | 0 | 1 | 0 | 0 | 0 |
| 0 | 1 | 0 | 0 | 0 | 1 |
| 0 | 1 | 1 | 0 | 0 | 1 |
| 1 | 0 | 0 | 0 | 1 | 1 |
| 1 | 0 | 1 | 1 | 0 | 0 |
| 1 | 1 | 0 | 1 | 0 | 1 |
| 1 | 1 | 1 | 1 | 1 | 0 |

**15-10.** Show the numbers in the accumulator and in the distributor at the end of each phase in the addition of the binary number 111000111 to the binary number 100110011.

**15-11.** Show the numbers in the upper accumulator, in the lower accumulator, and in the distributor, at the end of each phase of the multiplication, when the multiplicand 110001110 is multiplied by the multiplier 101100111.

**15-12.** Show the numbers in the upper accumulator, in the lower accumulator, and in the distributor at the end of each phase in the division of the dividend 11101111 by the divisor 10111011.

## REFERENCES

1. W. C. Irwin, *Digital Computer Principles*, D. Van Nostrand Company, Inc., Princeton, N.J., 1960.

2. R. S. Ledley, *Digital Computer and Control Engineering*, McGraw-Hill Book Company, Inc., New York, 1960.

3. M. Phister, Jr., *Logical Design of Digital Computers*, John Wiley & Sons, Inc., New York, 1958.

4. R. K. Richards, *Arithmetic Operations in Digital Computers*, D. Van Nostrand Company, Inc., Princeton, N.J., 1955.

5. R. K. Richards, *Digital Computer Components and Circuits*, D. Van Nostrand Company, Inc., Princeton, N.J., 1957.

6. *IBM 650 Data-Processing System Manual of Operation*, International Business Machine Corporation, New York, 1955.

7. N. V. Reinfeld and W. R. Vogel, *Mathematical Programming*, Prentice-Hall, Inc., Englewood Cliffs, N.J., 1958.

8. D. D. McCracken, *Digital Computer Programming*, John Wiley & Sons, Inc., New York, 1957.

9. J. Jeenel, *Programming for Digital Computers*, McGraw-Hill Book Company, Inc., New York, 1959.

10. M. V. Wilkes, D. J. Wheeler, and S. Gill, *Programs for an Electric Digital Computer*, 2nd ed., Addison-Wesley Publishing Company, Reading, Mass., 1957.

Chapter 16

# AND REDUCTION

## 16-1. INTRODUCTION

The demands for more and faster information from physical systems and devices used for space and nuclear research and development, and for industrial automation, have produced many new and effective systems for data acquisition and reduction. A partial list of the major components included in modern instrumentation systems includes: sensing elements, conditioning equipment, calibrating equipment, integrating equipment, analog computers, analog recorders, multiplexing equipment, analog-to-digital converters, telemetering equipment, digital recorders, digital plotters, high-speed camera and TV equipment, central-clock controls, and step-sequence controls.

The components included in any data-acquisition system will depend on the type of data taken, the information required as an end product, and the relative location of the components of the system. For example, the radio telemetering link is not required in the static test of a rocket engine fired in a bay adjacent to the instrumentation hut, but the radio telemetering link is perhaps the most important component link in a data-acquisition system for the flight test of a missile. A brief review of these components will now be given.

420

# DATA-ACQUISITION

# SYSTEMS

## 16-2. SENSING ELEMENTS[1]

The description of a representative sample of transducers in Chap. 11 included a comprehensive discussion of the sensing elements. It should be noted that an emf proportional to the quantity being measured is usually required as an input to the data-acquisition system from sensing elements. Therefore, transducers such as thermocouples, strain-gage bridges, piezoelectric devices, thermopiles, photoemissive cells, photoconductive cells, and photovoltaic cells are effective sensing elements. As an exception to this usual function of sensing units, some sensing elements produce a frequency which is a function of the magnitude of the quantity being measured. This frequency can be counted with an electronic counter to obtain the integral of the measured quantity or it can modulate a telemetering transmitter, and it can be reduced to a voltage with a discriminator. There are other types of inputs, but they will not be described here.

## 16-3. CONDITIONING EQUIPMENT

Conditioning equipment includes any equipment that assists in transforming the output of the transducer to the desired form or magnitude required by the next stage of the data-acquisition system. It also produces the required conditions in the transducers for them to work properly. This term includes a known constant-voltage source for strain-gage bridges, zero bridge-balance devices for strain-gage circuits, temperature-control devices for thermocouple reference junctions, and voltage amplifiers. For example the amplification of the transducer signal is adjusted to the desired gain by setting the gain of the amplifiers when a known voltage is applied to the input. Precise voltage-regulated power supplies produce the power for the strain-gage bridges. Thermostatic electronic controls keep the reference junction at the desired temperature, usually 150°F.

The bridges are balanced with servo devices that set the balancing resistor to a position which will produce a zero voltage at the output of the bridge. This servo device may be manually connected to the bridge circuit by the operator, or it may be connected to the bridge circuit by a magnetic clutch and switches.

### 16-4. CALIBRATING EQUIPMENT

Before each test there is a precalibration, and often after each test there is a postcalibration. This usually consists of a millivolt calibration of all input circuits and a shunt calibration of all bridge-type transducer circuits. The millivolt calibration is performed by applying a series of known voltages to all the input channels of the data-acquisition system. These voltages are usually in the millivolt range. A typical series of voltages applied during calibration includes 0, $+2.5$, $-2.5$, $+5$, $-5$, $+10$, $-10$, $+20$, $-20$, $+40$, $-40$, $+80$, and $-80$ mv. These voltages are applied to each input channel step by step, and all the digital recorders will record a series of a given digital number for each voltage step on a given input circuit. Similarly, the FM tape recorder will record a given frequency for each voltage step, and the galvanometer oscillograph or the strip-chart recorder will show a given displacement on the chart for each voltage step. Often, digital, FM, and galvanometer oscillograph data are taken from the same input channel.

The shunt calibration connects a shunt resistor across the unstrained active elements of the bridge-type transducers to produce an unbalanced voltage equivalent to a given percent of the rated output of the transducer. A common sequence of steps used in this calibration is 0, $+25$, $+50$, $+75$, $+100$, 0, $-25$, $-50$, $-75$, $-100$, and 0 percent. During the calibration, the digital and the analog outputs are recorded for each shunt used.

The steps are usually of a few milliseconds to 1 sec duration, and the process is produced with a set of stepping switches. The accuracy of the calibrating voltages is 0.01 percent or better. This particular system has one weakness. It excludes the calibration of the sensing elements and the conditioning equipment. There are some calibration systems, however, that apply known forces to the force-sensing elements of the load which calibrates the complete instrumentation system from the sensing elements to the readout system. A similar system is used for pressure-transducer inputs. The latter method of calibration is extensively used in wind-tunnel measurements.

When the calibration does not include sensing elements, these elements are usually calibrated in a testing laboratory prior to the test or at definite intervals. These tests include dead-weight pressure tests, weight or standard force tests for thrust transducers, and temperature-controlled oven tests for thermocouples and resistance thermometers.

## 16-5. INTEGRATING EQUIPMENT

It is often desirable to know the integral or summation of a quantity. For example, the time integral of the thrust during a static test of a missile engine is an important factor in evaluating the figure of merit of the engine.

There are several ways of determining the time integral of a quantity. An analog integrating circuit could be used for a qualitative test. It has the danger of becoming overloaded, and its accuracy is low. The digital measurements of the quantity could be added on a digital computer to acquire the desired summation. Another effective method applies the emf from the conditioning equipment to a saturable reactor in the resonant circuit of an oscillator. The change in reactance is proportional to the applied emf and produces a change in the frequency. This frequency is beat with a frequency equal to the frequency of the oscillator when the input is zero. The beat frequency, which is directly proportional to the input voltage of the oscillator, is amplified and applied to a counter. Usually, the range of the output frequency is 0 to 1,000 cycles per second, but frequencies as high as 100,000 cycles per second are used. A frequency range of 1,000 cycles per second gives an accuracy of 0.1 percent of full scale. A counter with a maximum count of 999,999 would integrate a full-load output for practically 1,000 sec, with a resolution of 1 count in $10^6$. This system of integration is extensively used in static tests of rocket engines. The counters may also operate a register that will record the accumulated integral at definite time intervals during the test.

## 16-6. ANALOG COMPUTERS

The function of a data-acquisition and reduction system is not only to record the data acquired by the sensing elements but to reduce these data to the desired form. For example, the position of the sting-balance support shown in Fig. 11-3 could be read into an analog recorder as voltages from positioning potentiometers. But the position of the sting-balance support is not the true position of the aerodynamic model under test, as the forces acting on the model bend the support. The true position of the model can be computed from the support position and the forces acting on the model. This true position can be effectively determined with an analog computer which will supply corrected voltages proportional to the true position of the model. Similarly, many desired quantities can be computed from the output voltages of the sensing elements. The output voltage of the analog computer can either be recorded in analog form or be converted to a digital form for recording and further computations.

It should be noted that analog computations are usually less accurate than digital computations, yet it is generally more economical to compute data that are adaptable to analog methods on an analog computer.

### 16-7. ANALOG RECORDERS

The methods of recording analog data have been discussed in Chaps. 4 and 7. They include pen-type strip-chart recorders, galvanometer oscillographs, FM magnetic tape recorders, and cathode-ray oscilloscopes with photographic equipment. The method used depends upon the frequency response that is required. Often, both galvanometer oscillographs and FM magnetic tapes are used to record the analog information and thus obtain a quick look at the data as well as the desired frequency response.

### 16-8. MULTIPLEXING EQUIPMENT[2,3,4]

*Multiplexing* is the process of sharing a single channel with more than one input. There are two main groups of multiplex systems, the *time division* of the channel and the *frequency division* of the channel.

**Time-Division System**

An example of a time-division multiplex system is shown in Fig. 16-1. It is a commutator with only one bar which successively connects the output of the device to one of the eight inputs. If the output of the commutator were connected to an instrumentation system, the system would read each input for a little less than 1/8 of 1 revolution. Thus the instrumentation system shares the time of each revolution with the eight inputs. This system is limited to the revolutions per minute at which good low-resistance contact on the commutator can be maintained. The system can be designed for any number of inputs.

A block diagram of an electronic time-division multiplex system is shown in Fig. 16-2. There are eight input circuits which are successively connected to the output circuit through a diode bridge. When junction *a* is positive with respect to junction *b*, the diodes in the bridge have infinite resistance, and the circuit between junctions *c* and *d* is effectively an open circuit. When junction *b* is positive with respect to point *a*, however, the

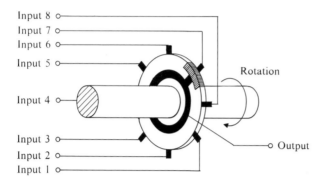

**Fig. 16-1.** *A time-division multiplex system using a mechanical commutator*

diodes have very low resistance and the bridge becomes a balanced bridge circuit with very low resistance arms, and the potentials of the junctions *c* and *d* are the same. Then the voltage at *c* is equal to the input voltage at *d*, or the circuit from *c* to *d* is a closed circuit.

Now the switching circuit that controls the potential at points *a* and *b* is operated by the coincident application of a clock pulse and a reset signal at the first and second inputs, respectively, of the first AND circuit of the control system. The clock pulse is of very short duration and has a magnitude of + 15 volts. During the remainder of the time, it is − 15 volts. The reset signal is generated by the operation of the preceding switching circuit. This reset signal is applied to the next switching circuit before the clock pulse is generated and it continues for a good part of the cycle after the clock pulse. It is + 15 volts during this part of the cycle and remains at − 15 volts during the rest of the cycle. These two pulses produce a short + 15-volt pulse at the output of the first AND circuit which is applied to the first input of the second AND circuit in this control system. The second input to the second AND circuit was already + 15 volts. These two inputs produce + 15 volts at the output junction *e* of the second AND circuit which is fed back to the first input of the second AND circuit. This locks the second AND circuit in the 1 position and keeps the output of the second AND circuit at junction *e* at + 15 volts as long as the second input to the second AND circuit is + 15 volts. The second input to the second AND circuit is a feedback circuit from the junction *e* through a time-delay circuit and a NOT circuit. The output of the time-delay circuit is also applied to the reset of the next switch to be operated. The +15 volts from junction $e$ will arrive at the reset of the next switch to be operated just before the next clock pulse, and the switch will operate at the arrival of the next clock pulse. At the same time the voltage through the NOT circuit will shut off the switch that has been in operation, and the potential of point $e$ will become −15 volts and will remain at this value until the two inputs to the first AND circuit of this switch are again both +15 volts.

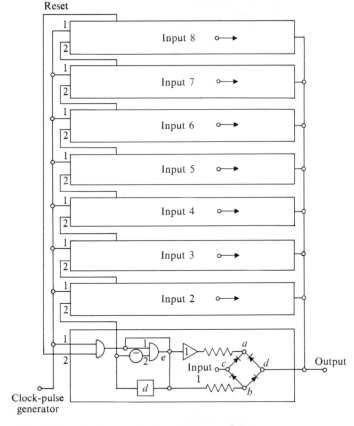

**Fig. 16-2.** *An electronic time-division multiplex system*

When junction $e$ is +15 volts, junction $b$ is +15 volts, and junction $a$, which is supplied from junction $e$ through an inverter, is −15 volts. This makes the voltage at $d$ equal to the voltage at $c$, and the input voltage 1 is applied to the output of the switch. When the junction $e$ is −15 volts, the reverse polarity is applied to junctions $a$ and $b$. This opens the circuit between junctions $c$ and $d$. This process continues through each of the eight switching circuits in repetitive succession at a rate determined by the clock pulse and the delay circuit. The number of inputs and switching circuits can be varied to meet the demands of the system.

Commercial circuits of this type have produced sampling rates of more than 10,000 samples/sec. Thus, if 80 samples were to be sampled at 10,000 samples/sec, each input would be read 125 times/sec. The time between samples is 100 $\mu$sec, and each input is read at intervals of 8 ms. The limiting factor in this system is the presence of switching transients. The time required to obtain a steady-state condition after switching is near 100 $\mu$sec. Other methods of sampling have produced sampling rates of better than $1.5 \times 10^6$ samples/sec.

There is one major difficulty with the time-division multiplex system. Each input is measured at a different time, and these values are not valid for comparison or computation if there is appreciable change in the magnitude of the inputs between samples.

A *sample-and-hold-circuit* is used to overcome this difficulty. Each signal input to the time-division multiplex system is connected to a circuit which is shown in Fig. 16-3. The first step in this procedure is to open

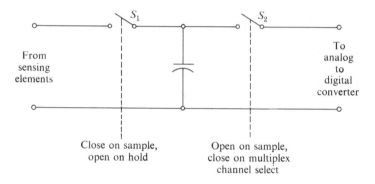

Fig. 16-3. *An elementary circuit of a sample-and-hold system*

switch $S_2$ and close switch $S_1$. This places an individual capacitor across each input, and the voltage across the capacitor, after a very short transient time, is equal to the input voltage. The second step is to open switch $S_1$. Then the voltage across each capacitor is the respective input voltage at the instant switch $S_1$ was opened. The third step is to close each $S_2$ switch at a given signal from the time-division multiplex system to connect each capacitor of the sample-and-hold system to the readout system at the correct portion of the time-division cycle. Usually, the output of the sample-and-hold system is applied to an analog-to-digital converter. Then all the digital outputs during one cycle of the sample-and-hold procedure is the value of the respective inputs at the instant the switches $S_1$ were opened.

## Frequency-Division System

The block diagram in Fig. 16-4 shows the arrangement of the components in an AM frequency-division multiplex system. Each input modulates an assigned subcarrier signal at comparatively low frequencies. These subcarrier frequencies are combined in a mixer circuit, and this combination modulates a main high-frequency carrier signal. This modulated high-frequency signal is transmitted to a receiver where the main high-frequency

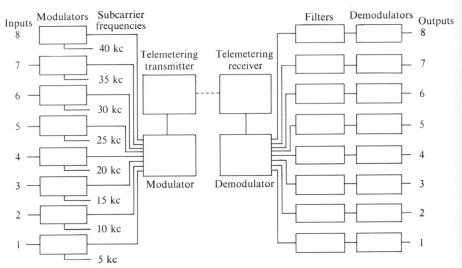

**Fig. 16-4.** *Block diagram of an AM frequency-division multiplex system*

signal is demodulated. This reproduces the combination of subcarrier frequencies. Each of the subcarrier frequencies is separated from the other subcarrier frequencies with band-pass filters. These subcarrier frequencies are demodulated to reproduce the individual input signals. The AM frequency-division multiplex system permits several signals to be transmitted over a single channel. The same is true of the FM frequency-division multiplex system described in Chap. 7. Frequency-division multiplex systems are well adapted to analog signals, as all input and output voltages are continuous, whereas time-division multiplex systems have discontinuous outputs and are well adapted to digital information, especially when sample-and-hold circuits are used.

## 16-9. ANALOG-TO-DIGITAL CONVERTERS

The methods for converting analog information to digital quantities were discussed in detail in Chap. 14.

## 16-10. TELEMETERING EQUIPMENT[2,4]

The general definition of telemetering requires that the readout be remote from the quantity measured and that the measured quantity be converted to an electrical quantity that can be transmitted to the desired location. This would include most modern instrumentation systems where the sensing elements are distributed throughout a plant or in a test bay, and the readout equipment is located in a control room or an instrumentation center. In modern instrumentation and data-acquisition systems, the transmission of information from a test bay or from components of a plant to a central information-recording center is often considered as a part of the data-acquisition system and not as a separate component of the system, unless special conversion and modulation equipment is required. The transmission of digital data from a data-acquisition system to a remote computer center and the transmission of information from a missile or a satellite to an instrumentation center are more distinctive examples of telemetering systems.

Telemetering systems often use either time-division or frequency-division multiplex systems to modulate the telemetering transmitter. Many types of modulation are used with these systems. When a frequency-division multiplex system is used with an AM subcarrier and the subcarrier amplitude-modulates the main carrier frequency, the system is termed an AM-AM system.

When a frequency-division multiplex system is used with an AM subcarrier and the subcarrier frequency-modulates the main carrier, the system is called an AM-FM system.

When a time-division multiplex system with an output similar to the one described in Sec. 16-8, where the amplitude of the pulse is proportional to the quantity measured, is used to amplitude-modulate the carrier frequency of a telemetering transmitter, it is termed a PAM-AM system, or a *pulse-amplitude-modulated–amplitude-modulated* system. When this time-division multiplex system is used to frequency-modulate a carrier, it is a PAM-FM system, or a *pulse-amplitude-modulated–frequency-modulated* system.

In some systems the time from a time-reference pulse to a second pulse is proportional to the magnitude of the measured quantity. This is termed the *pulse-position modulation,* or PPM. When this signal amplitude-modulates a carrier, the system is a PPM-AM system.

Other systems produce a length of pulse proportional to the measured quantity. This is *pulse-duration modulation.* When this signal amplitude-modulates a carrier, it is a PDM-AM system. Sometimes a pulse-duration-modulation system is called pulse-length- or pulse-width-modulation (PLM or PWM) system.

Some telemetering systems use a sequence of pulses to represent the magnitude of the measured quantity. This may be represented by the number of counts in a given time interval or by the sequence of counts and blanks in a given time interval. This is termed the pulse-code- or pulse-count-modulation (PCM) system. When this system is used to amplitude-modulate a carrier, it is a PCM-AM system. If it frequency-modulates a carrier, it is a PCM-FM system.

There are many devices to code signals for telemetering systems. Some of these are described in the references at the end of the chapter.

## 16-11.  DIGITAL RECORDERS[4]

Most digital information is recorded in a binary-number system, a binary-coded number system, or a binary-coded alpha-numeric system. The 1's and the 0's of the binary or the binary-coded systems are inscribed in

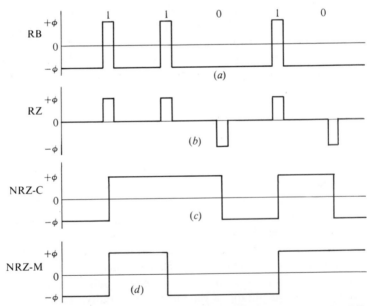

**Fig. 16-5.**  *Diagram of the binary number 11010 written in RB, RZ, NRZ-C, NRZ-M code*

several forms. The 1's may be holes punched in given locations on a paper tape or card, while the 0's are unpunched locations on the paper tape or card. The 1's and the 0's on a magnetic tape, drum, or disk may be one of several different systems.

In the *return-to-bias* (RB) system, the magnetic tape is biased to saturation in a direction defined as minus. The binary 0's have no effect on this tape, while the binary 1's saturate the tape in the opposite or positive direction for a short fixed distance on the tape, after which it returns to the biased saturation in the minus direction. A graphical representation of this system is shown in Fig. 16-5(*a*).

The *return-to-zero* (RZ) system is mentioned in Chap. 7. The tape is normally unmagnetized. A binary 1 magnetizes the tape in a positive direction for a short fixed distance and then returns to the unmagnetized condition of the tape. A binary 0 magnetizes the tape in a minus direction for a short fixed distance on the tape and then returns to the unmagnetized condition of the tape. A graphical representation of this system is shown in Fig. 16-5(*b*).

In the *nonreturn-to-zero-change* (NRZ-C) system, the tape is always saturated either in the positive direction or in the minus direction. The change of direction occurs when the value of the binary number changes from 1 to 0 or from 0 to 1. A graphical representation of this system is shown in Fig. 16-5(*c*).

In the *nonreturn-to-zero-mark* (NRZ-M) system, the tape is always saturated either in the positive or in the minus direction. The change of direction occurs when the binary number is a 1. A graphical representation of this system is shown in Fig. 16-5(*d*).

The format used to record data from an analog-to-digital converter is usually a parallel system. One common system employs a 16-channel magnetic tape. The range of the digital data is from 0 to 1999. These decimal data are written in *tens-zero-binary-coded decimal*. This code is as follows:

| Decimal | Tens-Zero-Binary-coded decimal |
|---------|-------------------------------|
| 0 | 1010 |
| 1 | 0001 |
| 2 | 0010 |
| 3 | 0011 |
| 4 | 0100 |
| 5 | 0101 |
| 6 | 0110 |
| 7 | 0111 |
| 8 | 1000 |
| 9 | 1001 |

The first four channels from the right record the units decimal digit. The next four channels from the right record the tens decimal digit. The next four channels from the right record the hundreds decimal digit. The thirteenth channel from the right records the thousand digit, 0 or 1. The fourteenth channel records the clock pulse. The fifteenth channel marks the beginning of the sequence of the time-division multiplex system. The sixteenth channel records the parity check. This channel marks a 0 when the number of 1's in the remaining channels is even, and a 1 when the number of 1's in the remaining channels is odd. On playback of the digital tape the parity is again checked and a disagreement of the playback parity with the recorded parity will produce an error indication and sometimes stop the system or take other means of compensating for the error.

Most computers use a parallel-series format. For example, one computer tape uses a 6-channel tape with 7 characters or rows of digits to produce one word input of 10 decimal digits plus sign. A tape-preparation unit is required to translate the 16-channel data tape onto a tape compatible to the computer input. This conversion is comparatively slow and cannot be performed at the data-recording speed. Usually, the data are recorded at a tape speed of

**Fig. 16-6.** *Block diagram of a tape-preparation system*

60 to 300 in./sec, with packing densities of 200 to 500 words/in. The playback for the tape-preparation unit is 6 to 18 in./sec. The tape-preparation unit is also capable of editing the tape and recording only that part of the tape that is required for further computation. A block diagram of a tape-preparation system is given in Fig. 16-6.

## 16-12. DIGITAL PLOTTERS

It is desirable to prepare a graph of the critical portions of the recorded and computed digital data to obtain a precise graphical comparison of the desired quantities. There are several types of digital plotters. Only one will be described here. It consists of a Thomson-Varley potentiometer operating in reverse. The digital number operates the switch contacts on the potentiometer, which produces a voltage that is porportional to the digital number. This voltage is applied to the input of another self-balancing potentiometer. This potentiometer sets the $Y$-position of an $X$-$Y$ recorder. When this potentiometer circuit is balanced, a solenoid on the writing head on the balance arm is energized. This places the desired mark on the chart. Usually, the balance head is moved in both the $X$- and $Y$-directions while the paper is stationary. The $X$-position is obtained by adding a $\Delta X$ for each digit read, and $Y$ is determined by the magnitude of the digital number. The plotting time is comparatively long. Usually, the first step in this procedure is to read a segment of the digital tape into a temporary storage unit. Then one digital number is read into the Thomson-Varley potentiometer, and the magnitude of the voltage produced is plotted on the $X$-$Y$ plotter. Then the next number in the temporary storage is read and plotted until all the stored numbers are plotted. After this, the next segment of tape is read into the temporary storage unit, and the procedure is repeated.

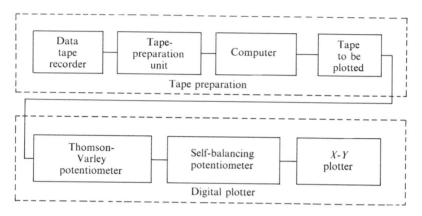

**Fig. 16-7.** *Block diagram of a tape-preparation system and digital plotter*

It will be remembered that the data recorded on the data tape and on the computer tape are consecutive samples of all the sensing elements. To plot the output of the consecutive data of one sensing element, the digital values from this element must be sorted from the digital data from all the inputs. This is usually done in the computer, and a new tape is prepared by the computer which has the desired data in the sequence required for plotting. A block diagram of this procedure is shown in Fig. 16-7.

**16-13. HIGH-SPEED CAMERAS AND TV EQUIPMENT**

In many industrial processes, aerodynamic testing, engine testing, etc., it is not possible to have the test operator view the equipment during test. Therefore, closed-loop TV is used to enable the operator to make visual observations of the test, and high-speed cameras are employed to obtain a continuous visual record to be used for further analysis. Cameras, remotely controlled from the central console, are used to obtain a visual record of the test. They are usually equipped with a marking device that records on the film the time intervals during the test. Even test number and run are often recorded on the film to identify completely each portion of the data.

## 16-14. PROGRESS MONITOR

The test procedure for a given system is usually fixed. The control console is often equipped with a progress monitor to ensure that all necessary functions are performed. As an illustration, typical operation of the progress monitor for the testing of a solid-fuel rocket engine will be described.

The preparation of this test requires the following:

1. All equipment must be turned on, and the tape transports must be in the ready position.

2. The START switch must be turned on. This switch will operate only when all the following conditions exist: (*a*) The deluge water pressure at the bay is correct. (*b*) All gates to the test area are closed. (*c*) The signal switch, which indicates that all the personnel in the bay area have been removed, is closed. (*d*) All warning sirens in the test area are operating. (*e*) The doors to the instrument house are closed.

A red light on the control console will indicate that the start operation has been performed. This operation starts the progress monitor. The individual steps performed by the progress monitor take place 1 sec apart. The number of the step being performed is indicated by the number in a window on the control console. The operations performed during each step are as follows:

1. The FM tape starts, the oscillograph paper starts at calibration speed (1/10 test speed), the millivolt calibration "homes," and the bridge-balance units "home." The "homing" time may last through several steps of the progress monitor.

2. The digital-tape transports start.

3, 4, and 5. The above operations continue.

6 through 20. The millivolt calibration of all equipment proceeds through the voltages 0, 2.5, $-2.5$, 5, $-5$, 10, $-10$, 20, $-20$, 40, $-40$, 80, and $-80$ mv. On the twentieth step, the calibrator "homes" to 0.

21. The progress monitor halts for several seconds to separate the millivolt-calibration sequence from the succeeding shunt-calibration sequence.

22. No operation.

23. The bridge-balance units are driven to the balance position.

24 through 39. The bridge-balance units proceed through the bridge-balance calibration positions 1, 0, 2, 0, 3, 0, 4, and 0 in the positive-calibration position and through positions 0, 1, 0, 2, 0, 3, 0, and 4 in the negative-calibration position. These positions connect calibrating resistors, either in series or in parallel, with the bridge circuit of the sensing elements, to produce an output voltage equal to the voltage output of the bridge at a given percent of full load.

40. The bridge-balance units are driven to "home" position. This may require more than 1 sec.

45. The oscillograph paper speed is changed to operating speed.

47. The firing signal goes on. Normally, a few seconds after the firing signal goes on, there is a signal from the engine instrumentation which shows that the ignition has started, and the test proceeds. When there is a major malfunction or when the test is completed as determined by the test operator as he observes the test on closed-loop TV, the engine is drenched with water by pushing a deluge button on the console. This ends the test run and begins the postcalibration. The oscillograph paper speed is reduced to calibrating speed, and steps 6 through 40 are repeated.

In other systems the operations performed by each step of the progress monitor will be determined by the requirements of the system.

## 16-15. CENTRAL-CLOCK CONTROL

The central-clock-control unit generates pulse-time signals as described in Chap. 11. These pulses perform two functions: (1) They trigger the multiplex system and the analog-to-digital converters. (2) They place timing marks on the analog recorders and the high-speed camera film for identification of the data taken on these devices. These marks may be a system of large and small marks that can be counted from an initial time mark, or they may record the time in serial BCD or binary numbers on one channel. Time recording is a very important part of an instrumentation system, and it may become very elaborate.

## 16-16. REQUIREMENTS OF A COMPLETE DATA-ACQUISITION AND REDUCTION SYSTEM

The components required for a data-acquisition system depend upon the number of inputs to the system, the number of samples per second required, the frequency response, and the accuracy. If a system required 2 percent accuracy and a frequency response less than 100 cycles per second, it could consist of sensing elements and oscillographs. If a system required accuracies of greater than 0.1 percent with a 500-cycles-per-second frequency response, and 100 inputs, it would need a sampling rate of 20,000 samples/sec, with sample-and-hold circuits and oscillograph records of the analog data. Similarly, a system requiring 150 samples/sec for each input and a frequency response of 10 cycles per second would need 1,500 to 2,000 samples/sec, with or without sample-and-hold circuits, and a d'Arsonval-type strip-chart recorder. If a system required a 10,000-cycles-per-second response, an FM analog recorder would be required. These systems are based on a few facts and the present state of the art. These facts include the following:

1. To reconstruct the frequency components from a set of digital data, there should be at least two samples per cycle.

2. The accuracy of a galvanometer oscillograph is 5 percent, which can be improved with adequate calibration.

3. An FM recorder has an accuracy of 5 percent.

4. The accuracy of a digital system with good calibration is 0.05 percent.

5. The frequency response of a galvanometer oscillograph is from 10 to 5,000 cycles per second.

6. The frequency response of an FM recorder is 10,000 cycles per second or better.

It is often desirable to filter the input to a digital system so that the digital data will be an average value and not a periodic point from an irregular input. These filters should have a very flat response up to their limit of 10 to 200 cycles per second, and then attenuate rapidly at higher frequencies. A few typical instrument systems will now be described.

An instrumentation system using a high-level multiplex system is shown in Fig. 16-8. The sensing elements may include strain-gage transducers for measuring pressures, thrust, and stress. Thermocouples and thermistors are used for temperature measurements, and position potentiometers are used to measure displacement.

The conditioning units include (1) a high-quality amplifier with a frequency response from 0 to 10,000 cycles per second, (2) bridge-balance units for the strain-gage and thermistor inputs, and (3) controlled temperature-reference junctions for the thermocouples. The amplifiers provide zero adjustment and gain control. The bridge balances are usually provided with a servo gun for balancing the bridges. Some bridge-balance units use a servo system which is connected to the respective bridge-balance potentiometers through magnetic clutches that connect the servo system in sequence to the bridge-balance potentiometers.

The multiplex system is usually a high-speed transistor or electronic device, with sampling rates of 10,000 to 20,000 samples/sec. The number of inputs varies from 10 to 200. Some multiplex systems provide two rates of sampling. For example, input channels 1 to 9, 11 to 19, 21 to 29, etc., may be sampled at 100 samples/sec, while inputs 10, 20, 30, 40, etc., may be sampled only 10 times/sec. It will be observed that each input to the multiplex system has been amplified. These inputs have a full-load voltage of approximately 1 to 5 volts. This increases the precision of the analog-to-digital conversion and reduces the percent noise. Sample-and-hold circuits are usually available for at least half of the input circuits. The system is generally provided with a patch board which allows the output of any channel of conditioning equipment to be connected to any channel of the multiplex system, with or without sample-and-hold circuits. With this patch board the rate of sampling of a given input can be chosen to fit the demands of the test. An instrumentation

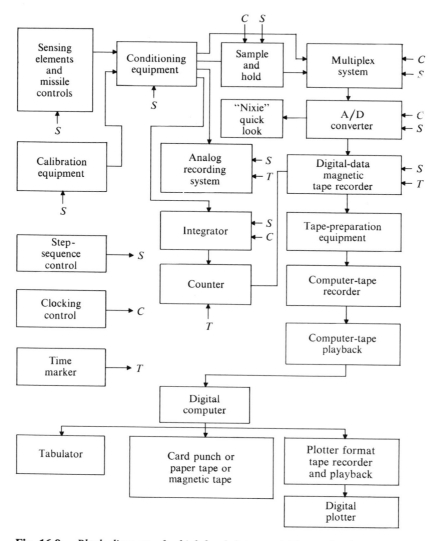

**Fig. 16-8.** *Block diagram of a high-level data-acquisition and reduction system*

system of this type is shown in Fig. 16-9. In this system the control console generates three distinct signals: (1) The 1-sec switching signal operates the progress monitor. This signal is marked *S* in Fig. 16-8. (2) The clock-pulse signal, which is the frequency of the sampling rate, controls the steps of the multiplex system, the analog-to-digital converter, and, in some cases, the readout of the integrating system. This signal is marked $C$ in Fig. 16-8. (3) The timing signal identifies the time on the camera film, on the FM and digital tapes, and on the oscillograph strip charts. This signal is marked $T$ in Fig. 16-8.

**Fig. 16-9.** *A modern instrumentation system* (*courtesy Hercules Powder Co.*)

The block diagram of an instrumentation system using a multiplex system that samples the voltages of the sensing elements before they are amplified is shown in Fig. 16-10. The voltages in this *low-level system* are usually 100 mv or less. This system has the advantage of using only one high-quality amplifier; there is, however, some difficulty in multiplex systems using this low voltage. Some systems have used mercury-wetted relays to reduce the resistance in the multiplex system.

The instrumentation system in Fig. 16-11 uses an AM frequency-division multiplex system which modulates the high-frequency radio transmitter. This system is used in missile and satellite flight instrumentation. The radio receiver produces the AM low-frequency signal similar to the output of the multiplex system. This signal is recorded on a magnetic tape recorder in the field and brought to the recording center for reproduction. This reproduced signal is filtered and demodulated to reproduce analog signals corresponding to the output of the sensing elements. These signals are usually recorded on oscillographs which are used for visual analysis of the data. If

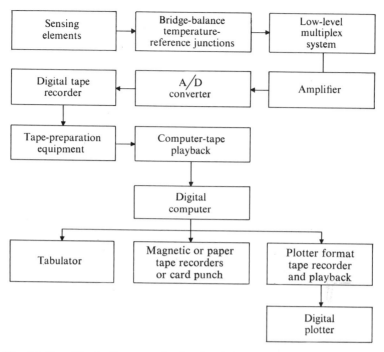

**Fig. 16-10.** *Block diagram of a low-level data-acquisition and reduction system*

digital computation is desired, a curve reader, such as the Bensen-Lehner "Oscar," is used to convert the analog data recorded on graphs to a digital number. The digital readout of this instrument is a punched card or punched tape.

Some instrumentation systems use an analog computer to make preliminary computations and scale corrections before the analog signals are sampled and converted to digital quantities for further computation. A block diagram of this system is shown in Fig. 16-12.

## 16-17. CHECKING THE PERFORMANCE OF A DATA-ACQUISITION SYSTEM

One of the most frequent sources of error in operating a data-acquisition system is the assumption that the precalibration and postcalibration of the system are sufficient to ensure that the data taken are accurate. These calibrations will indicate the linearity of the system and will give a scale factor for the recorded data for static operations, but they usually fail to account for the frequency response of the system and for errors produced by temperature gradients, mechanical vibrations, and noise. A complete performance test should include the determination of the following characteristics in each

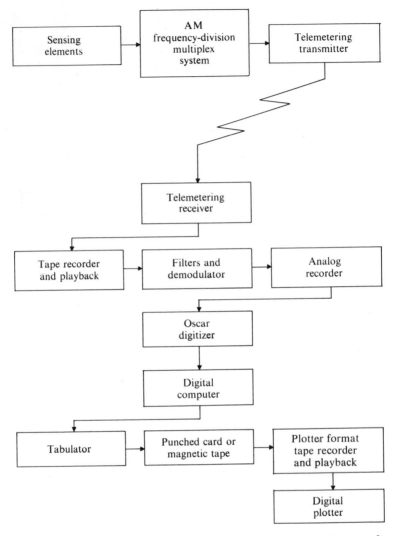

**Fig. 16-11.** *Block diagram of an instrumentation system using a radio telemetering link*

major group of components of the system: (1) linearity, (2) drift, (3) signal-to-noise ratio, and (4) response time or frequency response.

Methods of measuring these characteristics will now be discussed with reference to the major groups of components in an instrumentation system.

### The Digital System

LINEARITY MEASUREMENTS. The precalibration and postcalibration of a digital system are effective linearity calibrations. For example, consider the procedure for determining the linearity of a digital system which has a digital readout from 0000 to 1999, a sample-and-hold circuit for each input channel, and a 96-channel time-division multiplex system. Each input channel-conditioning amplifier is adjusted to produce a digital readout of 1000 with zero

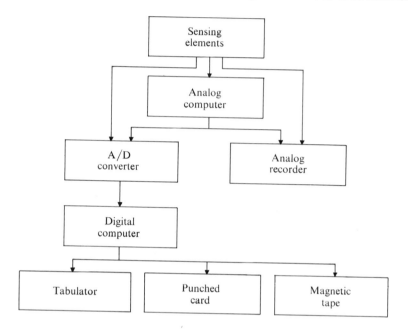

**Fig. 16-12.** *Block diagram of an instrumentation system which uses an analog computer in conjunction with a digital computer*

volts input, and 1900 with 80 mv input. A sample of the data obtained from one channel during a calibration cycle is as follows:

| Volts input | Digital readout | Linear output | Deviation from linear output |
|---|---|---|---|
| −80 | 104 | 100 | 4.0 |
| −40 | 556 | 550 | 6.0 |
| −20 | 779 | 775 | 4.0 |
| −10 | 888 | 887.5 | 0.5 |
| −5 | 946 | 943.75 | 2.25 |
| 0 | 000 | 1000.00 | 0.0 |
| +5 | 1057 | 1056.25 | 0.75 |
| +10 | 1113 | 1112.5 | 0.5 |
| +20 | 1224 | 1225 | −1.0 |
| +40 | 1451 | 1450 | 1.0 |
| +80 | 1900 | 1900 | 0.0 |

The line through the points (0, 1000) and (80, 1900) is chosen as the reference line. The linear values on this reference line, corresponding to the input voltages, are listed in column three, and the deviations from these values are listed in column four. The limits of the deviations are $+6.0$ to $-1.0$, giving the total maximum-to-minimum deviation of 7 counts or a mean deviation of $\pm 3\frac{1}{2}$ counts. Then the percent linearity is 0.184 percent of full scale. The same procedure would be followed for obtaining the linearity of each channel.

DRIFT MEASUREMENTS. The drift of a system is a function of time. The time period used for measuring the drift depends on the system. In solid-fuel engine tests, the test time is short, and the period between precalibration and postcalibration is usually less than 10 min. Thus a short time period of 10 min would give the value of the drift expected during a test. It is also desirable to determine the magnitude of the readjustment necessary over longer periods of time, and a long-time period of 24 hr would give the drift that could be expected from one day to another. Usually, both short- and long-period drift tests are made. The drift is the change in the digital output during a fixed period of time when the input is held constant. Several readings are generally taken. For example, a reading on the hour and 10 min after the hour may be taken during an 8-hour period, giving eight values of short-period drift. The largest value of drift gives the maximum or limiting drift; the probable drift can be computed by using Eq. (2-31). Similarly, the output with a given input may be measured at a given hour each day, giving several samples of the drift over a 24-hr period. It is to be emphasized that no adjustments of the equipment should be made during a drift test.

NOISE MEASUREMENTS. The noise of the digital system is manifested as an erratic change of count. It is the erratic deviation of the readout, usually observed for convenience during some fixed period of time, although it should be emphasized here that noise is not a function of time.

FREQUENCY RESPONSE. The input to a digital system is usually filtered to avoid periodic sampling of irregular inputs. The filters used for thermocouple measurements are flat to approximately 10 cycles per second, with a sharp cutoff for the higher frequencies. The filters used for thrust and pressure-transducer outputs are flat to 50 or 200 cycles per second and sometimes higher. The frequency response of a digital system is essentially the frequency response of the filters. In some tests the high-frequency response is measured by using unfiltered digital systems with high sampling rates.

The major difficulty in measuring the frequency response of a digital system is measuring the input voltage with the required accuracy. The input may be measured with a meter having an accuracy comparable to a Fluke voltmeter or a Hermach-Engelhard transfer volt-ammeter. These meters, however, measure the rms voltage, and slight variations in wave shape may produce deviations from the assumed sinusoidal input greater than the required accuracy of the system. Therefore, the peak value of the wave may be more easily compared than the rms value, as the peak values may be read directly from the digital data. An effective and accurate method of measuring the peak voltage is shown in Fig. 16-13. The output of a signal generator is connected to the voltage-dividing circuit normally used in the millivolt calibrations or an equivalent voltage divider which has resistance components that have an accuracy of at least $\pm 0.01$ percent. The voltage across the volt-age-divider circuit is usually 10 to 20 volts peak, while the voltage supplied to the inputs of the conditioning amplifiers is similar to the d-c millivolt calibration voltages. The range of these steps is from 0 to 100 mv.

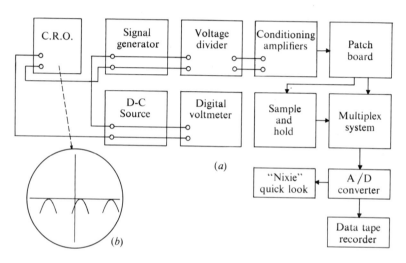

**Fig. 16-13.** *Block diagram of an accurate method of measuring the peak voltage of a sinusoidal emf*

The output of the signal generator is also connected to a cathode-ray oscilloscope in series with a bias voltage. The cathode-ray oscilloscope is set to maximum gain (minimum attenuation), and the horizontal sweep is adjusted to coincide with the center horizontal line on the screen with the vertical input short-circuited. Then the bias voltage is set to the voltage which will give the desired peak voltages. This voltage is measured to 4 significant figures with a digital voltmeter. Then the short circuit is removed from the vertical input of the cathode-ray oscilloscope, and the gain of the signal generator is adjusted until the peak of the pattern on the oscilloscope is tangent to the center horizontal line on the screen of the cathode-ray oscillo-scope. Under this condition the peak voltage applied to the voltage divider is equal to the bias voltage. A high-gain oscilloscope such as the Tektronix type 502 should be used in this circuit. Then the input voltage can be measured with an accuracy equal to the accuracy of the digital voltmeter. The frequency response is then measured with a fixed-input peak voltage. It should be within 0.5 percent over the desired frequency range, with a 3- to 30-db attenuation per octave at higher frequencies.

MEASURING CROSSTALK. An effective method of measuring the crosstalk is to apply 0 volts to all inputs of the digital system and adjust all conditioning amplifiers to give the desired 0 digital readout. Then connect a d-c voltage to the even-channel inputs of the digital system and adjust this voltage until all even-channel digital outputs are at rated value and record the output of the odd channels. The magnitude of these readings is the crosstalk. This procedure should be repeated with the d-c inputs replaced by sinusoidal inputs to the even channels.

### The FM System

LINEARITY CALIBRATION. The FM system has two distinct parts: the first records the FM signal on magnetic tape; the second is the FM playback unit that reproduces the signal from the FM tape.

The main unit of the first system is the FM modulator. It converts the input signal to an FM signal. For example, a commercial FM system has a center frequency of 54 kc with 0 volts input. It has a rated full-scale modulation of 40 percent with a 2-volt input. Then a +2-volt input would produce an output frequency of 75.6 kc. An input voltage of −2 volts would produce an output frequency of 32.4 kc.

Before a linearity calibration can be made on this part of the system, the output frequency of the modulator must be measured with an electronic counter when the input is short-circuited. If this frequency is not within 50 cycles per second of 54 kc, the center-frequency control should be adjusted until the correct frequency is obtained. Then a +2-volt input should be applied to the input, and the span control should be adjusted until the output frequency is 75.6 kc. The recording unit is then ready for linear calibration. The input voltage is varied from −2 to +2 volts d-c in the desired steps, the corresponding frequency output for each step is recorded, and the linearity is computed. This unit should have better than ±2 percent linearity. Note that the above values were chosen for a given example. The voltages and frequencies required for a given unit will depend upon the frequency and the input and output characteristics of the system under test.

After the linearity of this part of the system has been obtained, the values of the d-c voltages used in this calibration are recorded and played back on the second part of the system. Each discriminator is adjusted to give the rated voltage output when rated voltage is played back. Then the intermediate values are played back and recorded. The overall linearity is now computed. The linearity of the overall system should be better than ±2 percent. The d-c voltages in this calibration should be measured with a good digital voltmeter.

FREQUENCY RESPONSE. A typical FM system should have a flat frequency response from zero to 8 kc within ±1/2 db, and not more than 1 db down at 10 kc. The input and output of the complete system can be measured with a good a-c vacuum-tube voltmeter such as the Hewlett-Packard model 400 L. A nominal set of frequencies can be applied to the input with an a-c rms input voltage equal to 0.707 of the rated d-c voltage input. The output can be read directly on the output meter scale in decibels. Then one half the difference of maximum and minimum decibels during this set of measurements should not exceed 1/2 db for frequencies to 8,000 cycles per second and 1 db for 10 kc.

NOISE MEASUREMENTS. Apply a 400-cycles-per-second signal with an rms voltage of 0.707 of the d-c rated input to the FM system for several seconds, then play back and record the maximum deviation and the average voltage output. The noise level is the ratio of the maximum deviation from the average voltage, expressed in decibels. This should be less than −45 db.

DRIFT MEASUREMENTS. Apply a rated d-c voltage to the input of the FM system for 2 min. Repeat this procedure 10 min later and 2 hr later. The difference between the first and second readings gives the short-time drift. The difference between the first and third readings gives the long-time drift. This should be less than ±1 percent of full scale.

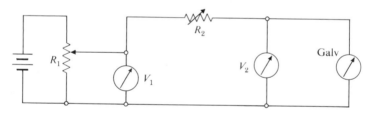

**Fig. 16-14.** *Circuit for determining the linearity and sensitivity of a galvanometer*

Another drift measurement that should be taken as a check on the operation of the FM system is the center-frequency drift of the FM modulators. Periods of 10 min and 1 hr should be used. More than 1 percent drift indicates a malfunction.

## Performance Tests of a Galvanometer-Type Oscillograph

Three characteristics are usually specified for a galvanometer-type oscillograph; these are the sensitivity, linearity, and the frequency response, which vary widely with the type of galvanometer used. The circuit in Fig. 16-14 is used to determine the linearity and sensitivity of the galvanometer. The resistance $R_1$ is adjusted to produce a 1-volt drop at $V_1$. $R_2$ is adjusted to produce a 1-in. deflection of the galvanometer. The voltage $V_2$ measured across the galvanometer is the inverse sensitivity of the galvanometer in millivolts per inch, or the reciprocal of this voltage is the sensitivity in inches per millivolt.

To measure the linearity, the voltage $V_1$ is stepped through the ten voltages listed below, and the deflections that should be obtained with a linear galvanometer are given:

| Voltage $V_1$ | Deflection in inches |
|:---:|:---:|
| 2.0 | 2.0 |
| 1.6 | 1.6 |
| 1.2 | 1.2 |
| 0.8 | 0.8 |
| 0.4 | 0.4 |
| 0.0 | 0.0 |
| −0.4 | −0.4 |
| −0.8 | −0.8 |
| −1.2 | −1.2 |
| −1.6 | −1.6 |
| −2.0 | −2.0 |

The maximum deviation from these deflections is the maximum linearity deviation, and this deviation expressed in percent of full scale (2.0 inches) should not exceed 5 percent.

The frequency response of galvanometers with high mechanical damping is measured using the circuit in Fig. 16-15(a). The gain of the signal generator is adjusted to produce 1 volt rms at $V_1$, and $R_1$ is adjusted to produce a deflection of 2 in. at 5 cycles per second. A nominal set of frequencies is chosen, depending on the frequency response of the galvanometer under test. The deflection is set at 2 in. for each frequency, and the voltage $V_2$ across the galvanometer is recorded. The difference between the maximum and the minimum voltage should not exceed 10 percent of the average voltage across the galvanometer.

Some galvanometers are not highly damped, and their frequency response is affected by the external resistance of the galvanometer circuit. The resistance required in the external circuit is always included in the specifications for these galvanometers. The circuit described in Sec. 3-21 should be used to obtain the desired deflection and external circuit resistance as shown in Fig. 16-15(b). Usually, the signal generator has a fixed internal resistance of 600 ohms. This resistance is not affected by the gain control, and the gain control can be used to obtain the desired deflection of the galvanometer, which will serve the same purpose as varying $R_2$ in Fig. 16-15(a). Then the voltage across the galvanometer is measured for each input frequency. The difference between the maximum and the minimum values of this voltage should not exceed 10 percent of the average value of the voltage measured.

### Overall System Performance

The overall performance of the system should be tested to determine its complete compatibility. This should include the operation of all digital channels in conjunction with all the FM and galvanometer oscillograph channels. The system should be checked with both the millivolt-calibration input voltages and sinusoidal input voltage to observe the response of the

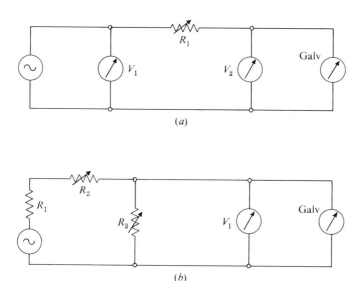

**Fig. 16-15.** *Circuits for measuring the frequency response of a galvanometer*

system with a qualitative test. This performance test is not a recalibration of the system but a test of its functional operation. Where possible, known inputs should be applied to the sensing elements, and the output should be measured to observe the accuracy of calibration and the complete system performance.

Most of the discussion in this chapter has been limited to data-acquisition system, but analog and digital computers are also important components of instrumentation systems. Problems whose solutions are known can be applied to these units to determine their reliability and accuracy. Only when the performance and accuracy of each component has been determined and the overall compatibility of the system has been established can the computed data be considered accurate and reliable.

## PROBLEMS

**16-1.** The voltage applied to the input of a digital-instrumentation system and the digital output are as follows:

| Millivolt input | Digital output |
|---|---|
| −100 | 1 |
| −80 | 204 |
| −60 | 407 |
| −40 | 601 |
| −20 | 802 |
| 00 | 1000 |
| 20 | 1197 |
| 40 | 1394 |
| 60 | 1592 |
| 80 | 1791 |

Determine the percent linearity of this system.

**16-2.** The data obtained during the measurement of the frequency response of a galvanometer in an oscillograph are as follows:

| Frequency in cycles per second | Voltage across the galvanometer, in volts |
|---|---|
| 5 | 0.257 |
| 50 | 0.262 |
| 200 | 0.263 |
| 500 | 0.263 |
| 1000 | 0.264 |
| 3000 | 0.266 |
| 6000 | 0.266 |
| 8000 | 0.258 |
| 10000 | 0.249 |

The deflection of the galvanometer was 2.0 in. (*a*) Determine the frequency response in percent of full scale. (*b*) Determine the average sensitivity of the galvanometer.

**16-3.** The output frequency of an FM modulator with the input short-circuited was measured on the hour and 10 min after the hour during an 8-h period. The readings are as follows:

| Frequency on the hour | Frequency 10 *min* after the hour |
|---|---|
| 54,421 | 54,416 |
| 54,402 | 54,399 |
| 54,397 | 54,396 |
| 54,374 | 54,374 |
| 54,364 | 54,360 |
| 55,352 | 55,349 |
| 55,344 | 55,342 |
| 55,340 | 55,336 |

Determine: (a) the short-time drift; (b) the probable short-time drift; (c) the 1-hr drift; (d) the probable 1-hr drift; (e) the 8-hr drift.

**16-4.** The voltage applied to the input of the digital system is constant over a 5-min period while the peak variation of the output was from 1982 to 1994, the initial output was 1985, and the final output was 1987. Determine: (a) the noise; (b) the short-time drift.

**16-5.** Outline the procedure for adjusting an FM modulator and measuring its frequency response.

**16-6.** List the advantages of: (a) a high-level multiplex system; (b) a low-level multiplex system.

**16-7.** Describe in your own words the procedure for determining the frequency response of a galvanometer.

**16-8.** Design a method for measuring the frequency response of an FM recorder using a motor-driven frequency generator, a potentiometer which produces a voltage proportional to the log of the frequency, and an X-Y recorder. What would you apply to the Y-input of the recorder? What would you apply to the X-input? What would be the shape of the trace? Would the pen trace the frequency response of the FM recorder? If the pen does not trace the frequency response, what could you add to the circuit to obtain a single trace of the frequency response?

**REFERENCES**

1. I. F. Kinnard, *Applied Electrical Measurements*, John Wiley & Sons, Inc., New York, 1956, Chap. 11.

2. *Reference Data for Radio Engineers*, 4th ed., International Telephone and Telegraph Corporation, New York, 1957, p. 538.

3. J. M. Gottschalk and W. J. Wasylenko, "Drum and Disc Storage," *Instrument and Control Systems*, April, 1961, p. 653.

4. P. J. Weber, *The Tape Recorder as an Instrumentation Device*, 2nd ed., Ampex Corporation, Redwood City, Cal., 1959, pp. 27–38.

5. "Revision No. 1 to the Final Test for the Data Acquisition System for Hercules Powder Company," *Minneapolis-Honeywell Company Report*, Beltsville, Maryland, P.O. no. BCCW-14-HO, 1959.

# INDEX

Acceleration, 251
Accumulator
 lower, 381
 upper, 381
Accuracy, 2
Adder
 full, 402, 403
 half, 399, 403
Address register, 375
Anderson inductance bridge, 198
Alternating-current
 bridges, 184
  Anderson inductance bridge, 198
  capacitance bridge with Wagner
   ground, 187
  inductance-comparison bridge, 186
  Heaviside mutual inductance
   bridge, 198
  Maxwell bridge, 199
  Owen bridge, 199
  resonance bridge, 198
  Shering bridge, 199
 power measurements, 112
  compensated wattmeter, 114
  polyphase measurements, 114
  thermal watt converter, 116
  wattmeter, 113
 reactive power measurements, 116
 recording meters, 128
 rectifier-type instruments, 102
Alpha particles, 271
AM-AM system, 429
AM-FM system, 429
AM frequency division multiplexing,
 428
Ammeter
 clamp-on, 144
 multirange, 77
 resistance, 80
 shunts, 76
Amplitude factors, 298

Analog-to-digital converters, 346
Angular velocity of a galvanometer, 38
AND operation, 387
Anemometer, 265
Arithmetic mean, 23
Arithmetic unit, 373, 376
Asynchronous computers, 406
Auxiliary computer equipment, 384
Averaging circuits, 284
Ayrton shunt, 56

Baldwin Piano Co., 367
Ballistic galvanometer, 58
Ballistic sensitivity, 47, 51
Beta particles, 271
Binary-coded decimal number, 337
Binary division, 414
Binary numbers, 324, 325
Binary-tens-zero-coded decimal number,
 431
Biquinary code, 341
Bismuth spiral magnetic intensity
 bridge, 275
Bolometer, 266
Boltzman's constant, 5
Bonded-resistance strain gage, 230
Boolean algebra, 387
 theorems, 391
Boolean equation
 function diagrams, 393, 400
 function table, 388
Bridges
 alternating current, 184
  Anderson induction bridge, 198
  capacitance bridge with Wagner
   ground, 187
  Heaviside mutual - inductance
   bridge, 198
  inductance-comparison bridge, 186
  Maxwell bridge, 199

Owen bridge, 199
resonance bridge, 198
Shering bridge, 199
direct-current bridges, 172
Kelvin bridge, 177
self-balancing bridge, 181
Wheatstone bridge, 173
Bridge sensitivity, 174
Bridge-T network, 188
Brooks inductometer, 187
Buffer circuits, 417

Calibration equipment, 422
Calibration of strain-gage circuits, 238
Cameras
high-speed, 433
Capacitance bridge with Wagner ground, 187
Card-preparation unit, 384
Carry, 398
Capacitor equivalent circuit, 194
Cathode-ray oscilloscopes, 165
Clamp-on ammeter, 144
Clock central control, 435
Clock pulse, 432
Colman Engineering Company, 366
Compensated wattmeter, 114
Complement
1's, 410
2's, 409
Computer auxiliary equipment, 384
Computer controls, 384
Computer operations, 377
Computer patch panel, 386
Computer program, 380
Computers
analog, 284
commercial, 318
digital, 372
asynchronous, 406
CDC 1604, 417
IBM 650, 374
IBM 1401, 417
IBM 7070, 417
IBM 7074, 417
Larc, 417
Philco S 2000, 417
Stretch, 417
Conditioning equipment, 421
Consolidated Electrodynamics Corporation, 368
Control unit, 373

Correction, 3
Coulomb friction, 297
Critical-damped galvanometer, 39
Critical damping resistance, External (CDRX), 53
Current galvanometer, 33
Current measurements, 74
Current measurements with a potentiometer, 218
Current sensitivity, 35
Current sensitivity of a galvanometer, 49
Current transformers, 142
Current transformer tests, 143
Cyclic-decimal encoder, 365
Cyclic-decimal-number system, 339

d'Arsonval movement, 70
Data address, 375
Data words, 375
Dead time, 10
Dead zone, 10
Decimal numbers, 324
Deflection factor, 4
Deviation, 23
average deviation, 23, 25
standard deviation, 24
Differential equations, 292
Differential transformers, 240
Differentiating circuits, 292
Digital computer, 372
Digital plotters, 432
Digital recorders, 163, 430
nonreturn-to-zero-change (NRZ-C), 431
nonreturn-to-zero-mark (NRZ-M), 431
return-to-bias (RB), 431
return-to-zero (RZ), 431
Digitizers, 346
Diode matrix, 350
Direct-current recording instruments, 95
Direct-recording magnetic tape, 155
Discrimination, 4
Dissipation factor, 192
Distributor, 376
Dividing circuits
electrodynamometer, 303
feedback, 305
servo-potentiometer, 300
Drift, 4
Drift measurements, 442, 445

Dropouts in FM tape, 159
Drum address, 375
Drum locations, 384
Drum storage unit, 375
Dual-trace potentiometer recorder, 226
Duodecimal numbers, 324, 325, 336
Duo-range potentiometers, 205
Dynamic analysis, 8
Dynamic characteristics of a galvanometer, 35
Dynamic error, 9
Dynamic range, 154

Electrodynamic instruments, 106
Electrostatic instruments, 111
Encoders, 346
  commercial, 366
  cyclic-decimal, 365
  positive- and negative-reading, 368
  spatial, 346, 360
    analog-to-binary-coded decimal, 361
  time-base, 346, 354
Errors, 3
  accidental, 22
  environmental, 22
  fractional, 16
  instrumental, 22
  known, 21
    combinations of, 21, 22
  limiting, 14
    difference of, 19
    product of, 19
    quotient of, 20
  machine, 22
  observer, 22
  probable, 25
    combinations, 28
  random, 22
  systematic, 22
Error-checking unit, 373
Equivalent circuit of
  capacitor, 194
  inductance, 193
  potentiometer, 220
  resistor, 193

Farrand Controls, Inc., 368
Feed-back voltage encoder, 346, 357
Fidelity, 9
Fixed decimal point, 375

Floating decimal point, 375
Flow chart, 381
Flowmeter, 264
Flux-linkage measurements, 62
FM tape dropouts, 159
FM tape percent noise, 162
FM tape recorders, 160
Fractional error, 16
Fractions, 342
Free period of a galvanometer, 39
Frequency comparison with a cathode-ray oscilloscope, 169
Frequency-division multiplexing, 161
Frequency measurements, 126
  electrodynamic-type meter, 127
  electronic counter, 128
  saturable-core-type meter, 127
Frequency of a galvanometer, 38
Frequency range, 7, 154, 442, 445
Friction
  coulomb, 96, 297
  static, 297
Full adder, 402, 403
Full-subtract circuits, 408
Function diagrams for Boolean equations, 393, 400
Function generator
  electronic, 310
  nonlinear-potentiometer, 306
Function table, 388

Gage factor, 232
Gage sensitivity, 233
Galvanometer
  angular velocity, 38
  ballistic, 58
    response, 60
  current, 33
    critical damped, 39
    dynamic characteristics, 35
    free period, 39
    frequency, 38
    logarithmic decrement, 42
    nondimensional response curves, 44
    overdamped, 43
    period, 38
    protection, 54
    relative damping, 39
    resistance, 48
    sensitivity, 45
    undamped, 38
    underdamped, 37

Galvanometer-type oscillographs, 153
  phase angle, 153
  relative amplitude, 152
Gamma particles, 271
Gas-amplification factor, 271
Gauss meter, 274
Geiger counter, 271
  external quenching, 272
  self-quenching, 272

Half adder, 399, 403
Half-subtract circuit, 406
Hall effect, 276
Heaviside mutual inductance bridge, 198
High-frequency power measurements, 263
High-level multiplexer, 437
High-speed cameras, 433
Hysteresis, 11
Hysteresiscope, 274

IBM 650, 374
IBM 1401, 417
IBM 7070, 417
IBM 7074, 417
Ideal transformer, 132
Ier register, 413
Index reading, 7
Index scale, 7
Inductance
  equivalent circuit of, 193
Inductance-comparison bridge, 186
Information bit, 375
Instruction cards, 383
Instruction words, 375
Instrument efficiency, 5
Instrumental errors, 22
Integrating circuits, 289
Integrating equipment, 423
Inverse sensitivity, 4
Ionization-detector chamber, 271
Ionization-type vacuum gage, 253

K-2 potentiometer, 211
K-3 potentiometer, 213
Karnaugh map, 393
Kelvin bridge, 177
Known errors, 21

Larc computer, 417
Librascope, Inc., 367
Limited error combinations, 17
Limiting error, 14
Linear change, 8
Linear measurements, 440
Linearity, 7
Load-ring force transducer, 245
Logarithmic decrement of a galvanometer, 42
Logarithmic decrement measurements, 52
Lower accumulator, 381
Low-level multiplexer, 439

Machine errors, 22
Magnetic-field measurements, 276
Magnetic flux and hysteresis, 273
Magnetic intensity bismuth-spiral bridge 275
Magnetic recorders
  digital, 430
  direct, 155
    conditioning devices, 154
    frequency range, 154
  FM, 160
Maxterms, 392
Maxwell bridge, 199
Measuring lag, 9
Megger, 87
Megohm sensitivity, 45, 50
Memory unit, 372
MicroSADIC, 368
MilliSADIC, 368
Minterms, 392
Mirror-type pyrometer, 267
Multiple-range potentiometers, 208
Multiplexing
  frequency division, 161, 428
  high-level, 437
  low-level, 439
  time-division, 424
Multiplying circuits
  electrodynamometer, 303
  feedback, 305
  serial, 412
  servo-potentiometer, 300
Multipoint potentiometer, 226
Multirange portable potentiometer, 216
Mumetal-wire magnetic intensity bridge, 274

453

Nixie tubes, 354
Noise, 4, 5
Noise measurements, 442, 445
Nonreturn-to-zero (NRZ), 164
Nonreturn-to-zero-change (NRZ-C), 431
Nonreturn-to-zero-mark (NRZ-M), 431
Normal distribution curve, 24
NOT operation, 389
Nuclear instruments, 269
Numbers
  binary, 324, 325
  cyclic decimal, 339
  decimal, 324
  duodecimal, 324, 325, 336
  octonary, 324, 325, 335
  sexadecimal, 324
  ternary, 324, 325, 333
Number-indicator switching circuits, 348, 351

Observer errors, 22
Octonary numbers, 324, 325, 335
Off-line operations, 417
Ohmmeter
  cross-coil-type, 86
  series-type, 81
  shunt-type, 85
Ohms-per-volt, 5
Operation code, 375
Operation register, 375
Optimum programming, 381
OR operation, 388
Oscillograph
  galvanometer-type, 148
    phase-angle, 153
    relative-amplitude, 152
    response, 151
    step-function response, 153
Oscilloscopes
  cathode-ray, 165
    frequency comparison, 169
    phase-angle measurements, 168
Overshoot, 10
Overdamped galvanometer, 43
Owen bridge, 199

PAM-AM system, 429
PAM-FM system, 429
PCM-AM system, 430
PCM-FM system, 430
PDM-AM system, 429

PLM system, 429
PPM-AM system, 429
PWM system, 429
$p$H measurement, 276
Parallel-recording system, 164
Parallel-T circuit, 189
Parity check, 164, 373
Percent linearity, 7
Period of a galvanometer, 38
Phase-angle measurements, 168
Phase-measuring circuits, 124
Phase-sequence indicator, 121
Philco S-2000 computer, 417
Photoconductive cells, 265, 268
Photoelectric cells, 265
Photomultiplier tubes, 267
Phototubes, 267
Photovoltaic cells, 268
Physical systems, 294
Piezoelectric devices, 245
Piezoelectric materials
  properties of, 247
Pirani vacuum gage, 253
Plotters
  digital, 432
Poisson's ratio, 231
Polar-to-rectangular transformation, 314
Positive- and negative-reading encoders, 368
Potential-transformer test, 139
Potentiometer, 202
  coefficient, 295
  current measurement, 218
  duo-range, 205
  equivalent circuit, 220
  K-2, 211
  K-3, 213
  multiple-range, 208
  protection of, 222
  recording
    dual-trace, 226
    multipoint, 226
    $X$-$Y$, 226, 432
  self-balancing, 223
  sensitivity, 219
  zero-suppression, 210
Power-factor measurements, 121
Power measurements, 112
  polyphase, 114
  reactive, 116
  voltmeter-ammeter method, 79
Pressure measurement, 252

454

Probable error, 25
  combinations of, 28
Probability curve, 24
Program register, 375
Progress monitor, 434
Proportional counter, 271
Pyrometer
  lens-type, 267
  mirror-type, 267

Q-meter, 192
Quantity of electricity, 58
Quartz oscillator, 278

Radiant-energy measurements, 265
Radio-telemetering link, 440
Radix, 323
Ramac, 417
Ramp voltage, 310
Random errors, 22
Range, 6
Reactive power measurements, 116
Read-punch unit, 384
Reading unit, 372
Recorder
  AC, 128
  DC, 95
    galvanometer, 148, 154
  magnetic tape
    digital, 163
    direct, 155
    FM, 160
  potentiometer, 223, 227
    multipoint, 226
    dual-trace, 226
    X-Y, 226, 432
Rectangular to polar transformation, 315
Rectifiers
  copper oxide, 103
  doped germanium, 103
  full-wave, 103
  half-wave, 103
  selenium, 103
  silicon, 77
Redundance check, 373
Redundancy, 164
Reflected binary-number system, 338
Register
  address, 375
  ier, 413
  operation, 375
  program, 375

Relative damping of a galvanometer, 39
Reluctance instruments, 244
Reluctance revolution counter, 250
Repeatability, 4
Residuals, 192
Resistance thermometers, 255
Resolution, 4
Resolvers, 313
Resonance bridge, 198
Response of ballistic galvanometer, 60
Response of thermocouples, 257
Response time, 9
Return-to-bias (RB), 431
Return-to-zero (RZ), 431

SADIC, 368
Sample-and-hold circuit, 427
Scale, 6
Scale range, 6
Scintillation counter, 272
Self-quenching Geiger counter, 272
Self-balancing bridge, 181
Sensing elements, 421
Sensitivity, 4
  ballistic, 47, 51
  current, 35
  current galvanometer, 45, 49
  gage, 233
  megohm, 45, 50
  transducer circuit, 238
  voltage, 45, 50
Serial adder, 402
Serial divider, 415
Serial multiplier, 414
Sexadecimal numbers, 324
Shielding, 195
Sine-cosine tapered potentiometer, 310
Sinusoidal change, 8
Spatial encoder, 346, 360
Speed of response, 9
Step function, 8
Sting balance, 236
Storage-entry address, 384
Strain gage
  bonded-resistance, 230
  calibrating circuit, 238
  unbonded-resistance, 237
Stretch computer, 417
Subroutines, 386
Subtract circuits, 408
Sum, 398
Sum of limiting errors, 17

Summing circuits, 286
Synchronous computers, 406
Synchroscope, 125
System performance, 447
Systematic errors, 22

Tabulater, 384
Tape-preparation system, 432
Telemetering
  AM-AM system, 429
  AM-FM system, 429
  PAM-AM system, 429
  PAM-FM system, 429
  PCM-AM system, 430
  PCM-FM system, 430
  PDM-AM system, 429
  PLM system, 429
  PPM-AM system, 429
  PWM system, 429
Telemetering equipment, 429
Temperature compensation, 263
Temperature control, 263
Temperature difference, 263
Temperature measurements, 262
Tens-zero-binary-coded decimal, 431
Ternary numbers, 324, 325, 333
Thermal conductivity, 264
Thermal detecters, 265
Thermal watt converter, 116
Thermocouples, 254
  bridge-type, 105, 107
  characteristics, 256
  vacuum-gage, 253
Thermometers
  resistance, 255
Theorems
  Boolean algebra, 391
Thermistors, 259
  current-time characteristics, 261
  resistance temperature characteristics, 260
  voltage-current characteristics, 260
Thermopiles, 266
Thévenin's generator, 175
Thomson–Varley potentiometer, 368, 359, 432
Time-base encoder, 346, 354
Time-delay control, 263
Time factors, 298
Time measurements, 278
Time-pulse generator, 278
Torque
  constant, 35

displacing, 34
restoring, 34
Townsend avalanche, 271
Transducers, 230
Transformers
  current, 142
  differential, 240
  equivalent circuit of, 135
  ideal, 132
  impedance, 136
  losses, 134
  phasor diagram, 135
  potential, 137
  ratio corrective factor (RCF), 139
Truth table, 388
TV equipment, 433

Undamped-current galvanometer, 38
Underdamped-current galvanometer, 37
Upper accumulator, 381

Vacuum gage, 265
Validity check, 376
Vane-type instruments, 109
  attractive–repulsive, 110
  radial-vane repulsive, 109
  tapered concentric-vane attractive, 110
Variable-capacity instruments, 242
V-brush binary spatial encoder, 362
Veitch diagrams, 393
Vibration measurements, 251
Volt box, 217
Voltmeters, 78
  multirange, 78
Volt-ohm milliammeter, 88

Wagner ground, 187
Watthour meters, 119
  alternating current, 119
  direct current, 91
Wattmeters
  compensated, 114
  thermal watt converter, 116
Wenner element, 215
Wheatstone bridges, 173
Wheatstone, Sir Charles, 173
WWV, 279
WWVH, 279

$X$-$Y$ recorder, 226, 432

Zener diode, 225